From Sticks and Stones, Antlers and Bones

FROM

Sticks and Stones, Antlers and Bones

JERSEY FARM IMPLEMENTS, MACHINES AND TRACTORS
4000 BC TO AD 1960

Mervyn Billot I.Eng., M.I.Ag.E.

JERSEY HERITAGE TRUST

First published 2006 by
Jersey Heritage Trust
Jersey Museum
The Weighbridge
St Helier
Jersey, Channel Islands
JE2 3NF

ISBN 0-9552508-0-3   978-0-9552508-0-4

Designed and produced by John Saunders Design & Production
Printed in China

Foreword

by Sir Philip Bailhache, Bailiff of Jersey

I remember a debate in the States in the early 1970s on a proposition to introduce some safety regulation to require tractors to have roll bars as a protection for the driver. As a member of the Social Security Committee I made an intervention in support of the proposition, but was thoroughly squashed by an elderly deputy from St Clement who had spent all his life in the agricultural industry. "He may be a clever lawyer", said the deputy, "but he knows nothing about agriculture." Sadly, my critic was right, in the latter respect anyway. He could have added an ignorance of machinery to my defects of knowledge too. I wish that I had had the opportunity to read this book thirty-five years ago.

At that time agriculture was still probably the most significant industry in the Island's economy, as it had been for millennia. The local community had essentially grown out of the rich soil of Jersey. Originally it was subsistence agriculture, but in more recent times important cash crops and their products had made it possible to earn a comfortable living from the land. In the eighteenth century it was cider, and for the last one hundred years or more the Jersey Royal potato has reigned supreme.

The scope of this history is impressively broad, beginning in Neolithic times and concluding in the twentieth century. No one can farm without tools, and the progression from simple hand-crafted implements to sophisticated modern machinery is a fascinating story. The author has carried out much research, and explored the archives of other places as well as his native island in order to paint on a broader canvas. This sets in context important local inventions like the potato planting plough designed by Jean Le Boutillier in 1835 and used for over a century both on flat land and the steep Jersey côtils. The result is an informative and comprehensive analysis of the development of agricultural tools and machinery over the millennia skilfully interwoven with vignettes of social history too.

The author is better qualified than most to have embarked on this task. He is a Jerseyman who was brought up and worked on the family farm in a rural community. During the war he joined the Royal Navy and saw active service abroad. Later he qualified as an engineer. His descriptions of the machinery are clearly written by one who understands how they work. I commend this book to anyone with an interest not only in agricultural machines but also more broadly in the history of the Island.

Foreword

by Anne E Perchard MBE

Congratulations are due to the author for undertaking this mammoth work. His undoubted enthusiasm for all things mechanical in agriculture shines through. He tells the story of the evolution of machinery from the first rough efforts of man to the work of today's very clever and sophisticated engineers – men who, especially since the agricultural revolution, have designed implements to make farming more efficient and prestigious and to alleviate the former hard and thankless toil of the agricultural labourer. The adaptation of machines to suit our Jersey conditions is well researched and most interesting. A fascinating collection of unique historic photos and statistics ensures that this part of agricultural heritage is recorded before it vanishes. I have memories of our first Miracle Milker and our first little grey Fergie in the 1950s – how excited we were – these were the tops! Now we marvel at today's modern dairy units and the massive multi-purpose tractors and machines that work the land. The progress continues.

Mervyn Billot's work spans the years 4,000BC to AD1960. His perseverance over the past 10 years in a ground-breaking contribution to this large subject deserves our grateful thanks for the unselfish communication of his knowledge. I am privileged to have been invited to write the foreward – it merits a large circle of readers. I like to think that many people will, as I have done, find great pleasure in reading this book.

Contents

Acknowledgements.

I wish to express my gratitude and acknowledge the help of the following organisations and people, Universities, Institutes, Museums and Companies who assisted me with this work.

Miss Mary Billot and Miss Sally Knight of La Société Jersiaise library; Le Couteur papers; Trinity Manor Farm Accounts 1820-21; Farm Accounts of Maison De Haut 1903 – 1922; La Chronique de Jersey, D.E. Payn (1940s); C.P. Le Cornu's 19th Century paper; Medieval Land Tenures in Jersey by Guy Fortescue Burrell de Gruchy; Larousse Librairie, Paris; Larousse Agricole, Encyclopédie de E. Chancrin et R. Dumont; Royal Jersey Agricultural & Horticultural Society and staff; the minutes of the Royal Jersey Agricultural & Horticultural Society year books; One Hundred Years of the Royal Jersey Agricultural and Horticultural Society published in 1933; Olga Finch, Curator of Archaeology, La Hougue Bie; The Royal Archaeological Institute and the Archaeological Journal; The Plough in Ancient England by F.G. Payne, National Museums and Galleries of Wales; The English Plough by J.B. Passmore M.Sc.; Sian E. Rees, Study for Ph.D. Mr. Jonathan H. Brown of the Museum of English Rural Life & Institute of Agricultural History, University of Reading; Reading Museum; National Museum of Antiquities of Scotland, Edinburgh; Wiltshire Archaeological and Natural History Society Museum, Devizes; the late Mr. Don Pallot and his sons Lyndon and Sam, The Steam Museum, Jersey; Jersey Heritage Trust; Encyclopaedia of Dates and Events ed. L.C. Pascoe; Mr. Vincent Obbard, Samarès Manor Museum; Mr. Charles Le Couteur; Mr. D. Wenner, DeLaval Limited; Mr. A.S. King Gascoigne Melotte (UK) Limited; Oliver Bone, the Curator of the Ancient House Museum, Thetford; British Museum, London Wall; London Museum, London Wall; Winchester Museum; Breamore Countryside Museum; Whitianga Museum, New Zealand; the British Library, London; John Moffat C.B.E., the Ivel Tractor; Mr. G. Stannard, Bristol Tractor Society; Magazines 'Vintage Tractor' and 'Tractor & Machinery'; Mr. Michael Vautier; Mrs. Anne Perchard MBE; Mr. Donald Le Boutillier; Mr. Jack Le Sueur; Royal Hotel, St. Martin; Messrs John and Andrew Le Gallais; Mr. David Levitt.

Lastly I owe a great debt to my wife who accompanied me around the many museums visited and helped to record the details and patiently put up with the many hours I spent at my computer which seemed to take on a certain urgency to get the job done!

Preface

It was in 1996 when Geoffrey Le Feuvre of the Channel Islands Group of Professional Engineers suggested to me that, as the only agricultural engineer in the Group, I should research the history of farm implements and machinery in Jersey and record it. The more I thought about it the more it began to dawn on me that it would involve a tremendous amount of research and investigation. Agriculture goes back thousands of years and so do agricultural implements, and it is a wide subject. The syllabus in my student days for aspiring agricultural engineers, produced by the Institution of Agricultural Engineers, covered a wide range of disciplines, not simply tractors and field machinery as so many people imagine but dairy machinery, farm buildings, farm roads, bridges, electricity, water and soil mechanics, etc. Before embarking on the academic studies, the syllabus required the student to spend a minimum of one year working on a farm. Fortunately I had been working on the family farm and others during school holidays and for two years after I was demobilized in 1946.

Having decided to respond positively to Geoff Le Feuvre's request and attempt to produce such a history, it more than concentrated my mind. I was anxious about the sources of information, but the more I thought about that the more they came to mind. Having been in the industry helped obviously, but Jersey has so many of its own developments and I have to admit I was just a little anxious not to miss anything. However, the more I researched, the more sources came along; with that anxiety partly satisfied it began to get exciting and I was enjoying it.

This book is a photographic record, where possible, with descriptions of equipment actually used in Jersey. If as in the case of the ard and early plough, that was not possible, I have used material from outside the Island. While researching the plough and its origins I realized I would have to go back to the beginning of the ard and trace the story through. This required research of work that had been carried out outside the Island. To my surprise, nobody appears to have produced the complete story from the beginning of the ard to the plough as we know it today. Previous work appeared in detail, in separate stages of the development, hence the many museums and universities from whom I received assistance.

I have also discovered that the conclusions one might draw from research are not necessarily correct. I am grateful to certain proof-readers for pointing out where I have got it wrong! I am sure that after publication somebody will tell me of something that is wrong and of items I have left out!

Research can be rewarding in many ways: for example, while looking through the year books of the Royal Jersey Agricultural and Horticultural Society I discovered that my late father, Jurat Francis Renouf Billot, was on the agricultural committee of the Society in 1933, when the Society celebrated its centenary. The annual Summer Show at Springfield that summer was a spectacular event which all sections of the public of the Island were able to enjoy.

I was recently reminded by my sister Gwyneth Billot that my father was involved in setting up the first museum display of farming tools and machinery at La Hougue Bie in the late 1950s and early 1960s, long before Hamptonne. He was very keen to show it to me, I remember. Mr. Ernest Le Conte, of St. Helier Parks Department at the time, told me that he and my father worked together to plant some of the many trees at La Hougue Bie.

People interested in family and social history will I hope find the story of Jersey blacksmiths and agricultural engineers of interest.

1 Setting the scene

Historical notes on agriculture in Jersey

Ancient land measure in Jersey, 1331

The normal holding of a tenant was one bouvée

1 bouvée = one-tenth of a carucate or 24 vergées
1 carucate = 6 old Jersey acres
1 old acre = 4 vergées
1 perche = 24 land feet
24 land feet = 24 Jersey square feet or 20.16 English square feet
1 bouvée one-tenth and two-thirds of an English acre

1 bouvée = 24 vergées

There were 534.5 bouveées or 12,838 vergées of arable land.

One bouvée was the area of land an ox could plough in one year. It was also a measure of land for which the tax was set to be paid to the seigneur, the duke or the king. The annual rent or firma per bouvée varied by parish, probably due to the quality of the land. It was paid in three instalments per year, at Michaelmas, Easter, and St. Paul's Day.

Grouville 10 to 14 sols
St. Saviour 6 to 10 sols
St. Martin and St Peter 8 sols
St. Mary and St. Lawrence 7 sols
St. Brelade 7 to 9 sols
(G. F. B. de Gruchy, Medieval Land Tenures in Jersey, *1957)*

Significant dates

1000   Ploughs were in use in the Island, but the spade and mattock would have been popular implements for cultivating the land. Areas under cultivation were small.

1600   It is suggested the first potatoes were grown at the request of Sir Walter Raleigh, the Governor. At about this time the enclosures of land began. Previously land was open, with little demarcation as we know it, taking the form of hedges on banks to protect the orchards from strong winds.

1607   Among the crops grown were flax, hemp, wheat, barley and oats, rye grass, vetches, beans, peas, and parsnips.

1666   The States adopted a policy of encouraging Islanders to emigrate because of the economic crisis and shortage of food to feed the population.

1673   There was insufficient grain grown in the Island to feed the population. The States put a restriction on building outside St. Helier and St. Aubin unless the property had twenty vergées of land.

1681   Many apples were not gathered due to a heavy crop and insufficient facilities for dealing with them.

1685   The population of the Island was 15,000 and there were 3,000 houses.

1699	The States set the *impôt* on imports to pay for a harbour at St. Helier to provide for forty ships and smaller vessels.
1700	The harbour at St. Aubin was declared 'terminé'.
1717	Parliament passed an Act to allow Island produce to be imported into England without duty or tax.
1734	The population of the Island was 20,000.
1768	The Chamber of Commerce was formed, the first in the English-speaking world.
1770	The situation in the Island was dire: many of the population were poverty stricken and hungry, and there were riots.
1771	The Code of 1771 marked the separation of the duties of the Royal Court and the States.
1778	A regular shipping service between the Channel Islands and England commenced.
1780	Potatoes were considered a luxury; most were grown in the garden and were not for sale. 10% of land was devoted to potatoes.
1781	Battle of Jersey.
1786	*La Gazette de Jersey*, the first regular newspaper.
1790	Another wave of French refugees arrived. Fruit trees were being planted: peaches, apricots, plums, pears, and cherries. La Société d'Agriculture was formed for farmers with fifty vergées, later reduced to forty then thirty vergées. At an early meeting they considered making eau-de-vie from local cider. 31 May: a landmark when the Society identified the Jersey breed of cow, 'les animaux de race Jersiaise', for the first time.
1792	In May, a three-day agricultural show was held in St John. 6,000 people attended.
1796	The show in St. John proved so popular it was held again and extended for five days, La Société d'Agriculture showing Jersey cows, 'les animaux de race Jersiaise', for sale. There were displays of farm tools, implements, and machines. A winnowing machine attracted considerable attention.
1800	The planting of apple trees was extended to about a quarter of all cultivated land.
1806	The population of the Island was 22,800.
1807	Growing potatoes for export began in earnest; but they were not earlies.
1833	The Royal Jersey Agricultural and Horticultural Society was founded.
1834	Jean Le Boutillier produced a potato-planting plough and followed that with a potato digger.
1844	Blight devastated the potato crop here and over the whole of Western Europe.
1871	The Channel Islands Exhibition was held in the buildings and grounds of Victoria College.
1878	Mr. de la Haye first introduced the Royal Jersey Fluke potato.

In early times farmers were subsistence farmers working with neighbours and the close community. Business was conducted by exchange and barter, rent was paid with cabots of wheat, little money or cash changed hands. Gradually this would change, but there were those who tended to continue with the old traditional ways. Cereals were grown to feed the family on the farm, including the extended family and the cattle, and were not for sale off the farm. The exceptions were those more ambitious go-ahead farmers who set an example to others.

The first potatoes were grown at the request of Sir Walter Raleigh whilst he was Governor of Jersey from 1600 to 1603. He would have been interested, having brought them from America. It is said he would have liked to see them growing in the garden of Government House, but he only visited the Island twice, in September 1600 and July 1602. Potatoes would continue to be grown, but only in gardens for the next two hundred years, while they were considered a luxury and not exported in any quantity until the early nineteenth century.

In the seventeenth century crops grown were wheat, barley, and oats. Oats were not regarded as of special value; they were grown on the poorer soils. Cereal crops were often undersown with grass seed, rye grass, etc. sown in late spring. Wheat was sown and often ploughed in with a shallow plough and harrowed just before Christmas or early January. Barley was sown in February or March. Other crops were vetches, i.e. a mix of cereals and beans and peas. Beans, peas, and parsnips were grown for both human and animal consumption. Also grown were hemp for rope and flax for linen.

C. P. Le Cornu, writing in 1859, says sickles were used for harvesting cereals. The crop was threshed with a flail on a threshing floor; a man who could thresh 400 sheaves in a day had done well. Straw for thatching was threshed on a threshing bench with a flail striking only the heads of grain in the sheave in order not to damage the straw and keep it whole, which was necessary for this use.

Research leads to the conclusion that in 1600 there were ploughs on larger farms with harrows and solid tine cultivators, with oxen providing the power to haul them. Ploughs were not widely used. Much of the land was dug by hand with the spade: deep digging was necessary to grow parsnips for the family and cattle on the farm. This suggests that there was still a lot of subsistence farming rather than commercial farming. To sow parsnips, a rake was used to mark the rows in a north–south orientation. Row width seemed to vary: some were 19 in. (48.2 cm) wide, and others were 4.5 ft (137.2 cm), which suggests seeds were sown broadcast in wide beds. Peas were planted 4 in. (10.1 cm) apart, the work being done by farmers' wives and other women. The work was finished by sowing parsnips and then harrowed in with a hand harrow to cover the seeds. After five or six weeks the peas would emerge and women and children would do the weeding, usually twice at the end of April, early May, and again in July and August. By the end of August the peas were maturing and the parsnips getting big enough to harvest. In September the cattle were turned out on the field to graze off the green leaf tops of the parsnips before lifting was done with a two-prong fork. When the peas were dry and hard they were milled into a flour or meal. About 10 per cent of the land was put down to parsnips; before potatoes, the parsnip was a staple in the diet of daily life.

Later in the eighteenth century two types of plough were in use, the first a shallow plough, ploughing down 5 or 6 in. (12.6-15.2 cm) deep at most, and a deep plough for parsnips probably 11–12 in. (28-30.5 cm) deep. So basically the first plough was a corn plough (or what one might call a deep breezing plough) and the second a really deep plough for growing root crops. The use of the plough for the average Jersey farm of the period would have led to very marked changes in sowing techniques and the opportunity to bring bigger areas under cultivation. A quarter of the agricultural land in the seventeenth century was in orchards; vegetables were considered a luxury—cabbage, cauliflower, asparagus, and carrots were grown in gardens. Towards the end of the century turnips were grown and fruit trees from France were planted: peaches, apricots, plums, pears, and cherries. Enclosures in the form of earth banks were constructed with hedging planted above to protect the orchards from high winds. This was not done to turn people off the land as in England.

In 1770 things had not greatly improved; the situation was grave once again. There were many poor people and the necessities of life were not readily available. There were riots among the discontented population. The problems were mainly food shortages, due largely to the backward state of agriculture and the system of farming. Much of the farmland was devoted to orchards, as exporting cider was profitable to the growers, and hemp was grown for making rope. In effect, not enough cereals and vegetables were grown to feed the population. St. Saviour had the most orchards of any parish in the seventeenth and eighteenth centuries. Apples were crushed, often in a presshouse or outside in the farmyard in a stone trough crusher with a large, horse-drawn stone wheel. In later years mechanical crushing mills were imported from England and France by some farmers.

The fertilizer in general use was seaweed, also known as vraic; it played an important part. The laws concerning vraicing in Jersey are very ancient and there is an official record to that effect: one of these laws received the royal sanction of Richard I when he was in Messina in 1191 while en route to take part in the crusades. The collection of vraic was controlled, detailing where and when one might gather it. Farmers with sickles and grappins, horses and carts, would go down to the beach and work waist-deep in water at low tide. The vraic was cut from the rocks as well as gathered from the shore. Vraic was often applied fresh to arable land before ploughing and to grassland. Alternatively it was used dry; it was also dried and burnt, and the ash was spread on the land for the most important crops. Ashes were stored in a dry ash store on the farm. Some farms had an ash store specially built for the purpose and these can still be seen today: there is an example at La Pompe in St. Mary. Vraic was sometimes collected according to type at certain times of the year for certain purposes.

In 1781 French forces led by Baron de Rullecourt invaded the Island. The Napoleonic wars continued, resulting in no amelioration in the 1790s of the Island's difficulties.

Formation of La Société d'Agriculture, 1790

The first meeting was due to take place at the home of Capt. Le Roux in St. Lawrence, but as a result of his sudden death it was decided to hold the meeting at the home of Capt. Goddard near the parish church of St. John. To be a member a farmer had to have 50 vergées of land and sell 300 livres of produce, equal to only £17 sterling because the *livre tournois* was valued at far less than the pound sterling. The aims of the new society were to improve the road system and the making of cider, to encourage the use of ploughs, and notably to make flour from potatoes. (This last aim shows that there is nothing new: in the Second World War during the Occupation large quantities of potatoes were made into flour, which was a great benefit.) The flour was not cheap but the modest cost of production brought a benefit to the producer. The formation of the new agricultural society relied upon public support for the development of three industries: sail-making, making hats, and producing candles.

The Society wanted to encourage the local production of these things which were of prime necessity. Presumably they used products from the farm for making linen for sails and hats.

At an early meeting they considered distilling cider to make eau-de-vie. A machine to cut and chop potatoes and turnips was demonstrated as was a plough for general use. Another matter considered was the making of starch from potatoes. At their second meeting, on 31 May 1790, at the home of Mr. J. Pepin of Grouville, membership was to be encouraged from farmers with 40 or 50 vergées. Of historic importance at that meeting was the identification of the Jersey cow for the first time, 'bovine de l'isle', 'les animaux de race Jersiaise', the dairy cow, and the selection of bulls all with good conformation (body shape). This was a good reason to have controls on imports of cows and bulls. They discussed the best way to nourish and fatten pigs for pork. A new model of butter churn was demonstrated. The preparation and use of lime in agriculture was considered.

A particularly interesting debate was the use of horses compared with oxen for work on the farm. Early ploughs were pulled by bullocks or oxen up to and during the nineteenth century; the animals were often shod. Three young oxen could plough 8 vergées in two days. The only advantage for the horse was that it was faster, particularly on the road. (Lord Bathurst had a bullock team in the 1960s on his estate near Cirencester. The author was surprised to see oxen ploughing in West Germany in the 1960s, but less surprising was to see them on a smallholding up in the hills in Fiji in the 1990s.)

Members' objections to oxen were that they had smaller feet or hooves than horses and they moved more slowly. However, oxen are easier to feed in winter with cabbages and parsnips, whereas horses need oats and hay. Oxen are less subject to ailments than horses, and can plough, harrow, and cart manure, and crush apples or grain. Oxen and horses often worked together in a team to haul the big plough. The oxen were put at the back because they were stronger and therefore better for pulling the plough the last few feet of the furrow up to the headland when the leading animals had already turned along the headland and were no longer able to pull the plough.

During the next two years the Society continued to give consideration to the production of calvados, as in Normandy, as indicated at a meeting in 1791 when making eau-de-vie was discussed again; a Mr. M. P. Anley had a distillery. It required 18 pots of cider to make 2.5 pots of good-quality eau-de-vie at 12 degrees alcohol, costing 18 sous. It was proposed to offer a prize of 10 livres for the best cider in July 1792 (£5 15s. at the 1940 rate or £120 in 1999). Prizes were to be awarded for the production of the best bottled cider. Apparently bottles were difficult to come by because the shows would only take place on condition that enough bottles could be found. It was also decided that the prize-winning cider would be sold in the pub nearest to the market. Barley straw was best as an underlay (presumably in the cider press); it was less trouble to use and the cider was better for it.

The Society went on to debate the problem of cattle exported to England that had originally come from France. (It was an abuse of an Act of Parliament to allow Island produce to enter England tax- or duty-free.) The States were to be asked to change the law controlling the import of cattle from France. There were 10,000 sheep in the Island at the time: one of the concerns of the Society was the number of stray dogs harming sheep; another problem was the rabbits. At the same meeting it was decided to offer membership to farmers with 30 vergées of cultivated land. At this time there were fifty-five members.

It was evident members were not satisfied with the quality of imported seeds. It was decided the members of the Society would send the secretary a list of all the seeds they needed, including clover, turnips, cabbage, etc., which would be obtained from a seed merchant recommended by the Society.

The suggestion was made that the Society should rent a farm in England to raise Jersey cattle on the spot and to sell them there to help overcome the abuse by people importing cattle from France to sell in England, passing them off as Jersey cattle.

At a meeting of the Society at the home of Mr Perrée near St. Ouen's Church, subjects discussed again were the attacks by dogs on flocks of sheep and crops. It was decided to ask the States to impose a tax on dogs with the aim of cutting down their numbers; also to persuade the States to enforce the seventeenth-century law which limited the area of orchards according to the number of vergées in cultivation. They discussed the best ways of fattening bulls and the best methods of harnessing bullocks to ploughs. It was recognised that the local cloth that was offered for sale was not as attractive as the imported material and it was decided that the word 'local' be added to the local material to encourage the Island industry.

Yet another proposal was to make cheese, which was not very well known generally. There was the question of organising a grand fair at St. John. A new type of cart was recommended, similar to a barrow but with wheels at the centre of gravity, which was better balanced (presumably a handcart). Lastly, the improvement of the mills was raised.

Unfortunately this society, which had proved so useful and full of promise during its first few years, gradually faded. The blame has to lie with the political parties: a situation had arisen which divided the Island and even divided families, creating great animosity. In 1825 another attempt was made to form a society: the press published notices inviting people who were interested to register at Hotel Paton in Halkett Place; the subscription would be 5 shillings per quarter. That society seems to have quietly disappeared; nothing appears in print about it after that date.

At the turn of the century, from the 1790s to the 1800s, farmers had plenty of work to get on with, having flax, hemp, and wool to prepare for spinning. Provisions had to be laid in for the farm for winter, candles had to be made, meat to be salted down, bacon to be smoked in the hearth. On the farm the farm cart and implements had to be maintained by the family. Different oils were brought in from flax, cod liver oil, and fish oil for lighting. From Ireland came clothing material, flannel and serge, from Newcastle coal and herring, from Russia soap, salt for making

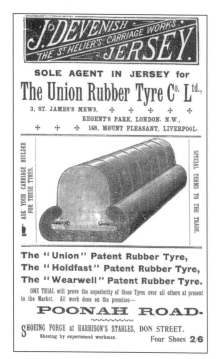

The above advertisement appeared in the 1903 year book of the RJA & HS

Ploughing in Jersey with four oxen and four horses.
This ploughing scene is thought to be in the north-west of Jersey. The oxen are in pairs as are the two horses before the oxen, and the two horses in front are one behind the other. It appears to be neighbours working together, each providing one or two horses and one or two oxen. This was common practice when ploughing with the Jersey big plough; no farmer would have enough horses and oxen to pull it. The strongest pair of oxen were always put directly in front of the plough because they were stronger than horses. When the leading animals reach the end of the furrow they turn on the headland; having turned they are no longer in line to pull the plough to the end of the furrow. The last two oxen will pull the plough the last few feet to the end of the furrow on their own.

butter, tobacco, and hemp. Luxuries were tea, coffee, mustard, dates, oranges, other citrus fruits, chocolate, and tobacco.

An example of a farm in 1777 was that of a Mr. Hubert of St. John. He farmed 68 vergées, having a house complete with sheds, lofts, pigsties, vegetable garden, apple and pear trees. Typical goods sold off the farm were 5,000 ballots (i.e. packages, probably cabots) of wheat, 1,500 of barley, and 1,000 of oats. He grew 3.5 vergées of peas and parsnips, 1 vergée of white potatoes and 2 vergées of big potatoes, and lastly 2,000 livres-worth of hay. He had two mares, one in foal, two cows, three heifers, eight pork pigs, and goats; some fern, a field of pears, and another of haricot beans. A second example was Tombette, having 58 vergées in St. Mary with 1,500 young shrubs of which 400 were grafted. Finally a Mr. La Cloche sold a 28-vergée farm in Rouge Bouillon!

In 1792 a fair or show lasting three days was held in St. John in May, which some 6,000 people attended. Having been so successful the show was held again in 1796. La Société d'Agriculture took great interest in showing Jersey cows, 'les animaux de race Jersiaise', for sale. The show was so popular, with so much going on, it was extended to five days. Apart from all the cattle on show there were also displays of farm tools, ploughs, harrows, handcarts, wheelbarrows, hand barrows, riddles or sieves for sifting flour and meal, harness for horses, yokes for oxen, and a winnowing machine. The winnowing machine was of a type made in 1790 by Jean Le Grand. who lived at the mill at La Hague in St. Peter. The machine was described as being 'very useful for blow cleaning grain, wheat and barley etc'. Fourteen people had made use of it and reported that the work done was economical and would recover the expense of purchase in three seasons.

Other items displayed would not have been out of place in the twentieth century: buckets, forks, scythes, rakes, and grappins, the last being recommended for unloading farmyard manure from carts or gathering vraic off the rocks and in the surf. The grappin was also used for cultivating between the rows of potatoes on small côtils and small patches of land such as around St.

Catherine. As a matter of interest, the grappin described in English publications is a fork with bent prongs or tines used for the same purposes in England. However, in Jersey a grappin with longer tines than average was used specifically for gathering vraic in the surf, particularly at St. Ouen's Bay.

Transport to and from the town to the show was interesting! A covered wagon drawn by no fewer than six oxen and eight horses transported fifty people at a time between St. Helier and St. John and back home again.

In 1794 an event of great importance took place with the introduction of printing and newspapers, which would lead to the spreading of news and information and eventually to a wider knowledge of the world outside the Island. Sea transport facilities were better, also improving communication; however, there was a greater population to feed.

The nineteenth century was the century of iron, steel, and electricity, the engineer and scientist, when men understood and made use of these materials in so many fields. In 1827 the first steam engine was constructed in Jersey for a mill and bakery in Phillips Street.

This advertisement appeared in the 1904 year book of the RJA & HS

At the beginning of the nineteenth century methods of cultivation were still very primitive. Many farmers continued to grow a mix of beans, haricots, parsnips, etc. In case of crop failure farmers grew a few potatoes or cabbages. Turnips were grown to feed the cattle through the winter months. The bigger, go-ahead farmers were being more commercial: to feed the population and make the Island self-sufficient was the aim. This was thought to be due to poor relations with other countries, presumably due to the continuing wars with France. The Island could not rely on imports; this fear resulted in a reluctance for change. Hemp continued to be grown for rope-making and flax was grown to make garments. Parsnips played an important part in feeding the population, as well as fattening pigs, and feeding the cattle. Peas were grown not only for human consumption but were dried and crushed with oats and parsnips for fattening the cattle.

The cider industry was in decline and, despite the restrictive laws, orchards still occupied about a quarter of the arable land. The planting of orchards had necessitated the planting of many hedges to protect the trees, their blossom, and their fruit from strong winds.

As the foregoing implies, at the beginning of the nineteenth century the Island remained in a poor state and the prospects for the future were not bright, but with innovations things slowly improved and the Island began to prosper. As time went on some municipal buildings were constructed, including the central market in Halkett Place. While General Don was Governor, having responsibility as commander of military forces and considering the continued menacing situation in France, he saw an urgent need to improve the roads. He pressed forward with the construction of many of our main roads for the speedy movement of troops in times of crisis. Following the defeat of Napoleon and the peace treaty, the maritime situation improved. Shipping between the Islands and the mainland was more frequent and more reliable, so improving communications, especially later when steamships were introduced on the routes.

In 1820 the Seigneur of Trinity travelled to the Isle of Wight and bought some agricultural tools and implements, seeds, fruit trees, pigs, and long-fleeced sheep.

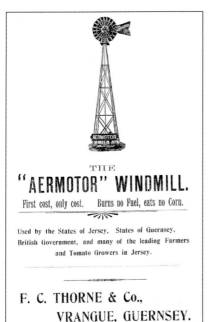

Advertisement, early 20th century

It is interesting to note an agricultural diary from Trinity Manor dated 1820:

On the 2nd October 1820 we began to plough Le Parc Mollet to sow rye to feed the cattle in the spring. The field measured 10½ vergées, one has to hurry to get the field in proper condition for the sowing. On October 18th we ploughed the field La Moyse du Sud to sow oats. October 30th we began preparing for the sowing of wheat. The cattle are fed with turnips, the cows are brought in each evening to the stables and those which give the most milk are fed with turnips while the others are fed with oat straw. December 1st. harrowed La Grande Garenne to sow the wheat seed. December 12th bought 18 cabots of vesce (vetches?) at 6/3 per cabot. Began feeding old hay to the cows. 28th Jan. 1821 The cows having finished the turnips from the Park are now going to graze in Le Clos Gruchy. We estimate that a third of the turnip crop have been eaten by field mice, they eat the interior and just leave the shell and the leaf making you believe that everything is in good order. February 1st Le Clos de la Promenade and du Park Blampied was an area of 29 vergées, we sowed just a little less than 23 bushels of English grain which represents 1½ cabots per vergée. The seed weighs exactly 32 Jersey lbs per cabot. The quantity of wheat sown in Le Clos de la Promenade was just slightly less than 1½ cabots per vergée. After the field had been sown flocks of birds came down on the field, then the hens and pigeons and the cows as a consequence the crop is very poor but it was not through lack of sowing enough seed. We calculate the two cabots are equal to one bushel English measure. A bushel of wheat seed contains 550,000 grains and therefore 3½ bushels per acre represents 1,925,000 grains.

Formation of the Royal Jersey Agricultural and Horticultural Society, 1833

It was a more settled period locally, giving the new Society a better chance of success. In 1940 when Payn was writing in the *Chronique de Jersey* it had been in existence for over a century. At the beginning the Society's efforts were not solely limited to the improvement of cattle. A committee had been set up: their mission was to visit farms, inspect the crops, give advice, and encourage new methods. 'Le banon', the laws on the right to graze animals on common land, was given consideration. The common lands were cultivated by different farmers, but after the harvest, cattle had grazing rights on that land. The Constable would announce the date when grazing could begin.

Growing potatoes for export began in 1807; they were not earlies, but were dug in the autumn. 1,200 tons were exported in 1811 and this had grown to 18,000 tons by 1842 before blight hit the crop.

Jean Le Boutillier's potato-planting plough and potato digger

In 1834 Jean Le Boutillier produced a potato-planting plough and followed that a couple of years later with a potato digger. Jean Le Boutillier was a young, innovative blacksmith who was asked by Col. John Le Couteur to make a plough to plant potatoes. After some time and experiment he demonstrated a planting plough to the colonel, who was pleased with the result and expressed the hope that in due course Mr. Le Boutillier might make him a plough to dig potatoes. The planting plough was a great success and in due course every Jersey farm had a potato-planting plough which was used every planting season and is still used today on the côtils.

Approximately two years after the planting plough Mr. Le Boutillier demonstrated his potato digger to Col. Le Couteur, who was delighted with it.

On 30 October 1837 Col. Le Couteur wrote to the secretary of the Agricultural Society of Great Britain and Ireland concerning 'a valuable invention by John Le Boutillier which may become of general utility to the agricultural world. For the information of the Committee at its next meeting. It is the construction and making of a plough for separating potatoes from the soil. John Le Boutillier had previously constructed a light one-horse plough for planting potatoes two years before, weighing 58lbs'. Le Couteur describes how 'it traces a furrow for planting at a set depth (and row width). It saves one horse because previously it required two turns of the plough at each furrow [i.e. two furrows had to be ploughed between each row of potatoes]. This light plough doubles the rate of work.'

Le Couteur says he has expressed the hope that Le Boutillier will show him an implement soon for taking them up (a potato digger). Describing the digger, Le Couteur says, 'Le Boutillier's potato digger is drawn by three horses working at an easy pace without stopping. It turned half an acre in 5 hours. Many people came to see it digging last week, this was in the last week of October.'

Writing to his son John at Sevastopol during the Crimean War, he describes the potato digger:

It has the breast of a Jersey plough and on the inside it has a wheel which rolls on the furrow bottom with teeth which catch the ground and rotate and through cogs drives a shaft with paddles or prongs which revolve as the plough advances, the potatoes which come over the share it throws them 5 or 6 feet. The prices are £3-10-0 for the digger and 30/- for the planting plough.

In a letter of thanks from John Le Couteur, Le Boutillier received a prize, a cheque for £5 from the English Agricultural Society, Cavendish Square, for his potato-digging plough shown at the Royal Show at Oxford on 17 July.

In order to protect Jean Le Boutillier's two inventions, especially the potato digger, Col. John Le Couteur wrote to people in England to patent the plough.

On 26 November 1838 he wrote to Queen Victoria asking her to grant a patent for 'the potato digging plough which dug potatoes with great rapidity saving much labour and good for comminuting the soil and mixing powdered manure with it'. If the petition is granted he asks 'that it be sent to the clerk of the Council, Mr. Lemare, for registering in the Royal Court because the patent would not have any force here'.

On 7 December 1838 he wrote, as President of the RJA & HS, to the Secretary of State, at the Home Department, London:

'Petition for John Le Boutillier who has already had two awards from the RJA & HS for two inventions, a potato planting plough and a potato digger.'

Le Boutillier's potato digger is at present on display at the museum at Hamptonne, St Lawrence.

John Le Couteur experimented with many varieties of potatoes and in the 1840s he planted a crop early in the year and also wheat seeds.

Following the building of the covered market, a public weighbridge was constructed at the harbour and 1848 saw the shipbuilding industry at its height. A step forward in education came with the building of Victoria College in 1851. In 1869 a water company was formed, with a storage and distribution system; in 1874 a railway between St. Aubin and St. Helier was constructed. However, two disasters in the century were the cholera epidemic of 1832 and the failure of local banks in 1873. The Island was still largely dependent on its agricultural industry and what it could produce; the fluctuation of the population also played its part. From 1734 to 1806 the Island population only increased by 2,000 to 22,800.

But after that the rate of growth increased by 10,000 every ten years; in 1851 the population stood at 57,000. The ease of communication and the affluence of refugees fleeing from France due to religious problems on the Continent, and, in addition, the choice of Jersey for a home by retiring army officers following the peace treaty, affected the local economy.

The first thirty years of the century saw great strides in local agriculture. Hitherto most work in agriculture was done by hand; little had been known about agricultural implements and simple tools like the hoe or seed drill. For example a two-prong fork for digging parsnips was used as a hoe, usually by women. Weeding was not considered important, thus farms were dirty with weeds. Much of the livestock was still in poor condition, particularly the dairy cow, and little was done to improve that. People were content with what they had, and although cattle were being exported it was done without realising the export potential that would build up into a worldwide industry before the end of the century.

The Society encouraged improved methods of agriculture and the use of new agricultural implements; it organised shows and exhibitions. In 1860 Ransome ploughs were in evidence; machines for crushing oats were made by a Mr. Biddle; mowing machines, seed drills, zigzag harrows, and scarifiers began to appear. In 1866 a Mr. Mauger invented a straw cutter (chaff cutter), yet another was invented by a Mr. Le Barr, and a winnowing machine had been built from the beginning of the century. Towards 1870 Mr. Le Cappelain of St. Peter's Iron Works began importing and making agricultural implements, later moving away from wooden frame implements into making the first iron and steel ploughs and cultivating implements in the Island. He imported several threshing machines and trussers, and portable steam engines to drive them.

In the middle of the century shows were organised to show and judge the usefulness of these new agricultural implements to encourage their use and development. The exchange of information and experience provided further help, in particular by those Jerseymen who had travelled and seen modern methods and systems. Some improvements resulted from the work of scientists in more advanced countries when that information was passed on to Jersey farmers, but more from persuading them to adopt more modern methods, tools, and implements. The consequence of using new methods and growing new crops resulted not only in the Island's producing enough to feed the population but also in its producing an important surplus for export which grew year by year.

Growing potatoes for export

Exporting potatoes began in earnest in 1807; they were not earlies, but were dug in the autumn. There were those in 1812 who still considered potatoes were a luxury and only grew a few in the vegetable garden. However, 1,200 tons were exported in 1811 and this expanded to 18,000 tons by 1842 before blight hit the crop in 1843, devastating it. The great development in the growing of potatoes was when they became more freely available and were exported to Brazil, Barbados, Portugal, Tenerife, and Gibraltar. In 1834 the variety of potato grown was Ash Leaf Kidney; then towards 1844 there was a new variety named Big Eyes, a round potato with big eyes and a fine skin. Another variety was a red skin potato named Phillips which was imported from Pelham in Hampshire; it had good keeping qualities and was stored through the winter and consumed until the new crop arrived the following year. There were also Scotch Reds and Jersey Blues. At that time potatoes were not stood as we do today to encourage the growth of shoots, but the potatoes for seed were cut into pieces, each piece having one or two shoots. These pieces were placed on the loft floor after it had been sprinkled with lime. As planting time approached the potatoes were taken out to the field and placed in little heaps to wait for planting time.

Blight

In 1844 potato growers were alarmed when there was a second severe attack of blight. (The Irish famine is of course well known but many other countries in Europe suffered from blight.) Parsnips were also affected. There was an urgent need to discover a means of combating the problem. Experience in previous years had shown the disease was brought on by climatic conditions in high humidity and was more prevalent in wet seasons and in the later digging areas, particularly after rain.

People near Bordeaux in France living beside a copper smelting factory noticed that a field of potatoes in the lee of the factory was unaffected by blight. This was investigated and resulted in the manufacture of copper sulphate spray, sold as Bordeaux mixture! Spraying the crop with Bordeaux mixture was the salvation of the potato. Years later it would also save the tomato crop from the ravages of blight (C. P. Le Cornu, 'The Agriculture of the Islands of Jersey . . .', 1859).

The origin of the Jersey Royal potato, or Royal Jersey Fluke

The Jersey Royal was first cultivated by Hugh de la Haye, a bachelor who farmed Bushy Farm at Mont Cochon. Years ago ploughing with the big plough was an opportunity for folk to work together and after a busy day there was usually a big meal served, washed down with plenty of cider and liquor. After the meal, the evening was spent singing, storytelling, and playing a card game called 'loup'. The party after ploughing was an occasion for each farmer to try to put on the best party.

To entertain the neighbours at his party, Hugh de la Haye fetched from the loft two potatoes remarkable for their size: one had sixteen eyes. The two potatoes had been on display on the counter of the office of Le Caudeys, the merchant on the Esplanade. Both of the big potatoes were cut up, each piece with an eye. These pieces were planted in a côtil in Bellozanne Valley on Hugh's farm.

When they were dug on Hugh's côtil the result was to amaze him: the potatoes from the one with sixteen eyes were all of a kidney type. At first the kidney shape disappointed him; the other potato produced round potatoes. He also noted that the crop of the kidney-shaped potatoes was much heavier and earlier than the others, so he decided to go on growing it. This potato became the Jersey Royal and eventually became firmly established in the Island.

The growing of parsnips on a large scale had been done for many centuries before, towards 1812, turnips were cultivated on a fairly large scale for feeding to cattle. In 1815 it was established that about 10 per cent of all arable land was devoted to growing parsnips. Hitherto turnips were relatively unknown to the Island and were just beginning to be used whereas they had been cultivated in England from about a century earlier. Chicory, a root crop similar to sugar beet and grown in the same way, was introduced around 1834 and ten years later was fed to cattle; but if fed in large quantities it made the cattle ill and so was grown less and less. Sorghum, a type of sweet grass, was tried and cultivated, but only for a short time. At the start of the century hops were grown for two or three years, but as the return did not cover the cost of growing the crop it was abandoned. Fruit trees were imported from France after an advert appeared in 1788 offering for sale pear trees, peach and apricot, cherry, plum, apple, and nectarines.

It is interesting to note in an official report in 1860 that the following crops were found on an average 45 vergée farm: 13 vergées of pasture, 5 vergées of potatoes, 6 vergées of turnips, 1.5 vergées of mangels, 8 vergées of wheat, and 10 vergées of clover. As we know, later two of the predominant crops were the potato and then the tomato. In a publication in February 1868 there was mention of the wonderful sight of peach trees in bloom at Mainland, Mr. Moses Gibaut's farm. It shows that here was a farmer trying to develop agriculture and introduce new crops.

A fertiliser used regularly was farmyard manure (FYM). It was only at the beginning of the nineteenth century that liquid manure was considered to be of value and collected from the stables to use on the land; hence the liquid manure tanks were constructed underground beneath the manure pits, the necessary drains were installed, and the liquid manure pumps were erected alongside. Burnt lime came to Jersey in 1792 and only eight years later it was used in agriculture. In 1812 lime was imported from Plymouth but the freight was so expensive that this was discontinued. In the same year seashells were used as a fertiliser; they were lifted from the seabed roughly 2 miles off St. Ouen's Bay on the west coast. During the month of October they were spread at 80 bushels per vergée on heavy land which was intended to be used for wheat. The result of the experiment showed that it was not only beneficial for the next two seasons but for the following five or six years. In 1839 artificial manures were first used.

A Mr. John Le Caudey had the idea of planting potatoes early and digging them early. Farmers quickly adopted the idea, digging in April and May, but it was not the Jersey Royal; that came later.

There were cattle on every farm and there were great numbers of poultry. In St. Helier at this time almost every house had a garden, which enabled townsfolk to keep poultry and other animals including rabbits and pigs. On 2 March 1867 there were as many as 300 pigs in the town.

Transporting cattle in 1820 was not without its problems; for example, to send a cow to Leith in Scotland the closest port to the destination was Newcastle. The rest of the journey had to be made on foot. A further problem of shipping cattle by sea was the necessity to have enough fodder for the voyage; it was impossible to know how long the journey might take with sailing ships. In those days many animals were lost because of rough seas during passages. A rough crossing in heavy seas to England in May 1835 resulted in twelve cows being tossed about one on top of the other. In 1850 a Mr. P. Motley of Boston, New Jersey, in the United States bought some cattle. He came back to Jersey in 1868 to buy more cattle and spent £500, which was a large sum at that time. The method of transport to the United States was interesting: a Mr. Dumaresq took charge of the transport. The cattle were put aboard a small steamship which sailed to Le Havre, and from there the cattle were shipped to Boston. Jersey cattle were exported to Ireland in 1846 and others to Windsor in 1851. At the World Show in Paris in 1856 there was a special class for Jersey cattle and sixteen animals took part. In 1867 a Mr. Le Bas exported no fewer than 2,041 head of cattle during the year.

When General Don was Governor of the Island he cultivated the arid lands of Les Quennevais in 1811. He created an enclosure of roughly 20 acres, sowing 12 vergées of barley, buckwheat, peas, rye grass, lucerne, and some potatoes, and other vergées were reserved for clover and sainfoin. In October 1851 there was a bigger experiment to grow crops on a much larger area of this barren land. Mr. Le Montais took charge of the project: it was a gigantic task to level out the sand dunes over an area of approximately 100 vergées. In the first year there was a good crop of turnips and mangels. Here and there lucerne was growing in the sand. The masses of seashells in the sand produced bicarbonate of lime.

There were few agricultural workers at the beginning of the century: all the work was done by members of the family without employing outside folk, and neighbours helped each other with ploughing and harvesting. Occasionally if extra labour was needed help was sought from the garrison, and they were paid 2 shillings a day and half that if they were fed by the employer. As an example, in 1849 a labourer of 24 years was paid 1s. 8d. per week over and above his food and was promised a small increase when he had become accustomed to farm work.

Jersey had a reputation for its excellent seeds, such as wheat, which were exported to England in great quantities. In 1851 a Jerseyman (probably Le Couteur) showed 112 varieties at an agricultural show at the Crystal Palace (presumably the Great Exhibition).

Statistics show the remarkable development of Jersey potatoes. In 1812, when the export of potatoes commenced, the quantity exported was 1,400 tons; in 1856 it was 4,960 tons; and in 1899 it was 65,000 tons, the value of which was no less than £330,421. Naturally the development of this industry had taken place to the detriment of others and was the reason for the significant decline in the cultivation of cereals. In 1890 the export of tomatoes began, with both the indoor and outdoor crop, and both crops expanded rapidly. This is a product of the development of the agricultural industry in the twentieth century, reaching a peak in the late 1940s. (The outdoor crop was to decline over the years.)

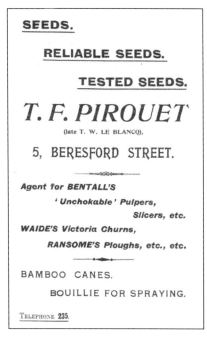

This advertisement appeared in the 1908 year book of the RJA & HS

In 1933 the Royal Jersey Agricultural and Horticultural Society published their book entitled *One Hundred Years of the RJA & HS, 1833-1933*.

In the book there are references to entries in the minutes of trials of farm machinery. Members had arranged exhibitions of new and improved agricultural implements and an ingenious machine for mowing a lawn (probably Buddings's patent for cutting the nap of carpets adapted by Ransomes of Ipswich for a lawnmower in 1832).

In 1835 it was reported that wheat was a staple crop and exported to England for seed. Hand weeding of the growing crop was stressed to provide a clean sample for export. Parsnips were also a staple, widely grown before the potato was broadly accepted. Potatoes had been grown for export and had shown promise, but after the losses due to blight, many gave up or reduced their dependency on them as a cash crop until a remedy was found.

Apples feature as yet another valuable crop widely grown for cider for export. Orchards were everywhere; every farm had its presshouse and apple crusher. Very few presses remain to be seen, having been removed to enable the old presshouses to be used for other purposes. There are still many stone apple crushers, which were often moved to become a garden feature.

In 1838 the conserving of liquid manure was stressed as a valuable fertiliser with a description of how it might be collected with a drainage channel from the cow stables leading to an underground holding tank or cistern under the manure pit near the stables, then going on to describe how it might be delivered.

In 1841 trials were conducted with washes, etc. for fruit trees, but there is no mention of the method of application. Trials were also conducted with fertilisers, notably guano, on crops in 1844, probably applied by hand. Two similar patches of potatoes were planted, one crop sown with guano and the other without. The patch treated with guano produced a 50 per cent increase in the crop.

Bordeaux mixture was introduced to spray against blight. Again no mention is made of the method of application. Pumps had been in use for many years, so it is quite likely that sprayers with a simple lever-operated piston pump were developed with a tank carried on the back, to be known as the knapsack sprayer.

The year 1846 was one of experiment, with trials of new machinery: horse hoes for weeding in root crops, probably the beginnings of the L-shaped hoe blade for weeding root crops and of a horse hoe for potatoes, probably the three-tine scarifier and the banking hoe. Special mention was made of a two-man hoe for potatoes. In 1857 trials of ploughs were to be carried out. Unfortunately there is rarely any record of the result and the conclusions drawn from the trials.

In 1871 the Channel Islands Exhibition was held in the buildings and grounds of Victoria College. It was described as the 'greatest event in the social life of the Island in the nineteenth century'. Complementary to the exhibition were field trials of new and improved agricultural machinery, including portable steam engines and threshing machines and ploughs. Unfortunately there were no reports of the results of the trials. The exception was the 1872 report, which mentions a trial of lawnmowers being conducted: 'Green's Patent' exhibited by Le Masurier and Vibert was found to be the best!

Green's were manufacturers of quality cylinder lawnmowers for many years. Ransomes' were the first in the world to manufacture a cylinder mower, adapting Budding's patent in 1832. It consisted of a cylinder or reel with helical blades on a number of discs mounted on a common shaft; beneath the reel was a fixed blade with a sharpened leading edge over which the helical blades passed, cutting like a pair of scissors. As the machine was pushed over the grass any long grass about to pass under the fixed blade was cut off to form a level, evenly cut strip of grass looking like a carpet. When the patent ran out many manufacturers copied Ransomes. Only the mounting of the cylinder, the number of blades on the cylinder, and the type of transmission to drive the cylinder differed between one machine and another.

In 1878 Mr. de la Haye first introduced the Jersey Royal Fluke potato. In 1883 at the RJA & HS

Le Cappelain threshing machine at Clairval in 1912. On a threshing day when one of Le Cappelain's many threshing machines was working there was always an atmosphere of excitement, hustle and bustle, and a sense of occasion. It was attended here by quite a crowd, the team operating the machine and some simply looking on, including the well-dressed gentlemen! Beards and moustaches seemed to be the fashion in those days. Le Cappelain's mechanic/driver is standing beside the portable steam engine as work stops for the photographer.

The team included the engine driver who needed to be supported by the farmer with a supply of fuel, either coal or wood or both, and a constant supply of water for the boiler. There were one or two men on the loaded van to fork the sheaves up onto the machine, a man on the machine to pass the sheaves to the feeder, who cut the binder twine and fed the sheaves in a steady flow into the drum. On the ground a man attended to the bags of grain from the delivery chutes, exchanging them as they filled up; he had to have a supply of empty bags. Another man raked away the cavings, the husks and short pieces of straw. Yet another man attended to the trusser, removing the trusses of straw and loading them onto a van. Lastly men with horses were required to move the vans, taking the empty van away and bringing a loaded van to the thresher. So there was quite a large team at work, neighbours helping as well.

Jubilee Show Mr. de la Haye exhibited a box of Jersey Royal Fluke potatoes. There is a report 'that Medals were to be offered for new and improved Agricultural Implements'. Unfortunately this laudable intention was not taken up; there were no entries!

In the report of 1885 there is a reference to the making of silage. One's immediate reaction on reading this was to ponder how they may have harvested the crop. They had reapers and horse-drawn hay rakes and buckrakes but little else except hand rakes, forks, and box carts. The report then went on to explain the need to compress the material in the silo, by making use of anything that came to hand, it would seem: large lumps of granite or timber for instance. Then the final test: would the cows eat it? Well, they did and they liked it!

The author recalls persuading his father to make silage in the early 1950s while he was an agricultural student, then watching with interest some months later as the heifers in a paddock near the farm buildings first sniffed it and nibbled it, followed by a very swift reaction as they chewed on jaws full of it, lifting their heads and looking round as if to say, 'golly this is good stuff!' Commendation indeed!!

Throughout the second half of the century there were references to butterfat and the making of butter, which became more frequent. It seems to have been considered urgent, leading to the arrangement for a travelling butter school from London to visit the Island. The result was so pleasing to the Society that the butter school was invited back each year to tour the parishes. Subsequently butter-making competitions were held at cattle shows using farmers' own cream separators, churns, and

Pre-First World War advertisement for Vermoreil sprayers

driers. During that period adverts promoting dairy equipment, in particular butter churns and cream separators, appeared in each annual report.

It was quite clear that the Society was having an uphill battle with farmers to persuade them to follow the school's ideas. It was quicker to grab a handful of clean straw from the bedding and rub it over the cow's udder to clean it and that was that!

In the Society's reports for 1901-2 it is stated that mechanisation of agriculture was also making advances in the Island, with reference made to the more general use of mowers or reapers and tedders in haymaking, and the reports refer to experiments carried out with types of potato-digging machines. Bamford's first Jersey Lily potato diggers appeared about that time.

In 1904 apples, of which there was a good crop, continued to be important and a good crop of potatoes was exported. In 1905 there is a reference to spraying against blight with Bordeaux mixture. One might wonder again what sort of machine they used; presumably the French Vermoreil knapsack with its copper tank, brass fittings, and rubber hose and lever pump.

It is advertised in the 1903 year book of the RJA & HS by Messrs. H. Becker of Beresford Street, St. Helier. One of these sprayers could be found on most Jersey farms where potatoes and tomatoes were grown in the 1920s and 1930s.

First World War

During the war potato diggers and mowing/reaping machines had to be purchased by farmers to help the willing hands of women and girls who were working in the fields because so many of the men were in the forces. Potato diggers had been in use since the turn of the century and reapers sometime before.

Tâch'ron is a Jersey French word for a 'fork', i.e. a team leader, with the potato fork. The team is composed of three people to dig and pick the potatoes, using a potato fork and two potato baskets. The digger is followed by the shaker who shakes the tops and arranges the potatoes for the picker. Finally comes the picker, who follows behind with two baskets, one for larger potatoes known as 'ware' and the other for the small potatoes known as 'mids', which were sometimes picked separately. The crash of 1929 and the world recession which followed had a dramatic effect on Jersey farming. There was massive unemployment in England and Wales, and the British Government requested the States to employ English labour. Men from England and Wales came over on the mail boat for the potato season and Bretons were no longer employed. However, unlike the Bretons, these men were not countrymen and had no idea how to use a potato fork. They frequently pierced potatoes with the fork and had difficulty recognising the original seed potatoes, picking them with the new ones.

Farmers found it expedient to buy potato-digging machines; these were all horse-drawn, one horse in the shafts and one in front in traces or long harness.

The summer shows in those years of the 1930s were great occasions: people flocked to Springfield to see the afternoon's entertainment just as they did for the Battle of Flowers, which in those days was also held at Springfield. Included among the entertainers for the Summer Show one year were the Cossacks with their horses; another year a cavalry regiment of the British Army performed riding tricks and musical rides. Most entertaining of all and fondly remembered were the Royal Corps of Signals with their Triumph motorcycles and horses. The dispatch riders made enormous leaps on their machines over a line of vehicles and horses including a covered wagon!

They performed a variety of tricks, ending with a mass of them climbing in an orderly manner on one machine to circle the arena. For the technically minded, motorcycles had girder forks in those days, before telescopic forks; the girder fork could take far greater punishment than the early telescopic fork. Outside the arena was a line of trade stands exhibiting tractors, implements, cars, delivery vans, lorries, agricultural sundries, and so forth, all of which added to the interest and excitement. The author as a schoolboy had many a pleasant hour wandering around those trade stands.

It was a happy occasion when the Royal Jersey Agricultural and Horticultural Society held its 100th birthday celebrations at Springfield during the Summer Show in 1933. The show included a wonderful procession of machines and farm transport past and present over its hundred-year history which circled the show ring before a large crowd.

It is interesting to note that the last toast of the Centenary Banquet in 1933 was...

'Speed the Plough'!

Hail to the agricultural machine! The author was delighted to note that his father, the late Francis Renouf Billot, is recorded in the publication as being on the committee in 1933. He later became a Jurat of the Royal Court. There was extra good news that year: the potato crop had done exceptionally well. Although prices were not particularly good the heavy crop had compensated.

A big advance in farm mechanisation in the late 1930s was the Ferguson tractor with its hydraulic lift system and three-point linkage. It would start a revolution in the design of tractors and implements still used today, some seventy years later.

The two pictures of the afternoon parade at Springfield in 1933 portray the history of the first hundred years of the Royal Jersey Agricultural and Horticultural Society with exhibits of their activities over that period. In front of the former grandstand is a lorry with the butter-making school followed by a milking demonstration, then a dairy lorry loaded with milk cans, followed by a milk delivery van. Next to follow is a demonstration of tomato packing with a grader and the tomato chips in which the tomatoes were packed for export, and then a lorry loaded with tomato chips ready to be shipped for export.

Afternoon parade at Springfield in 1933 celebrating the centenary of the RJA & HS (from Mr. Donald Le Boutillier's collection).

(*below*) The afternoon parade, 1933 (from Mr. Donald Le Boutillier's collection).

In this picture of the afternoon parade are a group of people in period clothing, the ladies in Jersey bonnets and all carrying the implements of the early days of the Society: a wooden pitchfork, a wooden hay rake, scythes, and sickles. Further back is a section of an apple crusher and press followed by a horse-drawn cider cart with an 800 gallon cask to carry cider to town for export, displaying one of Jersey's early agricultural exports when Jersey cider was a much sought-after commodity. The scene depicts an industry which was disappearing. Then come traditional ploughs pulled by horses, the breezing plough and the 'big plough' with men and their spades whose job it was to dig and tidy the furrow ends, and the modern tractor and plough. The changing way of digging and marketing the Jersey Royal potato is displayed next, with Bretons and a mechanical digger completing the scene. The latest application of mechanisation to dairying is demonstrated by the then up-to-date milking machine. There were probably three milking machines in use at the time, one at the farm of Mr. Riley at Trinity Manor, another at Mr. Arthur's farm Les Ruettes, St. John, and yet another at Mr. Peredé's farm at Fairview, St. Saviour.

JERSEY AIRWAYS, Ltd

DETAILS
of the

REGULAR AIR SERVICE

JERSEY to ENGLAND

may be obtained

from

HAROLD G. BENEST

(Bellingham's)

1 MULCASTER STREET.

An advertisement in the RJA & HS year book 1933.
To add to the pleasures of life in 1933 one could hop on a Jersey Airways plane on the beach at West Park and fly to England via Southampton, as advertised.

The dark clouds of war came ever closer and in 1940 everything would change with the German Occupation. The requirements of the local population brought about major changes to our agriculture at different times because the greater part of our production in normal times was for export. These official figures for the 1930s and 1940s published for each crop indicate the trends, to make a comparison with what was grown in 1939 in the last peacetime year before the Second World War and the figures for 1941. During the war and German Occupation there was no exporting, and it was important to produce as much at home as possible.

In 1939:

23,880 vergées of potatoes
12.5 vergées of rye
21 vergées of barley
2,939 vergées of root crops
10,014 vergées of pasture
134 vergées of wheat

In 1941:

6,500 vergées of potatoes
6,500 vergées of oats
400 vergées of rye
1,200 vergées of barley
3,500 vergées of root crops
12,000 vergées of pasture
12,000 vergées of wheat

The total figures indicate 4,359.5 extra vergées were brought under cultivation during the Occupation. Wheat production increased almost tenfold between 1939 and 1941. The areas of pasture and root crops for the cattle barely changed to provide the population with milk and meat. The changes were a return to that which had existed almost a hundred years before when the population depended mainly on what was grown in the Island. Growing cereals and fodder crops had been abandoned because it was easier and cheaper to import flour, wheat, straw, and hay, but there was always the appeal of the profit from potatoes and tomatoes, which despite several bad seasons brought quite a lot of prosperity to the agricultural community. There was a great growth in cultivating potatoes and tomatoes and this meant that all other crops were abandoned in their favour, so much so that from 1907 to 1938 the area under cultivation had increased by no less than 17,000 vergées and this was mainly taken up by potatoes and tomatoes. According to official figures in 1831 the number of vergées devoted to wheat was 5,823, which was quite a large figure. The total number of vergées devoted to arable crops was not as great as it could have been because large areas were in orchards, and there was quite a lot of land which had not yet been claimed for agriculture. Payn, writing in 1940, says that about 125 years before, Jersey wheat had had a good reputation in England and a lot of it was exported as seed for English farming.

The potato crop has varied enormously over the years:

1930: 17,337 vergées
1947: 11,002 vergées
1957: 20,204 vergées
1967: 14,827 vergées

Since then it has gone up to 31,835 vergées including 11,677 under plastic in 1997. There was a post-war boom with early potatoes after the First World War just as there was a tomato boom after the Second World War.

The tomato

The Hacquoil family were leading farmers in St. Ouen parish before and after the first war. They grew an enormous area of 100,000 tomatoes. They were very go-ahead people and early users of tractors. In 1912 they acquired a London bus for the benefit of their many staff; it was eventually parked in a field to provide shelter in inclement weather. François Le Maistre, whose family farm is in St. Ouen, remembers using it in more recent times.

Unheated glasshouses were known for many years as greenhouses. Today they are all known as glasshouses. They became popular with growers as the demand for tomatoes increased, leading to very extensive glasshouse construction, particularly after the last world war. Sadly the demand for local outdoor and glasshouse produce has declined in recent years. Tomatoes were first grown in the 1860s, but only in the garden for domestic consumption. The first tomatoes exported were from a glasshouse at Rozel Manor in about 1870. Mr. Paul Lamy of St. Martin was the pioneer. Having travelled to the USA as a young man, he saw them being grown in private gardens in Iowa, which was a corn-growing area where pigs were fattened on a large scale. Returning to Jersey, Mr. Lamy rented La Hougette in St. Saviour and was growing Indian corn (maize) as a second crop; having harvested the cobs he then fed the remaining growth to his cattle. He grew several vergées each year. He moved on to Bel Val, St. Martin, where he began growing outdoor tomatoes on a big scale, buying his seed from Mr. Gruchy of Les Prés, St. Clement, who had started growing tomatoes two years earlier.

There were problems with disease and humidity, among other things which affect the tomato. Bordeaux mixture, which was imported, was the most efficient spray against blight, but a mixture of blue stone and lime was just as effective and cheaper. A search began to find a tomato with a nice smooth skin to replace the rather rough skin type. A successful variety was grown by a Mr. Le Masurier, who named the tomato after his farm, to be known as Jambart Beauty. Other varieties introduced were Flying Dutch and the Frogmore, which produced big tomatoes. Sunrise became a most popular variety in later years.

Scientists found that the tomatoes contained certain vitamins which were good for human consumption. The press gave this wide coverage, so that tomatoes became popular in England and demand grew rapidly. This encouraged the search for better varieties to please the public in general. The merchants who exported the tomatoes purchased them at 3d. per lb and came to fetch them from the farm. Later, as the business developed and grew, the merchants continued to pay 3d./lb but the growers had to deliver them to the merchants in town; then there were fluctuations and gluts due to overproduction. Mr. Lamy grew up to 100,000 plants, and sometimes more.

The Veneer tomato basket advertisement, RJA & HS yearbook in 1909.
These baskets were the result of some hard work and trials to find the best package for tomatoes by Mr. A. J. Norman of the well-known company Norman Ltd.

The effect of power on the farm and in farming communities

Different countries were affected in quite different ways by farm mechanisation. Those with large populations of country dwellers were affected far more than others. The introduction of the threshing machine resulted in the Tolpuddle Martyrs, farm labourers in the south of England who saw their jobs threatened by mechanisation, but in the USA in the Midwest there was little or no labour to lose jobs. When the reaper was introduced by McCormick it was a boon to the farming families who could afford to buy it. In England the Industrial Revolution and the Enclosures Act forced thousands to move from the country into the industrial towns and cities to work in those 'dark satanic mills'.

The effect of farm mechanisation in Jersey was different again: most farms were family farms employing only members of the family with few people to be displaced. The main problem here had nothing to do with mechanisation, it was the effect on second and third sons with no farm to inherit. Instead they went to sea, or into the shipbuilding industry, and many emigrated to settle overseas. The Jerseyman has an extraordinary resilience for dealing with economic problems. Over the last hundred years the Island has imported labour to work on farms.

In 1912 the States rented La Chasse, St. Saviour, to carry out crop experiments with fertilisers, etc. The farm was occupied by the States from Christmas 1911 and it seems some crops were planted on the land even before that. After the First World War, Mr. T. B. Davis bought the States Farm in Trinity for the benefit of the farming community.

The early advantage of having a tractor for ploughing was that it did away with the need for neighbours to work together, each bringing their own horse to make up a team of at least four and often six to pull the big plough (*la grande tchéthue*), then working their way around the district helping each other to get their fields ploughed. The system had some advantages, as one plough would serve several neighbours working together, and it created a community spirit. The author's father remembered that after ploughing it was 'party time': having fed the horses they would crowd into the house for the evening meal and sit up late playing cards before dispersing. Others would sit up polishing the horses' brasses, not to be outdone by the neighbour's harness and brasses. Snatching a few hours' sleep before getting up at five to feed and water the horses and then have their own breakfast, they would then harness up to be in the field coupling up to the plough at first light. Neighbours worked together at harvest time to carry sheaves of cereals to the threshing machine, first on one farm and then on the next.

The farmers' wives would get together to cook a midday dinner for the men on each farm. Sadly mechanisation on the farm in Jersey in recent years has resulted in the farmer climbing on his tractor and going off to plough on his own. It has killed the need for neighbourliness and the old community spirit has largely disappeared.

Mechanisation did not come about with the arrival of the steam engine that was a part of the evolution in the provision of power. Mechanical devices began with the ox hauling the ard, followed by the working horse drawing cultivating implements, operation of water pumps for irrigation, the horse engine to drive barn machinery, and later the reaper and the binder and so forth. Steam provided the extra power to drive bigger barn machinery and bigger threshing machines which speeded up the work on the farm. Steam had a second part to play in that steam was driving the machine shops in the factories that produced the farm machinery. Then came the internal combustion engine to drive the tractor and the stationary engine, some American manufacturers going as far as naming their engines 'Farmer's Boy' and 'Farm Hand'. Then came electricity and the electric motor providing power at the point of use for the barn and dairy machinery. The potato-digging machines purchased by farmers in the 1930s greatly assisted the English unemployed brought over to dig potatoes. More recently the potato harvester has changed all that again: only three or four farm workers stand on a machine sorting rubbish from potatoes and the rest is done by the machine.

In 1939 there were 372 tractors, 1,258 horses, 914 lorries, and 312 potato-digging machines. In 1940 there were 438 potato-digging machines which was a substantial increase, due to loss of manual labour called into the armed forces at the outbreak of war. Many of the English and Welsh potato diggers in the 1930s were in the Territorial Army. It was their only source of income if unemployed.

In 1946 there were 1,036 horses and 344 potato-digging machines.

In 1985 there were 1,407 tractors including 95 tracklayers or crawlers, mostly the Ransomes MG2, 5, and 6, and there were 276 potato harvesters.

The use of power on the farm:

In 1870 one farm worker had 1.6 horsepower at his command.
In 1920 he had 5.3 horsepower at his command.
In 1933 he had 33 horsepower at his command.
In 1960 he had 40 horsepower at his command.

Between 1600 and 1800, 75 per cent of all labour was devoted to producing food.
In 1950 it was 10 per cent.
In 1800 it required three man hours to produce a bushel of wheat.
At the end of the nineteenth century it required half a man hour.
At the end of the first quarter of the twentieth century it required a one-quarter of a man hour.
By the 1950s in Jersey, thanks to the hydraulic lift, three-point linkage, and the power take-off (PTO), one man was doing what two had done before.
In spite of mechanisation the potato crop is still labour intensive, both to plant the crop and harvest it.

Sources: The foregoing was compiled from papers held by the library of La Société Jersiaise, the Le Couteur papers, and others including farm accounts of Trinity Manor 1820-2 and farm accounts of Maison de Haut 1903–22 and cuttings from *La Chronique de Jersey*, written by D. E. Payn in the 1940s and translated by Michael Vautier; other papers held by the Library of La Société Jersiaise; C. P. Le Cornu, 'The Agriculture of the Islands of Jersey . . .', *Journal of the Royal Agricultural Society of England*, 20 (1859); Guy Fortescue Burrell de Gruchy, *Medieval Land Tenures in Jersey* (1957); the minutes of the Royal Jersey Agricultural and Horticultural Society and their work *One Hundred Years of the Royal Jersey Agricultural and Horticultural Society* (1933).

2 The Beginning

Before considering the farm machinery of more recent centuries and the work it performs, it helps our understanding to look back to the beginning and examine the implements of the early farmer. It all began with very basic hand tools. The tillage implement is the one tool which has continued to be used from the earliest days of agriculture to the present time, and will continue to be used. Of particular importance were the stone mattock, the stone axe, and the flint sickle with which to clear the ground of trees and top growth before tillage could begin.

Jersey's first farmers, Neolithic people, have been the subject of considerable research by academics, which helps us to get some idea of the beginnings of our subject and what might have happened here in Jersey. However, some of it can be no more than an intelligent guess. It is not difficult to think of primitive man observing that, after flowering, plants like grasses or bushes created seed and berries which could be eaten, and the remainder of the seed or fruit which fell to the ground might germinate and grow, and then noticing that the process was repeated each year. He then realised that he could help the process to his advantage if he gathered that seed and planted it in a patch of ground he had prepared for it.

When man first took a branch from a tree or a piece of flint or stone and fashioned it to a point to scratch the earth to sow those seeds, he was not only learning to cultivate and farm the land but also learning a craft, to make simple implements and tools for agriculture. One can imagine the thrill when people saw those first seeds germinate and emerge from the ground, then later watched them grow and ripen, and the excitement of that first harvest and the realisation that they could grow their own food!

The first implements were limited to a very small number of materials listed in a little rhyme:

Wood and stone
Antler and bone

Of these, wood is the one material which was to remain in use to the present day, closely followed by stone in Jersey. Only the day before this piece was written the author collected a spade from his local blacksmith, Tom Marett, of St. Martin, who fitted a new wooden handle to a forty-year-old blade.

Where did it all begin? A very long way from Jersey!

Evidence points to the people of the Near East such as Sumeria, which is no longer a place name; it was beside the Dead Sea and included Jericho. It was thought to be the cradle of agriculture, where it was first practised in about 8,000 BC and possibly even earlier, there being flax and polished stone tools from that earlier period. The ever-growing population of Neolithic peoples expanded and spread very slowly north and west along rivers and estuaries and along the Mediterranean coasts, reaching these shores about 4,850 BC. Without any education and with no written language, development was painfully slow by today's standards, but as these people acquired skills in the use of materials for tools and implements, agriculture improved as time went on. The Mesolithic people living here when Neolithic people reached Western Europe were slow to adopt the Neolithic way of life.

The following calendar of events serves as a guide for the reader through the early part of this history. It was compiled by the author during research from several sources, some local, and the *Encyclopaedia of Dates and Events* edited by L. C. Pascoe. However a problem with compiling a calendar of events is the variation of opinion between sources, and some dates may have been revised by more recent research.

Significant dates

10,000 BC	Mesolithic period: trees and plants established.
6000 BC	Flint sickles, stone axes, mattocks, and adzes were in use, indicating the cultivation of crops in Sumeria and other parts of the Near East.
4850 BC	Agriculture in Jersey begins with the arrival of Neolithic people.
3500 BC	Wheeled vehicles were believed to be in use in Sumeria and craftsmen such as masons and smiths were active.
3250 BC	Beginning of Chalcolithic period in Jersey, lasting to 2,250 BC. Flat copper axes have been found in Jersey.
3200 BC	Ards and rakes (possibly harrows) and manuring in use by Egyptians who were using a 365-day and a twelve-month year.
3000 BC	Asses were used as beasts of burden. Utensils of precious metals and metal tools such as the sickle were in use (Middle East).
2800 BC	The Chinese are thought to have had a drill for sowing seed.
2600 BC	Manufacture of iron objects in the Middle East, but not widely used for several hundred years.
2350 BC	Wine in Egypt.
2250 BC	Bronze Age to 1500 BC in Jersey; stone tools continued to be used. Stone shares used on traction ards hauled by oxen; methods of joinery understood.
1860 BC	Copper mining in North Wales on the Great Orme.
1800 BC	Horses were being used in the Middle East as draught animals but were not yet being ridden.
1400 BC	In India iron tools and iron plough shares in use. .
1313 BC	Reservoirs and irrigation canal systems were in use in Egypt.
1122 BC	The Chinese completed a map of China.
1100 BC	Late Bronze Age in Britain to 500 BC. Tin mining in Cornwall, bronze made in England with Cornish tin and Welsh copper. Phoenicians importing English tin.
800 BC	Iron Age started in Jersey.
600 BC	The Persians were using windmills, canals and reservoirs, and irrigation was extensive.
500 BC	Brythonic Celts migrating to Britain in hoards from the Continent. The Celts were widely spread over Central and Western Europe. They were skilled in making stone tools and became good at working iron during the Iron Age. The skill to make iron tools and farm implements came from the Continent.
350 BC	Lathes were in use.
200 BC	Gears were in use in the Middle East to enable oxen to drive water wheels for irrigation.
54 BC	Start of Roman occupation in Britain. There followed a peaceful period of several centuries, benefiting agriculture and enabling craftsmen to improve their skills, especially with iron.
AD 410	The departure of Roman legions from Britain and Gaul was followed by the Dark Ages.
AD 500	Saxons of Teutonic race migrated to north-west Europe and Britain, where they introduced a heavy plough. They became the Anglo-Saxons.

Stone tools were some of the earliest tools used by people, the Palaeolithic, in Jersey; they were found at the first 'slaughterhouse' in the Island in a cave at La Cotte in St. Brelade, thought to have been in use from about 250,000 years ago. The tools were crude, made with stone simply by knocking off large flakes from big pebbles such as flint. Over thousands of years they discovered how to make better tools, how to grind them to produce a better cutting edge. Wild animals, rhinoceros and mammoths, could simply be driven over a cliff to be 'slaughtered', providing meat or food for a community of early people; but this was a result of hunting and droving rather than livestock farming. Amazingly the site was used on and off depending on the sea level over some 200,000 years. In recent years during digs at La Cotte stone tools were found including flint axes, knives or cutters, and scrapers.

The loam soil in Jersey, according to the late Dr. Arthur Mourant, was the result of violent wind and dust storms which swept over Europe in earlier times. The loess soil that covers the Island was deposited, having been carried on the wind from as far as present-day Poland, a thousand miles away. The evidence is best seen at Green Island where loess soil lies thickly over loose stone. In more settled times this enormous blanket of loess formed a soil base which, combined with warmer weather and rainfall, created ideal conditions for plant life. Trees and plants were well established by 10.000 BC in the Mesolithic period, long before the present-day sea level, which indicates this coastal area was fertile with a good climate and covered in vegetation, which would encourage people to settle.

When Mesolithic people inhabited this area from 10000 BC it was a very different coast compared with today: fertile lowland extended far around a major part of the high ground that was to become the Island. La Motte or Green Island was not yet an isolated island. While Mesolithic man may have experimented with plant life he was not a farmer. However, he did have tools— mattocks, hoes, the adze—and his arrows, made with the arrowhead set in resin to the wooden shaft, were used for killing animals and fish. The tools he had show that some primitive form of farming or gardening was being practised. Living on the coast he combined fishing with hunting with bows and arrows and gathering nuts and berries in the search for food, clothing himself in skins.

Neolithic farmers

There has been so much research on Neolithic people that there is plenty of evidence to support the claim that they were the first farmers in north-west Europe. They brought with them a way of life in which farming played an important role to provide food and clothing. They were skilled craftsmen and their culture of farming made them different from previous inhabitants of this area. They knew how to clear land of top growth, how to cultivate and make a seed bed, to sow seeds, harvest their crops, to grind and make meal, and to domesticate wild animals. They also knew how to make pottery, how to build and sail boats, how to build houses for themselves, for their livestock, and for the storage of harvested crops, and to store food, etc. in holes in the ground.

They knew how to make the tools to perform those tasks. Their hand tools were basic and primitive, but even so they were the forerunners of the agricultural implements and machines we use today. They had learned to fashion and polish stone implements as opposed to the rough flake tools of previous inhabitants. Their first implements in Jersey were stone axes, mattocks, adzes, flint sickles, querns, and hammers. The antler from a red deer was a useful source of material for making a share for the ard, and when cut and fashioned would make a useful pick by selecting and cutting out appropriate pieces. A piece of antler with two horns hafted to a stout stick made a two-prong grappin or pitchfork; the shoulder blade of an ox would make a useful shovel. The ribs were also used to make a hard point for the ard. With an axe and adze the people of this age would cut a branch from a tree to make a digging stick by fashioning it to a point at one end, or a narrow blade rather like an oar or paddle with which to dig the soil, in effect a wooden spade. By the third millennium this had developed further to make a heart- or triangular-shaped shovel. With these skills they were more inclined to settle, clear the land, cultivate the soil, sow crops of wheat, barley, rye, and flax, then wait to harvest the fruits of their labours.

However, the resulting change in the way of life was not quite as we might imagine. Farming formed only a part of Neolithic people's activities, their knowledge of farming was limited, and their very primitive hand tools limited the amount of work they could undertake and the area they could cultivate. Crops were grown in small plots or gardens; they were vulnerable to attack from wild animals, birds, disease, and drought without any protection as we know it. There were no sprays, no fertilisers, so they were still very dependent on gathering food from the wild, berries and nuts, hunting wild animals, and fishing. Over time they will have learned more because that was their inclination; they might learn the value of manure and ash as a fertiliser and green manuring and vraic.

The excavations at Le Pinnacle, St. Ouen, by members of La Société Jersiaise revealed what is thought to have been a settlement of Neolithic people from 6,000 and 7,000 years ago. It is sometimes referred to as a 'stone factory', where flint arrowheads, stone axes, mattocks, and adzes were found. The best-known implement is the axe, which was far more than the name implies. It was certainly an axe but by turning it along its axis through 90 degrees it became two more tools: an adze with which to make an ard or to hollow out a log boat, and also a tillage implement, namely a mattock. The mattock, the pick, the wooden spade or digging stick, and the ard (an early traction tillage implement) are man's oldest cultivating tools. The axe and flint sickle were used first to clear an area of land of trees, bushes, and top growth and the mattock to break open the soil and to clear the land of the roots of bushes and trees, which were then burnt off. The mattock was then used to cultivate the land. These implements would be simple to make with the primitive tools of the day but they would take considerable time. A stone axe would be sharpened when it became blunt but may have been used as a mattock before re-sharpening. Of the many stone axes in the collection at La Hougue Bie some have chips in the cutting edge, which suggests they may have been used as mattocks, becoming chipped on striking stones in the soil. Fortunately the basic materials Neolithic man needed for making implements of stone and wood were available in abundance in the Island. As we have seen he understood how to use bone, antler, and horn for making implements, and these too were available.

After thousands of years the mattock remains a very useful implement for breaking up the soil and should not be confused with the hoe, which is a lightweight tool for weeding between plants and rows of vegetables. Steel mattocks are still manufactured today and may be purchased in your local hardware store or garden centre.

There are no flint deposits in Jersey, so much of the flint found at Le Pinnacle was off the beach where flint pebbles could be found. Large pieces to make a useful flint axe or sickle had to be imported; there was a trade in flint and other stone implements in the Channel Islands. It is thought that flint was quarried in an area of Alderney before the rising sea levels covered it. Neolithic people's stone implements were used in the hand, and others were hafted to a wooden handle which, used with a swing, were more effective. A sickle made with a single piece of flint in the shape of a shallow curved blade hafted to a wooden handle may have been a rare luxury in Jersey in view of the scarcity of flint in the Island. So a sickle in Jersey was most likely to be made with blades of flint fitted closely along the inside curve of a piece of antler or branch of a tree suitably fashioned. The flint was knapped to make a continuous curved cutting edge. Knapping the flint to obtain a good spark, was an everyday job in the British Army in the days of the flintlock musket, from which the saying arises 'we must not be caught knapping!'

The sickle was used for cutting dry grass to store as hay for winter fodder, harvesting cereal crops and also to clear an area of land of top growth for cultivation. Neolithic man's collection of implements would have included a grindstone to polish and maintain a cutting edge on the stone axe or mattock and a quern with a shallow hollow in the middle together with a smaller pebble probably of dolerite used as a hammer, which would have a variety of uses from grinding nuts and extracting seeds to making flour or meal for food preparation. He may well have had tools made of antler as described above, such as a mattock, a fork, a pick, and a sickle. Horns were useful as they have a natural socket into which to fit the end of a stout stick or the nose of an ard to give a hard pointed tip; a horn will also hold water, making a useful drinking vessel. A piece of antler tens of thousands of years old is displayed at La Hougue Bie, indicating how durable this material is, so it is not surprising that Neolithic people found it useful. The author's father had a bull's horn which was filled with water to carry a carborundum stone to the field and keep it wet in order to sharpen a sickle or scythe in the field. It had a wire hook to attach it to a belt around the waist.

The antler and stone tools which follow are part of the La Société Jersiaise/Jersey Heritage Trust collection at La Hougue Bie, Jersey. (Courtesy of Olga Finch, curator of archaeology.)

Part of a red deer antler found at La Cotte de St. Brelade.
This red deer antler is of the Palaeolithic period, 40,000-80,000 years old. Probably the remains of a deer after it was slaughtered. The fact that it has survived for so long indicates how tough and hard wearing a piece of antler can be and why it was used as a tool.

Stone tools

Stone axe made of flint.
The flint axe's surface is rough and flaked. It is Neolithic c.4850 BC. The dimensions are 4 in. (10.1 cm) long and 1.5 in. (2.63 cm) wide. It was found at Les Chasse, St. Ouen, in 1959. The cutting edge was probably damaged in use. This axe may have been made from a stone or pebble picked up off the beach. Flint picked up off the beach is thought to be affected by a long period in the sea, making it flaky, but it could be the result of the process used to make and shape it.

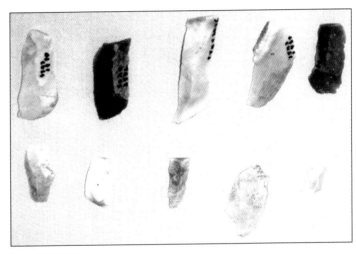

Mesolithic flint tools.
A selection of Mesolithic flint blades, 9000-7000 BC. The dimensions are approximately 0.625–1.25 in. (1.5-2.11 cm) long and 0.5-0.75 in. (1.3-2 cm) across. These fine blades are described as composite tools. They were probably made using tools made from mica. Even smaller fine blades like these above would need to be set in a curved piece of antler or hardwood to make a sickle.

Three stone axes and broken stone tools.
Three stone axes made of dolerite in the foreground. Neolithic, 4750-4250 BC.
Dimensions: from the left 4 in. (10.1 cm) long, 5.5 in. (12.73 cm) long, 3.5 in. (8.9 cm) long, 2.5 in. (6.3 cm) long, and the larger axes are 3 in. (7.6 cm) wide. Found at Le Pinnacle and probably made there.
Note the finish of the axes compared with the rough finish of the earlier stone tools. The cut marks are the result of archaeologists taking material to check the identity. In the background are some broken stone quarrying tools used for making axes; two of them originally had holes through them but have been broken across the hole. The broken tool on the right can be seen quite clearly. The holes were beautifully made and smoothed off.

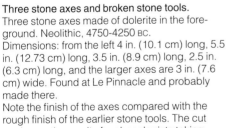

Neolithic stone axes of different materials found in Jersey

Selection of Neolithic stone axes, 4750–2850 BC, found in Jersey; from the top left:
(1) Flint axe probably from Normandy, blade 4.5 in. (11 cm) long, 2 in. (5 cm) wide.
(2) Dolerite axe probably from Brittany, blade 4.5 in. (11 cm) long, 2 in. (5 cm) wide.
(3) Jadeite axe probably from the Alps, blade 7 in. (17.7 cm) long, 3 in. (7.6 cm) wide.
(4) Dolerite axe made at Le Pinnacle, blade 8 in. (7.6 cm) long, 3 in. (7.6 cm.) wide, found at First Tower.
(5) Small axe made of fibrolite, blade 3 in. (7.6 cm) long, 1.75 in. (4.5 cm) wide.

This collection of tools from different places indicates that Neolithic man travelled quite extensively, bringing tools with him from different parts of Western Europe. These tools are beautifully finished, smooth and polished, indicating how the skill had slowly improved over many centuries. Dolerite rocks are amongst the hardest rocks found anywhere in the world.

Breton stone axe made of jadeite.
This beautiful stone axe known as a Breton torpedo axe of the Neolithic period is made of jadeite, probably from the Alps, c.4850 BC. Dimensions: 11 in. (8 cm) long and 2 in. (5 cm) wide. This is one of the largest and most impressive stone axes ever found in the British Isles, made at a time when Neolithic people were at the peak of their skill of stone tool making. The beautifully smooth finish has no damage to the cutting edge and it is still sharp today. Because it is the only one like it to have been found so far, it is thought it may have been a ceremonial piece belonging to a local leader. It was found when ploughing a field on a farm in St. Saviour.

Neolithic quern and stone hammer.
milling tools: ball hammer and quern for grinding grain into flour. The quern is made of granite. It is Neolithic, 4750-4250 BC, and was found in Jersey. The diameter of the ball hammer is 4 in. (10 cm) and the quern is approximately 15 in. (38.1 cm) across. Dolerite was a popular material for a hammer; the ball is beautifully shaped and finished and not simply a large pebble taken off the beach.

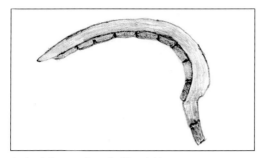

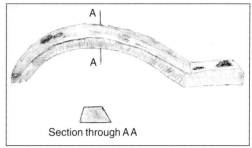

Section through A A

Author's impression of a flint sickle.
This drawing by the author is of a sickle made of antler or wood with flint blades inserted. Neolithic, c.4000 BC, approximately 7–8 in. (17.7-20.3 cm) long overall. The blades of flint were skilfully cut and knapped to shape and inserted probably with resin along the inside of a carefully selected piece of crescent-shaped antler or hardwood. The short stump at the end may be hafted to a wooden handle. The above drawing is the result of examining various sources and descriptions including *Larousse agricole: encyclopédie illustrée* and illustrates how such a sickle might look.

Author's drawing of a Neolithic flint sickle made from one piece of flint, c.4000 BC.
The Neolithic flint sickle is 7-8 in. (17.7-20.3 cm) long overall. The drawing gives a good idea what a well-made flint sickle looked like. Such a sickle might have been imported, like many of the axes in the Island, simply because there was no flint in the Island except for pebbles on the beach. Flint sickles continued in use through the Bronze Age to the Iron Age. This drawing is the result of examining various sources including *Larousse agricole: encyclopédie illustrée*.

It is remarkable that a tool like the sickle could be made with such a brittle material as flint, but having studied the skills of the Neolithic people, it is not surprising. If the reader has any doubts, just examine again the torpedo axe above. Neolithic people became experienced in selecting a suitable type of stone for one purpose or another, as they did with timber. As we see above axes were made of different types of stone, some imported, some quarried locally; dolerite was a favourite, being among the hardest rocks found anywhere. The deposit of dolerite at Le Pinnacle is a likely reason for it becoming a site to manufacture stone tools and implements. They were probably traded by barter with Guernsey and Alderney and elsewhere.

Some stone axes and mattocks found at Le Pinnacle were drilled to make a socket, including picks with a point at one end and a hammer head at the other; the tool makers had developed an effective and skilful way of drilling stone as the holes were beautifully made. The collection of quite small fine-pointed stone awls or boring tools from Le Pinnacle can be seen on display at La Hougue Bie. It is remarkable that they were able to achieve such a fine quality of finished work

Neolithic socketed stone axe and hammer.
This socketed stone hammer and axe is Neolithic, c.4000 BC. It was found near Thetford in Norfolk. It is 9.5 in. (24 cm) long overall. The axe is blunt after some hard use! It is amazing to us today that the socket was bored out using another piece of hard stone. (Ancient House collection, Thetford. Courtesy of the curator, Oliver Bone.)

with such a hard material and the primitive stone tools available to them. It must have tried their patience, as many were found broken across the carefully bored-out socket. Most stone has little tensile strength so the breakages are not surprising, but it is interesting that they tried and at times were successful. It took time to make the tools and to use them, but Neolithic man had no better methods and time was not a problem.

Such tools would have to be used with care to make them last; none would be tough enough or the assembly strong enough to take a lot of punishment. The stone axe for example would be used with small strokes for steadily chipping away at a tree to cut through it. Thetford Museum has an example of a socketed stone axe and hammer illustrated here.

It is thought the Island was able to support a population of about 3,000 people in the Neolithic Age, according to Olga Finch, curator of archaeology at La Hougue Bie museum. Farming activities were supplemented by hunting, fishing, and gathering fruit, which assured them of a food supply, giving them time to do other things such as improve their skills at making implements, clear and cultivate more plots of land, build boats and make expeditions to the neighbouring coast; and they found the time and had the skills to move and handle big, heavy stones with which to build the dolmens such as La Hougue Bie.

A collection of stone axes may all look pretty much the same to many people but the work to which they are put depends on how they are held in the hand or how they are hafted to the handle. A close examination of the wear and tear on the stone is a useful guide to their use: for example, if a stone is polished with a fine thin shape towards a sharp cutting edge it will be an axe or an adze; if it has lost the fine shape and the cutting edge is blunted with the odd chip knocked out of it, then it is more likely to be a mattock. They would sharpen a worn stone implement to restore it just as we would sharpen a steel cutting tool today. It is quite likely that as an axe becomes worn it will be used as a mattock.

Wooden implements

Among Neolithic people's implements was a stout wooden stick cut from the branch of a tree, then fashioned to a point at one end, with a stone mace head fitted onto the other end to add weight when digging the soil, sometimes known as a 'digging stick'. It may be fitted with a horn to harden the tip or fashioned in the shape of a blade, in effect a wooden spade to dig the soil as you would today with a spade or fork. The pointed stick with a horn tip and a stone mace was probably used first to break up the soil, followed up with the blade. It would have to be of a hard wood for the cutting edge to last. The depth of work was very shallow, perhaps no more than 3-4 in. (7.5-10 cm).

The stick was made in many different forms, some having one or two shallow bends to increase the leverage, so making it more effective to prise open and break up the soil. It was developed with little refinements added to it: a wider blade, a step or a peg above the blade upon which to place the foot to apply more body weight or leverage to penetrate and dig the soil more effectively. From this form it developed sometime later into the cas-chrom, later still into the foot plough, which is relatively modern.

In work the cas-chrom was first pushed with the body and foot into the soil, the handle was then pushed downward to lever up the blade to break open the soil, and it was then drawn backwards to repeat the process, continually working backwards. Depth of work was probably no more than 2 in. (5 cm). The cas-chrom continued to be used for many centuries up to the 1880s in parts of the west of Scotland, Wales, Spain, and Ireland. It is claimed that twelve men could cultivate an acre a day. Ash was a favoured timber, as it is today for the spade. The cas-chrom was developed further in quite a different way to become an ard that was hauled over the soil, which we will look at in the next chapter.

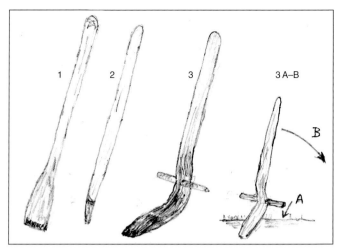

Wooden tools, digging stick, and cas-chrom.
Author's drawing of wooden hand tools, digging sticks, and cas-chrom for cultivating. Neolithic, c.4500 BC, to 20th century. Dimensions of various sticks 3 ft 6 in.–4 ft (110-20 cm) long. Digging sticks were made in several forms: (1) similar to a spade, (2) pointed stick tipped with horn on the point, (3) the cas-chrom with a foot tread to apply more weight to push it into the soil and with a bend to lever and break up the soil, still used but with an iron tip in the 19th century in Portugal, Spain, and in the Highlands and Islands. The expression 'digging stick' may not be the word used by the professional archaeologist but it is easily understood by most people. Today's digging stick is the spade. The author's drawings of the digging stick (1) and (2) are the result of examining various sources and indicates what such an implement might look like.

The next step forward was the ard, a traction cultivating tool hauled over the ground by one, two, or three men.

3 The Ard and Early Ploughs

'The Ploughman feeds us all.'

The January page of the Julius work calendar, Canterbury Cathedral, AD 1020.
The sharebeam was made of oak and the beam of holm-oak; the best ox for ploughing was a nine-year-old male and the best ploughman was a lusty fellow of 40 (Hesiad, Works and Days).

The plough and ploughing

The plough is a difficult implement to master, whether horse- or tractor-drawn. It is a highly skilled task: many people putting their hand to the plough for the first time have discovered this and experienced the frustration of failing to turn the perfect furrow. To be a good ploughman is a skill in its own right; to plough with a swing plough and a pair of horses requires the utmost skill. It may still be seen at ploughing matches today where they have their own classes. The most modern equipment, the multifurrow reversible plough, requires the close attention of a skilled ploughman to set the plough.

As a small boy brought up on a farm, the author often walked behind the horses and the big plough watching the soil being turned over by the mouldboard while his father was ploughing. He was fascinated by the furrow slice rising up the mouldboard, being turned and crumbled, then laid over inverted beside the previous furrow. Whatever had been on the top, weeds, grass, or manure, now lay buried under the clean, fresh soil. A field of freshly turned furrows, each one exactly like its neighbour, is a sight he would gaze upon and enjoy especially at the end of the day when the field was finished. Years later, as a young engineer with Ransomes, the famous plough makers of Ipswich, the author worked in the field developing new ploughs, and later with customers all over the country and parts of Europe, setting their new ploughs on their farms, and it still gave him the same pleasure. He had always taken the plough for granted and never given a thought about its origin. But while working on this history the question arose: what exactly was the origin of the plough?

The tillage implement has been man's most basic traction tool for several thousand years. It continues to be used at the present time and will well into the future. How did it become the implement we know today and when did it first come into use?

The history of the plough requires a wide-ranging examination of the many ages of man in Britain and Western Europe and the Middle East. We shall see how Jersey was affected by it. The modern plough in Jersey results from development in Western Europe, Britain, and Jersey over thousands of years. We have a fine collection of stone tools in La Société Jersiaise Museum at La Hougue Bie, for which we must be thankful. There are no other ancient agricultural artefacts in the Island so we make the huge leap of several thousand years to the last two or three centuries, filling that enormous gap by looking at developments on both sides of the Channel.

Throughout the history of agriculture since the beginning of the ard, two craftsmen stand out as major contributors to the production of farm tools, implements, and machinery. First the carpenter/joiner, followed by the blacksmith with the advent of the Iron Age. As time has gone on we have to thank the blacksmith for the major contribution to the advancement of farm machinery. From small beginnings in a blacksmith's forge in the country districts of the British Isles and later the USA, many small businesses became the modern-day international companies, world leaders in the production of farm machinery. Woodwork and ironwork continued to be used together until the middle of the twentieth century, from the humble spade to the wooden-frame threshing machine with an iron drum and concave. In Jersey the wooden plough gave way to iron towards the end of the nineteenth century, all made by Jersey craftsmen.

Before going any further a few words of explanation to help the reader not familiar with ploughs and ploughing. The mouldboard plough is an implement which turns the soil almost upside down, furrow by furrow, burying all that is lying or growing on the top, such as the trash residue of the previous crop, stubble, old grass, farmyard manure and vraic (seaweed) which has been spread on the land. The mouldboard plough leaves no soil unturned between furrows, whether it is a single-furrow plough or a multifurrow plough. It is the body of the plough that does the work. The body is composed of a share at the front that makes the horizontal cut at the furrow bottom. The share has a point and a wing, the width of which will vary depending on the width of furrow and the type of plough. Above the share on most ploughs is the coulter. Behind the share and coulter is the mouldboard, attached behind the share. The mouldboard is curved with a twist, or helix, to turn, twist, and mould the furrow slice over almost on its back to lean against its neighbour, the previous furrow slice. Also behind the share but on the side opposite to the mouldboard is a long vertical plate known as the landside, which absorbs the side pressure created as the share and its angled wing and the mouldboard are pulled through the soil. At the back of the landside is a heel that rests on the furrow bottom and helps with setting and maintaining the depth of work. The three components, the share, the mouldboard, and the landside, are held in place by an iron casting called a frog; on some ploughs it is a steel fabrication. The frog is almost hidden from view, being covered by the three components bolted to it. The assembly is called the body or in America the bottom. If a plough has three bodies in England it will be described as a three-furrow plough because it will turn three furrows; in America it will be called a three-bottom plough.

Above the share point is a knife coulter or rolling disc coulter suspended from the beam, which makes the vertical cut on the land side of the furrow slice, i.e. the side of the unploughed land. Beside or in front of the coulter is a skimmer: this is a small plough body that skims the top of the soil to remove the trash and drop it into the previous open furrow bottom. In Jersey the locally made 'big plough' has only a large skimmer, having no knife or disc coulter, but some modern imported big ploughs have a knife or disc coulter.

If the plough is a digger type ploughing a 12 in. (30 cm) deep and 14 in. or 16 in. (35 or 40 cm) wide furrow, the mouldboard will be deep and have an abrupt curve to crumble the soil as it lifts and turns the furrow slice. It is used on a mixed loam soil or light sandy soil of which we have both in Jersey. The general purpose plough, not used in Jersey but popular in England, will work between 5 in. and 7 in. (12-17.5 cm) deep at the most. It has a mouldboard with a long, slow-turning helix: the furrow is not crumbled but unbroken, and is simply inverted and pressed to lie against its neighbour; it is used on heavy clay land.

Some ploughs, usually confined to the West Midlands, the south, and South-West of England, have very long, shallow mouldboards measuring up to 4 ft (120 cm) long with a very slow turn to lean the furrow over against the previous furrow at a precise angle. A cast iron share known as a 'high-cut' share is cast with an upward curve at the middle of the wing to cut the furrow bottom high in the centre and produce a specially shaped furrow known as a 'high cut', or the 'oat seed' furrow. Each furrow slice must be sealed against its neighbour. The finished work looks like a

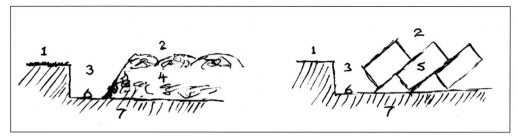

The furrow
On the left the furrow ploughing with a digger body as in Jersey, and on the right ploughing with a general purpose body:
(1) landside; (2) furrow side; (3) open furrow; (4) turned furrows, broken soil; (5) turned furrows, unbroken soil; (6) furrow bottom; (7) subsoil

Plough body details
(1) mouldboard; (2) frog; (3) landside; (4) heel; (5) share; (6) wing; (7) shin; (8) the hollow; (9) beam; (10) leg or stalk

piece of corduroy. Ploughing the oat seed furrow was done prior to sowing oats: the seeds were broadcast by hand and must not fall through any gap between the furrows but lie in the bottom of the V formed by the furrows leaning one against the other. It is very skilful ploughing performed with horses and beloved of ploughing match enthusiasts, but quite useless today with mechanical sowing machines!

The Jersey farmer uses the digger body, as it suits the Island's medium loam soil and produces a friable broken furrow requiring the minimum of further cultivation to prepare a seed bed. The author's father used to say in the potato planting season, 'plough in the morning and plant in the afternoon'. That is easy on our lighter loam soils but quite impossible on heavy clay soils in many parts of Britain, where they have to plough in the autumn and leave the winter frosts to break down and crumble the soil before planting in the spring. Between these two types of body is the semi-digger body, which has a slightly abrupt curve at the front of the mouldboard with a short twist or helix towards the back of the mouldboard; it is almost as long as a general purpose. They are very popular in the British Isles and are in general use in many parts.

Today's farmers with high-powered tractors and power-operated cultivators can get on the land and prepare seed beds in many areas in the autumn, provided the conditions are suitable, where previously the ploughed land would be left over the winter to weather and allow the frost to do its work.

The big plough (la grande tchéthue).
This horse-drawn Jersey big plough or digger plough at a demonstration by the Young Farmers' Club clearly illustrates ploughing in progress. The soil can be seen being turned by the mouldboard. In the foreground on the right can be seen the open furrow for the return leg back across the field. In this scene the furrow slice on each side of the work is turned towards the centre, known as 'gathering'; when the furrows are turned away from the centre it is known as 'casting'. The plough is drawn by six horses in pairs: the three horses on the right of each pair walk in the open furrow, the three on the left walking on the unploughed land. The horses are coupled to the plough with traces (chains) hooked at one end to the horses' collars and at the other to the red-painted wooden bodkins (whip-pletree or *batchu*). In the middle distance is the headland at the end of the furrow where the horses will turn and the plough is lifted out and laid on its side; the horses will draw the plough along the headland and will turn again into the open furrow in the fore-ground. When horses were working daily on the farm their tails would be cut shorter, to prevent them getting tangled in the traces and for cleanliness.

What may surprise the reader are the many different types of plough body, all variations of the three main types. There are many more different plough shares: Ransomes made between one and two hundred different cast iron chilled plough shares to fit general purpose and semi-digger bodies and a large number of steel shares to fit their digger bodies. All these different shares were to deal with the wide variety of soil types and the many different crops that are grown worldwide. Some need deep ploughing, some need shallow ploughing, others need a broken friable soil, others do not.

As described at the beginning, the conventional or traditional plough is an implement with a mouldboard; the share cuts the furrow slice and the mouldboard turns and inverts it. The resulting work leaves no unturned strips, thus bringing to an end the need to cross-till, so important with the ard which had served for thousands of years.

To distinguish between a modern traditional plough and a one-way plough: the former has one or more fixed bodies that turn the furrow slice in the same direction, usually to the right as seen when walking behind the plough; the one-way plough has a minimum of two bodies, one ploughing to the right and the other to the left, and a rapid means of changing over from one body to the other. The traditional plough necessitates ploughing 'round and round'. So, when starting to plough, the first furrow is made ploughing across the middle of the land to be ploughed, from one end of the field to the other. On reaching the end the ploughman lifts the plough out and proceeds to turn 'round' the end of the open furrow before dropping the plough back in work to plough back up the other side, turning the furrow slice towards that first open furrow at the centre. This practice is known as gathering. The practice known as casting is to plough along one side of the field, turning the furrow slice towards that side of the field rather than towards the centre, and on reaching the end the plough is lifted out of work and the tractor and plough are driven to the opposite side of the field in order to plough back along that other side turning the furrow towards that side.

If a field is particularly big, then to save time hauling the plough along the headland all the way from one side of a large field to the other, the field is divided into lands. Each land would be, say, 100 yards wide; there may be several such lands in a large field. Care has to be taken in measuring and marking out the lands before ploughing to make them parallel. Because of our small fields in

Jersey, ploughing in lands is unnecessary, and ploughing with a one-way or reversible plough does away with the need for lands.

The one-way plough necessitated a different way of ploughing. The ploughman started ploughing his first furrow along one side of the field, casting each furrow towards that side of the field, and continued simply ploughing back and forth, working his way to and fro, until he reached the other side of the field (as practised by most ploughmen in Jersey today).

Tractor-mounted one-way plough.
This tractor-mounted one-way plough is a two-furrow reversible with digger bodies, ploughing in Maufant. The picture illustrates one-way ploughing quite clearly: the land on the left is ploughed and that on the right is unploughed. Ploughing began along a hedge on the far left of the field and will finish when the last furrow is ploughed along the hedge on the right. Each time the tractor and plough reaches the headland the plough is lifted out of the ground and reversed or rotated, so changing the two left-hand casting bodies for the two right-hand casting bodies; meanwhile the tractor turns on the headland and enters the same open furrow and ploughing commences in the opposite direction.

Whatever the type of plough, soil, or crop to be grown, the first job is to plough. For many years in Jersey, after the farmyard manure had been carted in January and spread on the land, ithe land was ploughed, marking the start of a new season.

Back to history

The early part of the story that follows is the author's own conclusions resulting from researching the subject. Historians and archaeologists do not always agree with each other. For example, more recent work may be found to lead to different conclusions from previous work.

Because of the huge gap and our limited knowledge of implements and tools in Jersey between the Stone Age, Bronze Age, and Iron Age up to the Romans and Vikings, we have to look outside the Island on either side of the Channel to see what was being done, the implements used, and guess what might have influenced the Island's farmers' choice of implements and tools during those gaps.

In the previous chapter we saw how stone and flint axes and sickles were used to clear the ground of top growth before tillage could begin. The soil was cultivated with the mattock, digging stick, or cas-chrom. At some point it occurred to our ancient forebears, probably in the Middle East, that it would be quicker to pull the cas-chrom or an implement like it over the land to be cultivated rather than use the digging stick and mattock. To make the implement, a tree was selected with a stout branch that formed a V with the trunk of the tree. The branch was cut out by taking a substantial part of the tree trunk with it, sufficiently heavy to provide some penetration when fashioned to a point. The branch was cut to a suitable length to form a beam. The beam was grasped by two men to pull the implement along. In a later development a handle or 'tail' was let into the back for a third man to hold the implement steady, keeping the point in the soil as it was hauled along. So the 'ard' was born, and it would remain a basic tillage implement for over 6,000 years in Western Europe and to this day in some parts of the Third World.

It is important to distinguish the difference between the ard and the plough. Having described the plough above in some detail, it is only necessary to say that the plough with its wide share, skimmer, and mouldboard will turn a furrow slice to cover completely any top growth and previous crop residue. The plough cultivates all the land, leaving no soil unturned. The ard in all its forms has neither a wide share nor a mouldboard, but merely has a point to penetrate and tear open and stir the soil. The ard cannot cultivate the whole area of topsoil; it will leave a strip undisturbed between each pass necessitating cross-tilling. It is in effect simply a single-tine cultivator!

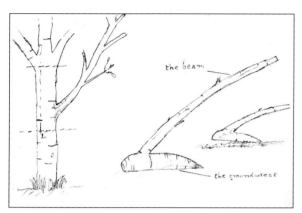

The original ard or crook ard.
To make the ard, the tree trunk was cut through at the horizontal dotted lines in the drawing above and trimmed to a point at one end. Any little twigs and small branches were trimmed off the branch so that it formed a beam. The groundwrest was 25-30 in. (63-76 cm) long and the beam approximately 6 ft (200 cm) long.

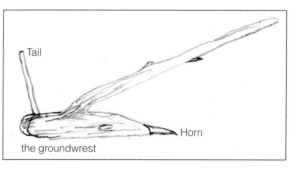

An improved crook ard with a tail and a horn on the point of the groundwrest.
As time went on the people learnt new skills such as joinery and to bend timber to suit their needs, and so the bow ard was developed. Time and effort were put in to make the bow-shaped beam for the ard. The trunk of a young elder, birch, or elm tree was bent over and forced to the ground and pegged to clamp it to the ground. After some time, when it remained in the desired shape, it was cut down and 'smoked' or seasoned over the hearth for several months with the groundwrest. The tail or stilt cut from a beech or oak tree was also seasoned over the hearth, then all were brought together and assembled.

The crook ard was the first ard in the Neolithic period. Two men would grasp the beam and haul it over the ground. Depth of work with the ard varied depending on the condition of the soil but it was rarely more than 4 in. (10 cm), and maybe 5 in. (12.5 cm) on land previously cultivated. As time went on depth of work improved. In work, what became known as the groundwrest was dragged along at a shallow angle to the ground. When joinery was understood the ard was constructed in three parts: the beam was curved or bowed and fitted in a mortise in the groundwrest and the handle known as the tail was fitted in a second mortise at the back; this is known as a bow ard, illustrated below. A third man held the tail to steady the ard in work. Some shares were made of horn, others were a specially shaped stone or bone, while still others were made of hardwood.

The bow ard was widely used for many centuries. While no complete ards have been found in the British Isles many parts of ards have been found there.

The ard developed into different types and varied from place to place depending on materials available, soil type, and the whims and fancies of the farmers in a given area. Bow ards were widely used in Britain and in many parts of Western Europe. The long, wooden spear share was not discarded in some places, even in the Iron Age. It continued to be used on both the bow ard and the groundwrest type.

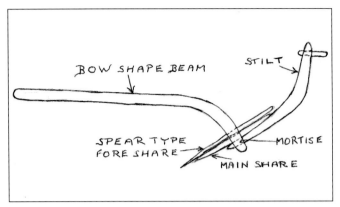

Bow ard with stilt (tail) and share.
The foreshare, main share, and stilt (formerly the tail) are fitted through a mortise in the beam almost at right angles. The beam is 8-9 ft (240-300 cm) long, the stilt complete with share 3 ft 6 in.–4 ft 6 in. (140-170 cm) long. The wooden spear foreshare is 21-7 in. (52-67 cm) long. The main share, which may be arrow shaped, is 20-1 in. (50-3 cm) long. The share may be of stone, bone, or spear type, made of hardwood such as oak. This type of bow ard might achieve depth of work of 6 in. (15 cm). A bow ard and a crook ard dug up in a peat bog in Denmark were made of birch; the bow ard had a stilt made of oak. Replicas of recovered ards have been made and experimented with to see how they worked.

As time went on the ard developed into two main types, of which the only common feature was the bow-shaped beam. In Britain the share and stilt were mortised through the beam at a steep angle to the ground and the assembly wedged or pegged in place. The stilt was approximately 3 ft (100 cm) long. The less popular crook ard with the groundwrest, beam, and tail was worked with the groundwrest almost flat on the ground. Both types were used in Western Europe, so it is not unreasonable to assume they were probably used in Jersey.

The front of the groundwrest on the crook ard became known as the sharebeam, to which the share was fitted. The sharebeam was cut to provide a slot or mortise into which the share was fitted and pegged in place. A hardwood, spear-type arrowhead share set at an acute angle to the soil proved to be the best for deep work. Once virgin land had been cleared of top growth and it had been burnt off, the soil was broken up with the mattock and the ard. The ard worked to and fro across the area to be cultivated; the process was repeated at right angles to the previous work to achieve a more effective result. Any remaining clods were broken up with mattocks. Cross-tilling (or cross-ploughing) became general practice up to Roman times, resulting in rectangular and square-shaped fields.

Tillage in the Bronze Age

By the beginning of the Bronze Age in Britain, 2000 BC, the British Isles had changed considerably since the early Neolithic period. The climate had changed: it was warmer, resulting in rising sea levels. Jersey and neighbouring islands had been isolated by the Neolithic period. Great storms had washed away any of the fertile soil remaining between the Island and Les Minquiers and the east coast and Les Écrehos. Ashore in the Island and on the mainland on both sides of the Channel the warmer weather encouraged the progress of agriculture, large areas of land had been cleared of bush and forest, and there was more crop growing, expanding up to a peak around 1500 BC. Wheat had been grown since 3500 BC in Britain; another crop was barley. Oats, peas, and beans were introduced into the British Isles during the Bronze Age. The ard had become an important piece of equipment just as the plough is today and over the next thousand years the ard did not appear to change.

Some time before the Bronze Age the ard was being drawn by oxen; various ideas were tried to 'harness' them to the ard. A rope around the necks or shoulders of the oxen was not very satisfactory, neither was a wooden beam attached to the horns of a pair of oxen, and the animals did not like it. The yoke resting on the animals' shoulders proved most satisfactory. The yoke was made from the trunk of the linden tree or lime tree and selected for being the right diameter and of suitable length for two or four beasts. Like the ard it was seasoned over the hearth. At first, beyond making it round, little attempt was made to achieve a bow for each animal.

Late Bronze Age rock carvings and drawings in caves in the Alps, in northern Italy, and others in Sweden, together with the numerous hoards of tools and shares which have been uncovered and examined by archaeologists, give us some idea about these implements and how they were used. Some cave drawings are silhouettes looking down on the scene, but the ard is turned on its side at the back to show a side view of the stilt but not the beam, and very little detail of the implement is shown, except that it is T-shaped, the stem of the T being the horizontal beam and the bar across the top of the T being the upright stilt. The stilt is curved, set at an acute angle to the soil and extending upward to form the ploughman's handle above the beam. Other carvings and drawings illustrate the ard in great detail such as at Littlesby in Denmark, also showing the agricultural scene, the spring sowing, etc.

Each drawing depicts the oxen and how they were yoked into teams of two, four, or six beasts. The six-abreast team was harnessed to a single long yoke but this seems to have been rare; more common were teams of four abreast or in pairs in line ahead. Teams of four abreast resulted in half the team treading over worked land, but this was regarded as useful as it broke up any clods, as one might roll today after ploughing. The drawings depict the caller of the oxen in front of his team facing the animals and walking backwards, holding onto the yoke and calling to his oxen to coax them along. The ploughman is holding the stilt or tail and in some cases a third man is helping the ploughman. The ox driver or caller walking backwards in front of the oxen is perhaps surprising but this was the usual method for many centuries. About a quarter of an acre or half a Jersey vergée was tilled in a day. This was probably as much as the oxen hitched in a very primitive manner to the ard and the caller walking backwards all day could cope with. There were frequent stops for various reasons, such as changing a broken share, the implement clogging up with top growth and weeds, and resting the animals at the end of each leg across the field before setting off again. Tilting the ard to the right was common practice as it helped to turn the soil on its side.

Oxen were trained to the yoke: difficult animals were placed between two quiet beasts and led until they learned. To yoke the ard to a pair of oxen, the beam on the ard was made longer to enable the beam to rest on the yoke. The beam was lengthened to 8 or 9 ft (250-300 cm). The pitch, i.e. the angle of the share point relative to the ground, determined the depth of work, as it does today; depth was adjusted by hitching the beam further forward or backward on the yoke. The further back the beam was hitched, the deeper the work.

Different methods of yoking oxen were widely used over Western Europe from Sweden to the Alps: most were just two abreast and all were hauling bow ards. There are drawings with one, two, and three people; most have three, the ploughman holding the stilt, the caller in front of the oxen facing them and calling them with his hand on the yoke walking backwards, and a boy on the left of the oxen ready to assist, one with his right hand on the stilt. Most drawings are silhouettes looking down on the scene; they do not attempt to illustrate the bow shape of the beam on the ard but they all show the ploughman tilting the ard over to the right.

It was a major advance when oxen were yoked to the ard, making a big improvement to the depth of work and output, enabling larger areas to be cultivated. Tillage with oxen and the ard was well established by the

Copy of a Bronze Age cave drawing of ploughing with a stilt ard and oxen.
This drawing by the author is similar to one of many Bronze Age cave drawings in the Maritime Alps. It illustrates a team of oxen at work yoked two abreast to a bow ard; the oxen appear to have enormous fearsome horns! The beam will be bowed, and the bowed stilt has been turned on its side in the cave drawing.

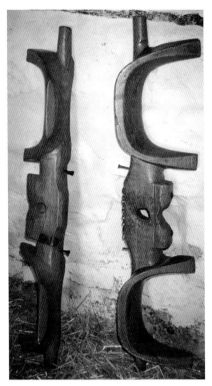

Jersey ox yokes standing on end.
These two ox yokes have been turned on their ends and propped against the white-washed wall of the stables at Hamptonne Country Life Museum in St. Lawrence, Jersey. They are for yoking two oxen to implements and carts, etc. The dimensions are: 4 ft 3 in. (127 cm) long; neck arches 13 in. (33 cm) at 3 ft 3 in. (1 m) centres. They are carved from one solid piece of hard timber (lime and linden wood were the early choices) and made by a craftsman who specialised in making yokes in the 18th or early 19th centuries. The two illustrated above were carefully carved and shaped, making them comfortable for the oxen. In Jersey, ox teams would plough yoked in pairs one pair in front of the other.

Yokes varied from age to age and place to place and varied in length for two to as many as eight oxen. In medieval times some ploughmen preferred to yoke their oxen up to eight abreast rather than in pairs, one pair in front of the next. Old pictures show yokes as being a simple rounded length of timber, while others were little more than a plank of wood. Ards were still in use in the 20th century such as the version called 'el Cambelo' (the ard) in Spain, and were followed up with the mattock.

Bronze Age and remained as the method of tillage through the Iron Age and the Roman occupation. It was so widely used, it is reasonable to speculate that although there are no artefacts in Jersey to prove it, the ard may well have been used here. We have the evidence of oxen being used in the Island in medieval times. The bouvée was a land measure before AD 1000 and was the area of land a pair of oxen and a man could cultivate in a year. They continued to be used in Jersey in the eighteenth and the early nineteenth centuries.

Today we may assume copper and bronze must have been thought of as new and exciting materials but they do not appear to have had any great impact on the tillage implement. It is thought by one authority that the Beaker People brought bronze shares with them to use with the ard in Britain. Perhaps it was simply to try them, but it did not become common practice. A well-shaped bronze share would have made a big improvement to the performance of the ard to penetrate and burst open the soil, compared to wood, bone, and stone shares, making it easier to pull through the soil. But bronze is a soft material and would wear quickly and be expensive. Many farming folk would have been skilled at making shares of the three well-tried materials of stone, bone, and hardwood; they were plentiful and remained the favoured materials, and bronze was never given a second thought. No bronze shares have been found in Jersey.

In 500 BC the Celts were migrating to Britain, bringing with them their skills with stone tools and later with iron. The development of the groundwrest or sole-type ard was an improvement of the earlier crook ard and bow ard. It became more popular in Britain in the first century BC some four hundred years after the beginning of the Iron Age in the British Isles. Its rebirth probably came from the Continent with the migrating hoards of Celts whose skills probably resulted in small improvements to the ard and the yoke. Making the yoke with bows in it ensured a more comfortable fit on the ox; that alone would increase the output of the ox team.

But the limitations of the ard remained. It was only capable of breaking up and stirring the soil. Cross-tilling was still necessary to ensure the land was well broken up, the animals' hooves helping in the process: square and rectangular fields can still be seen on the chalk lands in the south of England. However, all these developments of the ard did mean man could depend on a more extensive and intensive type of farming capable of growing more and supporting a larger community. As the use of the ard was so widespread over such a long period of time in what is now France and the British Isles, and continued through Roman times, it is reasonable to assume they were used in Jersey, but which of the many types is anybody's guess. Bone shares remained a favourite by the sea, where large rib bones were obtainable from big fish washed up on the shore, but they were also made from the ribs of slaughtered oxen. Well-made stone tools would cut quite large bones to shape, even to a small wing on one side, in an attempt to lift and turn the furrow. Stone shares were also specially shaped and were reversible so that when one end was worn the share was turned end for end. Sandstone, where it was available, was popular because it was easier to shape with a stone chisel; stone shares were also shaped with a wing.

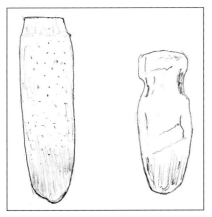

Stone shares.

Stone shares like these were used from the Stone Age to the Middle Ages. They are oval in cross-section, having a waist at the trunk and the surface pecked to provide a grip to wedge it in the mortise. They measured between 10 and 16 in. (25-40 cm) long and 2 .5-3.5 in. (6-8 cm) wide. These are sketches of two types of stone shares found on different sites of ancient homesteads in Orkney and Shetland during 'digs' and detailed research conducted by Sian Rees. Similar shares were found in Denmark. It was found that the wear on these stone shares tells us a lot about the ard and how it was used, such as tilting the ard to one side during work, a practice found in many parts of the world where the ard was used in an attempt to turn the soil before the development of the mouldboard.

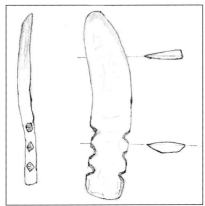

Bone shares.

Bone shares like those illustrated here 12 in. (30 cm) long and 3.5 in. (9 cm) wide) measured much the same as stone shares. They varied in length from 8 in. to 14 in. (21-35 cm) and in width from 3 in. to 4 in. (7.5–8.3 cm). The drawing shows the side view and underside; the side view is on the left. The notches on the sides are for wedging or pegging the share in place in the sharebeam and varied in number between two and three on each side, some having more on one side than the other. Because of the natural curve on bone shares they have to be fitted at an angle in the sharebeam in order to present the point along the line of draught, otherwise the curve would cause the ard to sheer off to one side in work. The northern isles were largely treeless; stone and bone were the only materials available. Clamping these shares and a wooden supporting share with wedges and pegs was to continue for many centuries; pegs continue to be used to the present day, with modern socketed cast iron shares on general purpose bodies (not used in Jersey).

In the late 1950s hoards of stone implements were found across parts of Britain, along with some individual examples. A hoard dug up in a peat bog at Donneruplund in Denmark revealed items such as the ard, and a second in a bog at Hvorslev produced two wooden shares made of maple. Long wooden shares are known as foreshares and were all supported along their length by a main share on the bow ard, as illustrated here, and on some types with a groundwrest. Both the main share and the foreshare penetrated the soil, and in some types the main share had an arrowhead.

Wooden spear shares.

These wooden shares were made of maple or oak and used on the stilt ard and spade ard. The dimensions of the head are approximately 8 in. (20 cm) long and 4 in. (10 cm) wide. The length overall varied from 1 ft 10 in.

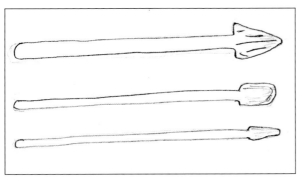

(56.2 cm) to 3 ft 9 in. (112.5 cm). The wooden share was probably used more widely than any other material on the stilt ard up to the Iron Age; its great virtue was that it was easy to make where there was woodland. Wooden shares worked an inch (2.5 cm) deeper than stone or bone shares; the spade ard, with its particularly steep share angle of 60 degrees, worked more deeply than any other ard. During the Iron Age the iron spear-type, or bar point, share replaced many of the earlier hardwood spear-type shares.

How shares were fitted to the ard

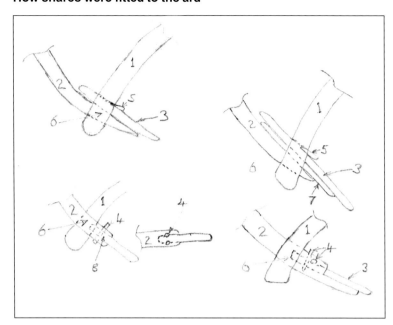

Different methods of fitting shares to the beam of the stilt ard:
(1) beam; (2) stilt; (3) foreshare; (4) peg; (5) wedge; (6) mortise; (7) main share; (8) socket.

As the drawings indicate, there were very different methods of fitting shares to the stilt ard. Wooden shares were simply fitted into the mortise and wedged. Stone and bone shares were shorter and required a different technique of pegging in two planes, one or two vertically and one across horizontally. Wood, stone, and bone shares were used countrywide, whichever material was available, through many ages from the Neolithic to the Celtic people.

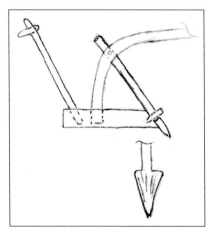

The spade ard.
The spade ard with the bowed beam and a tail are mortised into the groundwrest. The spade share is made of oak and is passed through a mortise in the beam and pegged to the front of the groundwrest. The dimensions of a spade share are between 3 ft 6 in. (105 cm) and 4 ft (123 cm) long and the length of the arrow-shape head is 8 in. (20 cm). The angle of the share relative to the soil surface is 55-60 degrees. The share has a long tang or stem to extend up and pass through the mortise in the beam. Their use was not so widespread as other types of ard but this was an effective implement, working the soil to a greater depth than other ards.

It was remarkable what the people in the Neolithic period could achieve with stone axes and adzes and the limited skills of carpentry and joinery at their disposal. Evidence of the ard, which as said above probably started in the Near East, has been found in many parts of the world from Asia Minor across to Western Europe. The ard remained in much the same form for up to 1,500 years in Western Europe. But the cultivation achieved with it was sufficient to grow a cereal crop, as anyone who has read *Ploughman's Folly* (1945) will know; the American author, Edward Faulkner, was able to show how good cereal crops were obtained after only lightly scuffling the soil sufficient to bury the seed. The system was being practised in England in the 1960s.

There was a dramatic change of climate following the eruption of Mount Hekla volcano in Iceland in about 1000 BC. The climate was colder, and people living high up in hill country were forced to move down to lower, more sheltered, warmer levels, leaving their well-defined drystone wall field systems and homesteads. It is these areas that provided archaeologists and researchers with the opportunities to dig and find new artefacts and ancient methods of tillage.

It was only in the late 1950s that hoards of stone implements were found in storage pits on Stone Age homesteads in parts of Britain. In the past many stone tools were dismissed as simply more stone axes, whereas on examination of the wear they have been shown to be stone shares. A study by Sian E. Rees in 1979 examined hoards of stone and bone shares found in heaps

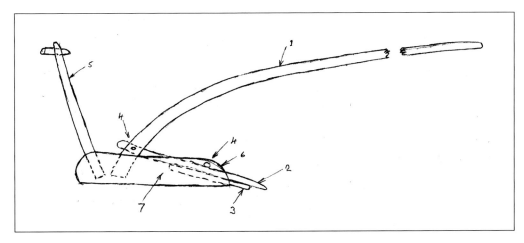

The Celtic ard:
(1) beam; (2) hardwood foreshare; (3) 'main' support share; (4) peg; (5) tail; (6) sharebeam; (7) groundwrest.
This Celtic all-timber ard is a more advanced ard benefiting from joinery and is made of several components.
The dimensions are: beam 10 ft (300 cm) long, groundwrest and sharebeam 2 ft 6 in. (75 cm) long, wooden
spear-type share 2 ft 3 in. (70 cm) long.
The improved crook ard or Celtic ard comprises the groundwrest and sharebeam; the long, spear-type
foreshare passing through both the sharebeam and the beam ensures a strong construction, but when fitted
with stone and bone shares they were only half the length of the spear type so were both pegged and wedged
into the sharebeam. This ard eventually spread widely over Western Europe and Britain replacing the bow ard
and stilt ard.

and in pits like those for storing wheat and other precious items on abandoned Neolithic homesteads in the Shetlands and Orkneys and elsewhere. It is suggested there may be similar hoards in
the rest of the British Isles that have not yet been found.

The research on these stone implements is therefore quite recent. The work proves that stone
shares were used to provide a hard-wearing point. Rees examined the wear on stone and bone
shares, uncovering the land in fields surrounding the hoards to expose the surface of the subsoil.
She found the scoring marks made by the shares and she was able to match the wear marks on the
stones with marks on the subsoil to determine that the stones were shares. Similar score marks
dating back to 2800 BC have been found in Wiltshire.

Sian Rees discovered the share point marks of cross-ploughing on the surface of the subsoil
during her research. Many of the stone shares were worn on one side, indicating that the ard was
held at an angle as it was drawn along in an attempt to turn a furrow which matched the score
marks on the surface of the subsoil. It has also been possible to measure the angle of tilt which
varied between 3 and 20 degrees. As the ard had no mouldboard, tilting it in work was done in an
attempt to throw or turn the furrow. Tilting the ard to one side to turn the furrow is still practised
today in parts of Asia and is illustrated in photographs of tilling with ards and oxen, in a way
similar to a couple of thousand years ago!

A problem of identifying stone shares was that many were broken in the trunk at the point
where they protruded from the sharebeam and when discarded were thrown in the hoard; some
were incorporated in drystone walls; some may never have been found. What is of interest to
Jersey is the Viking influence in the use of stone shares, which have been found in all parts of
Viking settlement from the Orkney and Shetland Isles, Scandinavia, to areas in the east of Britain
such as Lincolnshire, and in the north of France! Which poses the question: were they used here?

The stone share continued in use through the medieval period until quite recent times, long
after the ard had been abandoned in favour of the mouldboard plough. This is understandable if a
farmer had an outcrop of suitable stone nearby. It was cheaper for him to make his stone shares

when he had time and the skill rather than buy in manufactured iron shares. We may have them lying around in Jersey in a heap in the corner of a field which has been seen but ignored for decades simply because it is in a spot which is not worth working, and the reason why the heap accumulated there in the first place. It is a question of knowing what to look for!

Tillage in the Iron Age

In the fifth century BC farmers from the Low Countries introduced iron shares into Britain, which was well before the Romans, who are sometimes thought to have brought iron shares with them. They may well have done but they were not the first!. It was more likely the migrating Celts, who were skilled craftsmen with stone implements and tools and had quickly become skilled with the new material iron! The iron share made a big improvement to the performance of the ard to penetrate and burst open the soil and made it easier to pull. A highly successful innovation also thought to have come from the Low Countries was the knife coulter, which is still in use unchanged today. It was simply a large knife with a stalk (like a handle) that was fitted vertically through a mortise in the beam over the point of the share. Its purpose was to make a vertical cut in the soil above the share point, doing away with the need to have a steeply angled share. The share could now be much flatter, and the overall effect reduced the load to haul the ard through the soil. Later Celtic arrivals in Britain in the first and second centuries AD brought ploughs rather than ards with them!

The Roman period brought about a more peaceful and settled way of life, resulting in a growing population. The keeping of livestock and the greater use of ox teams encouraged the cultivation of larger areas of cereals and other crops, which was necessary to feed a increasing population as the hunter-gatherer way of life had almost disappeared. The Romans not only brought iron shares with their ploughs, they also brought the turnwrest plough, a form of one-way plough; but cross-ploughing was still considered necessary in Roman times.

The Iron Age has made research a little easier as iron shares have been found in various parts of Britain from the Roman and pre-Roman period and are on display in various museums. Some shares are almost 'as new', others are part-worn, and many have partly rusted away. Among them are tanged and socketed iron shares of the spear and chisel type, indicating the variety of shares of different lengths and widths for a variety of ards or ploughs of different design. The earliest iron shares found in England suggest the sharebeams to which they were fitted were at a much more acute angle to the soil than those for the same period on the Continent. The stilt ard remained a popular implement in Britain, whereas the ard on the Continent had an almost flat sole or groundwrest. In some cases the wooden spear-type share was fitted with a small cast iron socketed share over the nose or point to provide a hard-wearing point. Early iron shares were narrow but had widened by the Middle Ages. Even so, in the sixteenth century there were still spear-type shares with a wing in use. Yet another share in Roman and Saxon times was the Saxon cast iron asymmetrical share, found in Norfolk; examples are displayed in the Thetford Museum. Similar shares from the Roman period have been found in London, preserved in the mud. They are all large with a socket and shaped like a large arrowhead. It is suggested they may have been used on Roman one-way ploughs, of which there were several types. Early mouldboard ploughs in Roman times had cast iron mouldboards and some used a wroughtiron share.

The mouldboard plough and other animal draught cultivating implements were already in use in the Middle East and had been for several hundred years, which would have influenced Roman thinking. These advances in technology took time to reach Western Europe and to benefit the people of Jersey, but we have no firm archival evidence in the Island.

On an ard with a tanged spear-type iron share the tang passed back through the sharebeam and also through the beam above, making quite a strong unit, and on a share with both a tang and a socket it was an even stronger arrangement. They had a small wing on the furrow side of the share; it was at the most 1.5 in. (3.7 cm) wide.

In spite of all these many different shares, the implement remained little more than a single-tine cultivator, although it was beginning to look more like a plough, and with tilting, it turned a furrow of sorts on its side; but it was still necessary to cross-plough. In Britain as time went by the ard with a groundwrest, a knife coulter, and a flat share eventually replaced the simple T-shaped ard. General practice was to set the knife coulter to cut through the soil on the land side above the share point, and this practice remained as the ard developed into a plough. Behind the share and sharebeam on some implements the groundwrest was shaped on the furrow side with a curve to help turn the furrow slice, which was completed by the ploughman tilting the implement toward the furrow side; but that only turned the furrow slice on its side, and did not achieve complete inversion. It was a step forward, but cross-ploughing was still deemed to be necessary to achieve complete cultivation of the land. Agriculture anywhere in the world is one of those conservative industries where there are those who like to continue as they have always done, so cross-tilling was to continue for many more centuries through the Roman occupation.

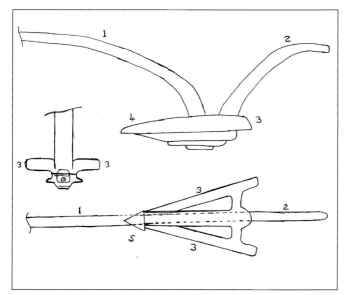

The Sussex one-way plough: (1) beam; (2) tail; (3) groundwrest; (4) sharebeam; (5) cast iron share. Iron was used to make not only the shares and coulters but also the brackets such as a drawbar or fittings for the coulter. The wooden frame was largely assembled by joinery, a practice that was to continue until the end of the 19th century when the wooden-frame plough gave way to the iron plough.
A late variation of the ard had a wedge-shaped groundwrest for one-way ploughing; it was known as the Sussex plough. It is an Iron Age, Roman/Celtic implement pulled by two oxen. It has a wooden frame and iron fittings, and the usual tail and bowed beam and mortise for the share assembly. The interesting thing about this implement is not only the way it is made with an unusual assembly of pieces underneath the groundwrests, but its having in effect two groundwrests in a V formation. The groundwrests were used alternately. The ploughman leans the implement first to one side, assisted by the assembly underneath to hold it over while tilling in one direction, and then at the end of the furrow, having turned the implement round for the return direction, he will lean it over on the opposite side to plough the other way.

At this time there was an advance, with another type of tillage implement that looks more like a plough. It has two vertical components: the frame was strengthened by an upright known as the sheath which was fitted between the beam and the groundwrest immediately behind the sharebeam, and both a stilt and tail provide two handles to form a rectangular frame. The point of the share protruded forward and downward to engage the soil. The groove was under the share-beams on some frames and on others at an angle on the top. Another alternative was to fit an iron share with a socket onto the nose of the sharebeam, held on with a peg. It has an iron knife coulter with an attempt to make a mouldboard, which at first was little more than a rectangular flat piece of timber or plank attached at the back of the sharebeam to the top of the groundwrest and set at an angle with the top edge out toward the furrow side, in an effort to turn the furrow right over rather than on its side.

The sheath and rectangular frame would feature on wooden-frame ploughs over many centuries. The big Jersey wooden plough has a rectangular frame. The rectangular frame was to last until the iron-frame plough came into use in the late nineteenth century in Jersey. The iron frame came into use earlier in England. The knife coulter would last with very little change to the present day.

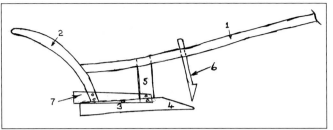

The classic rectangular plough frame:
(1) beam; (2) stilt; (3) groundwrest; (4) sharebeam;
(5) sheath; (6) knife coulter; (7) mouldboard.
The classic rectangular wooden frame ard/plough with iron fittings and stone or iron shares with a little plank for a mouldboard as described. The beam was long so that it could rest on the yoke.

While the rectangular frame was to dominate the wooden plough design for many centuries, over the years there were changes to the groundwrest, which includes the sharebeam; other changes were to the stilt and tail (or handles!). The final conversion from the ard to the plough came when mouldboards of different types were fitted. At a much later period the wooden mouldboard was carefully shaped with a helix and covered with sheet metal cladding to extend the wear.

Iron shares, coulters, and a spade sheath of the Roman period or earlier.
Of the two shares, the spear-type is displayed diagonally across the showcase. It is made of wrought iron. The cast iron socketed chisel-type share is mounted on the wall behind the two coulters. The spear-type share and knife coulters were made by a blacksmith and the cast iron chisel share by a foundryman. The two Roman Iron Age knife coulters each have a square-section stalk.
The dimensions are: 27 in. (67 cm) long, the blade 3 in. (7.5 cm) at its widest point. The shorter one is 21 in. (50 cm) long and 4 in. (10 cm). Made of wrought iron, possibly by a military blacksmith. Found at the Silchester site, and now in Reading Museum.

The iron spear-type share eventually replaced the earlier hardwood spear share. The share was laid on the supporting mainshare and both were passed back through a mortise in the sharebeam and the beam of the ard, where it was clamped with a wedge to make a firm fitting. The small cast iron socketed share on the back wall of the showcase was fitted over the point or nose of a wooden share or the sharebeam, and pegged in place to provide a hard-wearing point. Blacksmiths often had a foundry as well as a forge. At a much later period the St. Peter's Ironworks and the Grandins were both blacksmiths and foundrymen.

Iron spear-type socketed chisel share in Devizes Museum.

An iron share made by a blacksmith in the Roman Iron Age, AD 50-375. The dimensions of the socket are 2 in. (58 cm) long by 3.5 in. (9 cm) across the wings. The chisel point to the back of the wings of the socket is 13 in. (35 cm) and the tang is 10 in. (25 cm) long, and the chisel is 1 in. (2.5 cm) wide. The socket is to secure the share into the mortise in the sharebeam; the tang passes back through a mortise in the beam and is wedged. The wings help to burst open the soil and create a small open furrow. The share was found at the Box Villa site in Wiltshire and is in Devizes Museum. It was used for stony ground such as the flinty and stony soils of parts of Wiltshire. Modern ploughs use a device known as a 'bar point' together with a separate wide wing share. Bar points are used on stony soils and are very popular in Scotland.

Saxon cast iron asymmetrical share (Ancient House Museum, Thetford).

The picture on the left is of a cast-iron socketed asymmetrical share and shows the socket quite clearly with a wing on each side. The dimensions are 12 in. (30 cm) long by 4 in. (10 cm) wide. This is similar to the asymmetrical shares found in the London area. They were fitted directly to the nose of the sharebeam. Made by a foundryman of the Roman or possibly Saxon age and found in Norfolk.

Asymmetrical arrowhead shares of the Roman Iron Age found in the London area (London Museum, London Wall).

This share was found at the Walbrook Valley site in London, where it was preserved with others in the mud flats. The dimensions are 12 in. (30 cm) long, 4 in. (10 cm) wide, and the open socket size 3 in. (7.5 cm) wide and 4 in. (10 cm) long. There are similarities to the Saxon share found in Norfolk, indicating a wide-spread use of this type of share over a long period of time. Having no peg hole, they were probably a tight fit on the sharebeam and may have had a peg fitted across above the share.

Socketed Roman Iron Age knife coulter found at Sparsholt.

An early Roman iron knife coulter found on the site of a Roman villa at Sparsholt by David Johnston (who has been involved in research in the Channel Islands). The knife coulter is socketed in the stem into which a hardwood stalk is inserted, which in turn is clamped to the beam of the ard directly over the point of the share. Dimensions: 18 in. (45 cm) long, the blade 4 in. (10 cm) wide. (Courtesy of Winchester Museum.)

Crops known to have been grown in England in Roman and Saxon times and probably here in Jersey – were wheat, barley, rye, oats, flax, peas, and beans, for human consumption and cattle fodder. The Romans are known to have had the harrow, a square wooden frame with wooden tines, drawn by horses rather than oxen. Horses were faster so the harrow was more likely to shatter the soil into smaller fragments, so creating a finer tilth. Unfortunately we have no firm archival evidence in the Island.

The Romans were methodical: the square and rectangular fields resulting from cross-tilling in southern England and East Anglia would have suited their tidy minds. Many of those ancient fields are surrounded by drystone walls clearly marking out their shape and size. One sample is 60 ft wide by 260 ft long (18.6 m x 80 m), measuring about half an acre or roughly one Jersey vergée; others were larger, up to 4 acres (about 8.5 vergees). Just as Sian Rees's work clearly shows the marks of cross-tilling on the surface of the subsoil in the north, so these very old fields in the south and in East Anglia produced similar evidence. However, in others there is evidence of parallel tilling, or ploughing as we know it, showing quite clearly the angle of tilt up to 20 degrees as described above to turn the furrow. The discovery of the parallel tilling is indicative of an early primitive plough, so the plough as we know it was not far away.

The groundwrest and sharebeam were the forerunner of today's frog, landside, and heel. The modern frog, either of cast iron or a steel fabrication, is the component to which all the parts that comprise the 'body' of the plough are fitted: the share, the mouldboard, the landside, and the leg or shank. The body does all the work of cutting and turning the furrow slice (see the numbered drawing on page 32). It is notable that the knife coulter was in general use long before the mould-board. The mouldboard began to appear during the Roman occupation, but were not necessarily introduced by the Romans.

Just as there was a reluctance to stop cross-tilling, so there was also to stop using stone and bone shares in favour of iron. No doubt with iron tools such as a hammer and chisel it was possible to produce a more appropriately shaped share.

The turnwrest plough was an expression sometimes heard even in the twentieth century. The turnwrest was a one-way plough popular in Roman Britain: it had in effect two groundwrests arranged so that only one operated at a time; one turned the furrow to the right and the other to the left. The turnwrest rotated along its length, hence the name turnwrest. At each end of the field the ploughman rotates the turnwrest from one side to the other, so changing the direction that the furrow is turned relative to the plough. One-way ploughs were fitted with the asymmetrical pointed cast iron shares,such as the Saxon share and those found in Iron Age sites in the London area. They appear to have been made over quite a long period and a large area, suggesting that it was a successful design.

The knife coulter on the one-way plough was clamped to the beam over the point of the share using an iron figure-of-eight-shaped bracket that hung on a peg on the top of the beam. A wooden wedge passed through the bigger loop and was so placed that it clamped the coulter in position. At the end of each furrow the ploughman, having rotated the turnwrest, removed the wooden wedge and coulter, the figure-of-eight bracket was swung over the beam, and the wedge and coulter refitted to hold the coulter over on the opposite side of the beam. It was on the left when turning the furrow to the right, and moved to the right when turning the furrow to the left. The adjustment was quick and simple.

Other one-way ploughs had a detachable mouldboard, or ear as it was called, which again was simply a flat, almost triangular board. Instead of rotating a turnwrest at each end of the furrow, the mouldboard was taken off one side and attached to the other side of the plough. At the same time the knife coulter was adjusted to the appropriate side, as described above, before setting off across the field in the opposite direction. This system continued to be used on the heavy Kent one-way plough right up to the end of the nineteenth century.

While there was a wide range of mouldboard ploughs and shares to suit all the various conditions in the country there were many people who continued to use the ard. Ploughs and shares varied over the country depending on the skills of the local ploughwright, the demands of the ploughman, and the type of soil; some were heavier than others. There were cast iron socketed shares and forged wrought-iron tanged shares, all of various lengths, widths, and sizes. In some conditions a plough might need some downward pressure on the beam to provide more pitch to aid penetration, so a boy was employed to ride on the beam; this practice continued, surprisingly, up to the 1830s.

Teams of oxen for tillage varied in number from two to eight yoked abreast or in pairs in line ahead. One cannot fail to wonder at the difficulties of finding a straight length of timber approximately 24 feet long to make a yoke for eight oxen and the difficulty of turning such a team at each end of the furrow. Very likely the eight-abreast team was unusual and would have been abandoned with the advent of the mouldboard plough. Thereafter teams would have been yoked in pairs in line ahead, each pair having a yoke and a rope attached to it, passed down between each pair and joined to one rope attached to the plough drawbar, as illustrated on p. 000.

The following piece of twelfth-century Welsh/Celtic law is interesting as it gives us some idea of life in those far-off times. The law refers to the man in charge of the oxen as a 'caller' and not a driver. The law states, 'it is the duty of the oxen caller to be gentle and to call the team so they shall not break their hearts'! In addition it is the duty of the caller to provide the yoking gear. The law also specified how the resulting work was to be shared out, a quarter for the ploughman, a quarter for the driver or caller, a quarter for the owner of the plough, and the remainder shared between the rest of the people. Everybody was bidden by law to 'bring his own contribution to the field'! Presumably this meant to work, perhaps using mattocks to work the difficult corners, to provide spare shares to replace a worn one, and extra oxen to relieve a lame animal in the team, etc. Ploughing was a big event for the community: to get one's share of the land and resulting crop and harvest one had to be there, which it is said tended to crowd the field with 'helpers'!

It was to be the eleventh century AD before a truly curved wooden mouldboard was made covered with sheet metal nailed to it. As ever, development continued to be painfully slow!

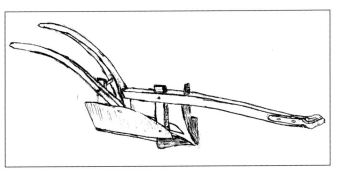

The plough complete with mouldboard.
Here at last is an implement we can describe as a plough! It is an early swing plough; like the ard it has no wheels, and it has the classic rectangular frame with a long beam and a groundwrest/sharebeam forming the horizontal components joined by the verticals, the tail (landside handle) and the sheath towards the front of the groundwrest. The share is cast iron with a socket and the mouldboard is a plain, flat, triangular piece of timber fitted to the sharebeam and groundwrest held out by the stilt at an angle across the furrow. The stilt is supported by a stave between the stilt and the tail. The beam slopes downward at the front to the iron draw-hitch to improve the line of draught. The line of draught is the imaginary line between the centre of power, i.e. between the shoulders of the pair of oxen nearest to the plough, and a position two to three inches back from the point of the share. The plough hitching point has to be along this line or as near as possible. To achieve that the front of the beam has to curve downward. This is important on all ploughs but particularly so with a swing plough.

The knife coulter is fitted in a mortise in the beam; on some ploughs the tang was beaten flat and hammered to wrap tightly round the beam, the point directly over the share point. The plough now has two handles, the tail on the land side and the stilt on the furrow side. On the other side of the rectangular frame can be seen a narrow pointed plate: this was to become known as the 'landside' or slade; its purpose is to counter the effect of the share and mouldboard to push the plough sideways. This type of plough lasted many centuries from the late Celtic period and through the Saxon era to the medieval age.

The ard was a relatively light implement, and so too was the early plough that derived from it. In the fifth and sixth centuries, when the Saxons migrated and settled in Britain, they brought their ploughs with them. These were said to be heavy ploughs with a wheeled forecarriage. At first they settled in the south-east, where they ploughed more deeply than before, possibly using a steeply angled share to reach the desired depth. Deep ploughing requires a plough with bigger, stronger heavy components; such a plough will be easier to handle with a forecarriage. Furthermore a heavy, deep-digging plough requires a big team of six or eight oxen to haul it. Lighter Celtic ploughs did not need wheels and became known as swing ploughs, which do not plough deeply and need only two or four oxen. There were variations then just as there are today with modern tractor ploughs.

Ploughs were made by a carpenter and a blacksmith working together. The blacksmith was responsible for the iron components, the fittings, the adjustable iron draw-hitch, the knife coulter, and the cast iron share, if he was also a foundryman, as many were. Depth of work was little more than 3-4 in. (10 cm).

14th century-medieval mouldboard plough.
The 14th-century medieval mouldboard plough is complete with rectangular frame. The curved mould-board is supported by the stilt and fitted above the groundwrest. It has a line of rivet heads indicating that it is covered with sheet iron. The stilt is supported by a stave to the tail. The knife coulter is fitted in a mortise in the beam with a wedge. There is a little artistic licence: knife coulters never have more than a slight curve, and all those in the museums are straight. A wooden mallet is carried on the beam to hammer and tighten any loose wedges or pegs. Note the details of the ox team and the manner of yoking the oxen to the plough. The beam does not rest on the yoke; it is shorter and curved downward towards the soil surface; the purpose of this is the all-important 'line of draught'. The ox on the right of each pair would be walking in the furrow bottom.

Saxon wheeled plough.
The Saxon/medieval wheeled plough is a heavier and deeper-digging plough. This type of plough lasted through to the 16th century with slowly evolving improvements. The forecarriage has two equal-diameter wheels; the nearer wheel in the picture is the furrow wheel that runs along the bottom of the open furrow. The frame has a shortened rectangle more like our own later wooden ploughs. The cast iron share is fitted to the sharebeam and the knife coulter is fitted in a mortise in the beam. The mouldboard in the Saxon period would have been a flat board as illustrated, previously supported on the groundwrest and at the back by the stilt. It was improved with a curve and a slight twist, or helix, and in the late medieval period it was sheathed with iron, and finally the mouldboard was made of an iron plate pressed in a forge to give it the appropriate shape, as illustrated, but it needed the support of a substantial timber frog behind it to keep its shape. The frog replaced the groundwrest.

The basic components of the 16th-century plough are the classic rectangular frame evolved from the Saxon period but shortened, with a long beam and a groundwrest/sharebeam forming the horizontal components joined by the verticals, the tail (landside handle) and the sheath towards the front of the groundwrest. On some ploughs the sheath was adjustable up and down to alter the pitch. The mouldboard (both the curved and flat type) is supported by the sheath at the front and by the stilt at the back and is mounted above the groundwrest. It has a landside supported at the front on the groundwrest or frog and the tail. In due course the frog would replace the groundwrest and sharebeam. The stilt (furrow-side handle) is supported in turn by two staves fitted between the stilt and the tail that holds them apart. The wheels are of equal diameter, but in a later century the furrow wheel would have a bigger diameter to compensate for the depth of the furrow to level up the crossbeam in work. In time some craftsmen specialized in making ploughs, and were known as plough-wrights.

The ox driver in medieval England walked beside his team when the team was formed up in pairs in line ahead rather than walking backwards in front, as he would do with an abreast team. In fourteenth-century Wales the four-abreast team was abandoned in favour of yoking oxen in pairs in line ahead. However, in Scotland, the Isle of Man, and Ireland the four-abreast team and the long yoke continued to be used into the early nineteenth century. Teams of horses were ploughing from the thirteenth century and sometimes formed part of mixed teams of horses and oxen. It was argued that horses were faster than a team of oxen; even so a team of oxen would plough at 1.5 miles an hour and it is said that was as much as the driver could cope with, without getting exhausted! In a mixed team the horses were at the front and the oxen were at the back, directly in front of the plough, as they had the greater strength to pull the plough those last few feet to the headland. This was because, as each pair of horses or oxen reached the headland, they had to turn and after turning onto the headland they were no longer able to pull the plough. In Jersey in the nineteenth century mixed teams of horses and oxen were not uncommon.

The National Museum of Antiquities of Scotland claims to have the oldest surviving design of plough in the British Isles. It is a copy of the Shetland plough thought to be of Viking influence! It is quite different from the ploughs we have examined so far.

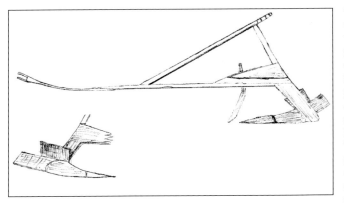

The Shetland plough of Viking influence. Did the Vikings bring it here?
The iron jaw hitch, or drawbar for hitching with a pin to the team of oxen, is riveted to the underside of the wooden beam. The plough has the usual adjustable iron knife coulter, fitted to the beam and wedged. The iron winged share is 1 ft (30.5 cm) long and the wing 4.5 in. (11.25 cm) wide, the socket is 4.5 in. (11.25 cm) long. The share is virtually horizontal with very little pitch, and has a socket to fit on the sharebeam. The wooden mouldboard is in three parts, a lower mouldboard with an extension at the back and a short wooden board at a sharper angle nailed above to complete the assembly, designed to invert the furrow slice.

Depth of ploughing was only 3 or 4 in. (7.5-10 cm), Shetland having a very thin layer of soil over a rocky and stony subsoil. It has a triangular frame above the beam to strengthen the beam. The tail or handle is incorporated in the triangle, which adds strength to the assembly with a high standard of joinery. The position of the handle enables the ploughman to walk beside the implement rather than behind it. The dimensions are all approximate: overall length 8 ft (240 cm), the wooden beam 5 ft (152 cm) long, and the iron drawbar and jaw 2 ft 6 in. (75 cm) long and 3 in. (7.5 cm) wide. The body of the plough is 2 ft 9 in. (83 cm) long. The wooden mouldboard is an assembly of three pieces of timber which is 1 ft 9 in. (53 cm) long overall. The knife coulter has a cutting edge of 12 in. (30 cm) and the stalk is 9 in. (22.5 cm) long. The plough is lightweight and handy, requiring only two oxen, and went on being used until fairly recent times. A woman in living memory remembered it being used in her childhood, probably in the mid-19th century. The Vikings eventually settled in what became Normandy and some are thought to have settled here in the middle of the Island, so the question arises, did they bring a similar plough with them?

From the end of the sixteenth century many improvements have been made to the plough. The Norfolk plough based on a Dutch design had an iron mouldboard and a wrought-iron share. The rectangular frame, heavy groundwrest, and sharebeam were discarded as in the Shetland plough in favour of a strong triangular frame made up of the handle or tail, a deeply bowed beam, and a sheath. The sheath and handle were curved at the join to take the share and mouldboard, and the back of the mouldboard was supported by the tail or handle, making for a lighter plough. It could be drawn by just two horses; one man could handle both plough and horses.

In the seventeenth century the Dutch began to use a rolling disc coulter instead of a knife coulter, so reducing the draught load, the disc having only a rolling resistance. It was adopted by some British manufacturers, notably Ransomes of Ipswich. In the eighteenth century several farmers and ploughwrights in Britain were experimenting with further improvements to the plough, particularly to the iron mouldboards and iron hitches or hakes/draw rings at the front of the plough to which the whippletree or bodkin was attached, and in turn the horse to haul the plough. The hake was made with both horizontal and vertical adjustments, using a series of holes or indents to fit the coupling chain to the bodkin, so adjusting the pitch and line of draught. The work resulted in the Rotherham plough and Arbuthnot's improved Rotherham plough. The Huntingdon plough of the 1780s is interesting in having a mix of old and new. It has an iron rolling disc coulter, a wooden mouldboard carefully curved with an iron shin and an iron lead onto the wooden mouldboard and a Ransomes iron share. Another plough of that period is the big heavy Kent plough, a one-way plough with a long, straight, movable mouldboard that is changed from side to side as described on earlier one-way ploughs. The frame is a traditional rectangle with a long, straight, heavy wooden beam resting high on a forecarriage with big-diameter wheels, and a long knife coulter. It was favoured by the farmers of the county to the end of the nineteenth century but needed a big team of horses or oxen.

A young ironmonger from Norwich who had been experimenting with cast iron shares that he manufactured and sold in large numbers throughout East Anglia produced the chilled cast iron share in 1803. Quite by accident he discovered that when molten iron fell on a piece of iron, the surface in contact with the cold iron was particularly hard. He experimented further using a sand mould with an iron base, which produced a share with a hardened surface under the cutting edge of the share, so extending the life of the share. The young man managed to raise capital and moved his business to Ipswich beside the dock, on the River Orwell, where he formed the company in his own name as Ransomes. In the 1850s Ransomes were manufacturing the 'A' plough, with a single handle to which fifty varieties of mouldboards could be fitted! Ransomes made a single-furrow digger plough for the American market in the 1880s, fitted with a disc coulter and a seat known as a sulky. Single-handle ploughs were still in use in England in the nineteenth century and some had a detachable second handle.

An early plough in Jersey was the corn plough, with a wooden beam, a rectangular frame, and a wooden block carved to shape to support a sheet-metal mouldboard. The working depth was at most 6 in. (15 cm) and often less. It was used in the autumn after harvest to prepare the land for sowing winter wheat and spring-sown oats or barley and other spring-sown crops. In its earliest form it was a swing plough, i.e. without wheels, but had a wooden forecarriage toward the end of its heyday. It needed only one horse and on some occasions two, when both horses walked in the open furrow one in front of the other or abreast, one in the furrow and one on the land. The corn plough was probably the only plough on the Jersey farm until the middle of the eighteenth century, when the 'Jersey big plough', *la grande tchéthue*, became a firm favourite. It was a heavy

The 19th-century wooden Jersey big plough (note the rectangular frame).

La grande tchéthue, or the Jersey big plough. This picture clearly shows a much shortened rectangular frame, the sheath close behind the wooden frog supporting the iron sheet metal mouldboard, and note the very large skimmer, almost a plough in itself and replacing the coulter. At the back, the stilt, no longer forming a handle, but instead supporting two handles. The landside and heel are in one piece, forming the base of the rectangle. The wooden forecarriage has the larger-diameter furrow wheel on the right. Note the wooden crossbeam between the wheels with its range of adjustments to ensure the plough beam rests in the right place for width and depth of furrow.

deep-digging plough with big wooden wheels on a forecarriage and a range of adjustments. It featured a substantial heavy wooden block or frog, moulded or carved to support the wrought iron mouldboard, iron share, and landside and the traditional rectangular frame. Rather than a knife coulter, it was fitted with a large, deep skimmer almost like a small plough body for skimming off the vraic where it had been spread on the land or the residue of the previous crop, depositing it into the open furrow. Before the skimmer came into being, a second light plough, probably a corn plough with two oxen or horses, went in front of the big plough to clean off the top of vraic or old debris. Some farmers changed the practice by light ploughing or breezing in the autumn before deep ploughing in the following January or February.

Why did the Jersey farmer change to a heavy, deep-digger plough? Hitherto parsnips and potatoes had been considered a luxury and were grown in the farm garden; when it was realised they were a saleable product they were grown as commercial field crops, and when milk began to be sold more dairy cows were kept and parsnips also fed to them. Both crops required deep cultivation to grow successfully. It was probably the last major development for the animal draught wooden plough in Jersey. The corn plough became known as a 'breezing' plough (*tchéthue à brîsi*) after certain changes to the body which made it more like a shallow digger with an abruptly curving mouldboard to crumble the furrow, similar to but very much smaller than the big plough. It was for autumn work, to sow cereals and to clean up the land to lie fallow preparatory to deep ploughing in the early spring.

In 1880 Théophile Le Cappelain, of St. Peter's Iron Works, began to design and manufacture the Jersey big plough with an iron beam and took advantage of the new technology, using an iron frog and a stiff mouldboard that needed only the minimum of brackets and stays to hold it in place. The forecarriage remained much the same, with a wooden block to support the beam and wooden carriage wheels, but in due course the forecarriage was made with steel wheels.

20th-century iron, twin-furrow Jersey horse plough.
We now move to more modern implements, for example Le Cappelain's self-lift ploughs, which were quite different with a very different frame. They were often twin-furrow ploughs with two beams, each carrying one body. The wheels had their own separate axles (with two right-angle bends) or, as on the plough shown here, the stalk was fitted at right angles to the wheel axle and bolted at right angles to a shaft across the top of the frame. When the shaft is rotated by a control lever the wheels move vertically up or down through an arc to raise the plough in and out. The control levers had a latch that engaged in a succession of notches on a quadrant to hold the plough in the raised position and to control the depth of work. These control levers were brought to the back of the plough so that the horse driver could operate the controls and also drive the horses. They were to look very similar to the tractor ploughs that would later come on the market.

This twin-furrow horse draught plough could at first glance be mistaken for a trailed tractor plough. The two handles at the back and the adjusting levers quickly dispel that thought. Of the two control levers, the one at the front controls the width of the front furrow and the one at the back in front of the handles raises and lowers the plough in and out of work and will set the depth of work. The levers are adjusted by an operator on the ground.

The next generation of these ploughs would be made with a tractor drawbar and the control levers extended forward for a tractor driver to reach them without leaving his seat.

In the twentieth century, when the first tractors arrived, Ransomes developed an automatic lift, operated by a rack engaging a gearwheel at the hub of the landwheel to raise the plough out of work at the headland. A trip lever operated by a 'pull' cord controlled by the tractor driver brought the lift into operation; it was connected through a linkage to operate on both axles to lower the wheels relative to the plough frame, so raising the plough out of work. A second sharp pull on the cord released the lift mechanism and the plough was lowered into work. All other control levers would be led to the front of the plough within easy reach of the tractor driver, who could operate them without leaving the seat of the tractor.

The whole process of development from the very beginning of the ard into a plough lasted for several millennia. Animal draught implements had been in use in the Middle East for a thousand years before the technology reached Western Europe. Farmers in the past had a tendency to be conservative. The ancient farmer seemed content with the ard as the main tillage implement. The developments in the last millennium have been rapid by comparison and extremely rapid in the twentieth century.

The story of the plough in the twentieth century continues in Chapters 6 and 11.

Sources:
F. G. Payne, 'The Plough in Ancient Britain', *Archaeological Journal*, 104 (1948); J. B. Passmore, *The English Plough* (1930);
Sian E. Rees, study for Ph.D.; Museum of English Rural Life, University of Reading;
Reading Museum; National Museum of Antiquities of Scotland, Edinburgh;
British Museum, London Wall; London Museum, London Wall; Devizes Museum;
Winchester Museum; Oliver Bone, curator, Thetford Museum; Jersey Museums Service;
Mrs. Olga Finch, curator of archaeology, La Hougue Bie, Jersey.

4 The Bronze and Iron Ages and the Effect on Agriculture

Copper: the Chalcolithic period

The Bronze Age having been studied by many academics, the information one gleans does vary depending on whose research one reads! In the wider world the Bronze Age appears to have lasted over 2,000 years in three phases, an early phase up to 1500 BC, a middle phase to 1000 BC, and a late phase to 500 BC. In Jersey it is thought to have started in 2250 BC, lasting until 1500 BC.

Approximately 4,500 years ago in Britain, a revolution was about to begin with the discovery of metals: the first was copper. Over many centuries metals would eventually affect the everyday lives of all people, but it was to be a very slow process. For example, during the Bronze Age there were few copper or bronze tools or implements used in agriculture. Copper axes and sickles were made but their use was not widespread. Three copper axes have been found in Jersey, one each at La Moye, Le Pinnacle, and La Pouquelaye. One of them is thought to date from 2200 BC. Copper does not appear to have been used to make a share for the ard, although it was probably tried. The metal would be too soft, compared with stone, and would wear away too quickly; furthermore it was probably rare and expensive. In effect it was of limited use in agriculture, and the people were probably quite content with the wood and stone, antler and bone tools to which they were accustomed.

However, through this period new skills with metals were learned. For 400 years the only copper tools likely to be used in agriculture were axes and the odd sickle. Other items were ornamental pieces and jewellery, or weapons such as spears. The real advance came when tin was discovered and it was found that when mixed with copper in the right proportions (10 per cent tin to 90 per cent copper), bronze was the result, a much harder and more durable material.

Copper having been discovered on the Great Orme, near Llandudno, in North Wales, it was mined from 1860 BC and continued into Roman times, starting again in the late seventeenth century and on into the late nineteenth century. Tin was being mined in Cornwall from 1100 BC and was still being mined there in 1997. When copper mining started in North Wales, tin was imported to make bronze before mining began in Cornwall. A bronze axe found at Le Pinnacle is thought to have come from Wales. The early flat copper axes were cast in a single open mould; the exposed side of the casting would like any liquid settle flat after pouring, thus one side of the axe was flat when it was removed from the mould.

As we have seen, copper is a soft metal but has the property to become work hardened, that is, it can be hardened by hammering it and using it. For example, hammering the cutting edge of a blade or axe would harden it, so helping to preserve a sharp cutting edge, but in spite of that, being a softer material, the copper axe would become blunt more quickly than stone. Copper can be annealed with heat, making it soft and malleable, when it can be hammered to restore the shape or cutting edge and hardened again. Various ideas were tried by smiths to harden copper including arsenic, which seems highly dangerous, but it was only when it was mixed with tin that they had any success. Tin on its own has a limited use; it is most valuable as a constituent in alloys such as bronze, solders, bearing metals, and coatings such as tin plate for canned foods.

Bronze was being imported into Britain from quite early on: a bronze axe found only 3 miles from the Great Orme in North Wales has been dated to 2500 BC; the blade was hafted to the handle with binding in the manner of the stone axe. This was something out of the ordinary because it was to be another 500 years before the Bronze Age proper began in Britain (c.2000 BC), and several centuries before copper was mined on the Great Orme.

Symmetrical bronze shares were tried on the ard in Britain but apparently it did not go beyond that. However, apart from a flat copper axe, no bronze items of any description have been found on the sites of early Bronze Age agricultural settlements in Jersey such as La Moye, and this is not confined to the Island but is true of the rest of Western Europe.

By the time the Bronze Age reached north-west Europe and Britain, the world had moved on, it was warmer, and sea levels had risen. Clearing and burning off top growth and woodland had reduced the areas for hunting and gathering; as a result the people were more dependent on agriculture, but by now they were more skilled at farming. In Jersey they were able to combine fishing with their farming activities and hunted for seals on the offshore reefs. In Britain there were settled farmsteads and country hamlets. During the earlier centuries people did not hesitate to abandon land when it was exhausted and move on to clear a new area. Over time the deserted land would have rested, becoming fertile and productive again, only to be settled on once more by later generations. These people were more interested in cattle, and searched for land suitable for both arable and pasture. While the landscape had changed, the remaining forests and woodlands were extensive, providing many of the needs of the community. In a world without oil, gas, and coal, gathering firewood was an almost daily chore. One has only to recall the many oil paintings of times past, perhaps a thatched cottage, a track passing by, and someone carrying a bundle of wood wrapped in sacking over a shoulder or on the side of a donkey. Woodsmen provided timber, which had so many uses, building houses, making implements, etc. Bark was stripped from trees for tanning leather, which caused many more trees to die. There were the charcoal makers, and as before there was food such as berries and chestnuts to gather, acorns for pigs, and areas for cattle to browse and graze. Finally there was hunting wild pigs for food and fun.

A major change was the wheel: people were able to build carts and use oxen for haulage. Bronze tools, such as axes, knives, and saws, were used to build carts, using the hardwoods such as oak for the axles and wheel hubs. The ard was adapted for animal draught mainly by lengthening the beam to hitch it to the yoke. Skills had improved; stone and bone shares, for example, were much more skilfully made, with greater precision to fit them to the ard.

Mixed farming was practised, keeping cattle for beef, milk, leather, and for hauling implements and general haulage; sheep were kept for meat rather than wool; and one or two goats, pigs, and poultry were kept primarily for meat. It is not known when poultry were first kept for egg production. Subsistence farming for the extended family or community was still the rule. The major activity on the land was growing cereals: wheat, which had been grown since 4500 BC in Britain, barley, from which they made malt, and later on oats were grown. Apart from feeding themselves, when these crops were harvested people fed their livestock. Flax was grown for clothing. Later in the period peas and beans were introduced into Britain and grown in garden-size plots.

A site in Gwithian, in Cornwall, has revealed a small farmstead where there is evidence of mixed farming at the end of the second millennium BC. It has a cluster of small fields with criss-cross furrows left by cross-tilling with the ard. Rubbish found in the furrow bottom indicates manuring of the land. Stone tips or shares were found on the edges, indicating that stone shares were being used on the ard.

Provided one has the skill and the correct materials, it is not difficult to make copper castings to produce an axe and a variety of implements, as shown by the excellent demonstrations organised by the Jersey Heritage Trust and a visiting specialist at the Archaeology Reconstruction site at La Hougue Bie in Jersey. A skilful operation of the kiln was demonstrated for smelting copper. The air blast necessary to pass through the kiln was created by regularly squeezing two soft leather bags or bellows into it from opposite sides, raising the temperature to 1,000°. That is the necessary temperature to turn the mined ore into metal, using charcoal. A further skill is in making the moulds into which the molten copper is poured to make the castings. When the moulds and casting have cooled, the mould is opened, the casting is taken out and fettled, i.e. the rough edges removed, and, in the case of a cutting tool, beaten with a hammer to harden the cutting edge.

Demonstration kiln for smelting copper; the temperature must reach 1,000º (La Hougue Bie, 2001).

A two-piece type mould for making a copper axe.
A two-piece mould open after a new copper axe has been taken out to cool. Note the stone axe fitted in a socketed handle and two wooden axe handles being prepared for a socketed bronze axe which will require a three-piece mould.

Samples of tools made in the kiln.
Samples of axes in the making: on the left are two palstave axes made with two-piece moulds and below them are two socketed axes made with three-piece moulds. On the right are flat axes of an earlier period made with a one-piece mould; they are waiting to be fettled to clean off the flashing at the sides. Also displayed is a bronze dagger (at the top of the picture).

Bronze axes were more widely used, along with other cutting tools as previously listed including knives, razor blades, and sickles, which would appeal to farming communities. Bronze tools such as saws and chisels were probably useful to craftsmen such as carpenters to improve joinery and make better-quality products such as the ards and carts.

During the Bronze Age, a new culture came into being, influenced by the Beaker People, so named for the design of the beakers from which they drank and in which they stored liquids and foodstuffs. Pieces of their broken beakers have been found in passage graves, especially at First Tower, west of St. Helier. They were particularly skilled potters and bronzesmiths.

Some uses of bronze in Jersey can be found by looking at the items in hoards uncovered in the Island and the other Channel Islands, Brittany, and the south of Britain. Flat copper axes have been found in hoards at La Sergenté in Jersey, Alderney, Little Sark, Guernsey, and in Brittany. Bronze axes were found in hoards at the Town Mills, near St. Helier. A large bronze axe was found in Cobo measuring between 7 and 8 in. (18-20 cm) long with a 6 in. (15 cm) cutting edge. On Longy Common in Alderney a bronze sickle and a Breton bronze axe were found. A second Breton axe was in a hoard in St. Helier, where the most common items were swords, knives, bowls, and razors. In its collection at La Hougue Bie, La Société Jersiaise has several bronze axes with palstaves, wings, or sockets. Two have been assembled to handles by museum staff to illustrate how it was done. The collection includes an axe thought to have come from Wales. Were any of the knives found used as hoe blades when fitted to a suitable handle?!

In southern Britain, Late Bronze Age sickles have been found in various parts, many in the London area, all with a crescent-shaped blade, some more curved than others and all tapering to a point. The blades are between 5 and 6 in. long (12-15 cm), between 1.5 and 2 in. wide (3.5-5 cm) at the handle. The blades are thin, between 0.125 and 0.18 in. (0.3-0.5 cm), and ribbed along their length to build in strength. Some had sockets for fitting a handle and some had a rivet through the socket; all that remains of the rivets today is two stumps. A range of bronze hand tools were made in France, including sickles, mattocks, saws, and spades; all the mattocks were socketed for fitting to a wooden handle and one or two look similar to the mattock you would find in your local garden centre today. As time went on, a widespread trade in bronze items developed.

In view of that trading, it seems reasonable to think that there may have been some of those French tools in Jersey, but no evidence has been found to confirm that. Unfortunately Jersey has an acid soil, in which metal objects, such as the very thin blade of a sickle, will deteriorate, if left lying in the soil over the centuries. The hoards that have been found in Jersey were buried in earthenware containers, contained broken, worn, or damaged items, and are thought to have belonged to bronzesmiths—probably their stock in trade. They would have been melted down and new products cast, recycling the bronze. But nothing has been found with an agricultural application.

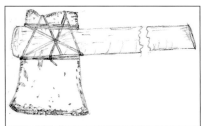

Flat copper axe found in Jersey.
This is a flat copper axe of the Chalcolithic period (c.2200 BC). Dimensions: approximately 8 in. (20 cm) long and the cutting edge 5–6 in. (12.5-15 cm). Three flat axes of this type were found in Jersey, one each at La Moye, Le Pinnacle, and La Pouquelaye, and another at Cobo in Guernsey. The open flat mould method of casting would continue into the early Bronze Age. They were hafted to a wooden handle with binding in much the same way as the stone axe.

Bronze

Bronze knife and socketed axes.
The knife is from c.800 BC, found at La Moye, and the socketed axes are of the Breton type, 700-1000 BC. Dimensions of the axes: length up to 5 in. (12.5 cm) and width 1.25 in. (3 cm).
Socketed axes were made with a three-piece moulding, two to form the axe and one to form the socket. One is tempted to wonder if the knife might be the blade of a hoe, but it seems unlikely, as bronze even in the Late Bronze Age, was too valuable for such a mundane task.

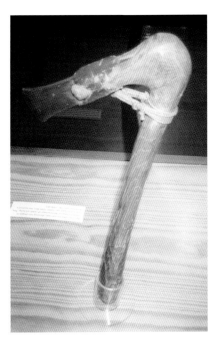

Winged bronze axe hafted to a handle by museum staff.
The wooden handle for a Bronze Age winged axe was cut from a suitably shaped V where branches of a tree divide. The short leg of the V is inserted between the wings and clamped by hammering the wings tightly around the V, and bound tightly through the ring at the top to the handle. Dimensions: the blade is 5 in. (12.5 cm) long and 1.25 in. (3 cm) wide.

A socketed axe fitted to a handle.
This socketed axe from the same period as the one above is hafted by inserting the short leg of the V handle into a socket in the axe and binding it with twine to the handle. The dimensions are the same as the one above.

Which would be the stronger is difficult to say; probably one is as good as the other. Both were found in the hoard at La Sergente. Both axe handles were made by the Museum Service staff as examples of the finished axe. All these bronze axes are part of the Société Jersiaise/Jersey Heritage Trust collection at La Hougue Bie. (Courtesy of the curator, Olga Finch.)

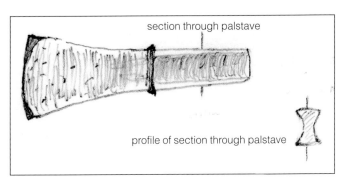

section through palstave

profile of section through palstave

The bronze palstave axes were probably a forerunner of the winged and the later socketed axes. Only two moulds were used to cast the palstave axe. The overall length was on average 5-6 in. (12.5-15 cm). The handle would have been made to the same shape as the handle for the winged and socketed axes; the palstave was hafted by inserting it into the wood up to the collar, and bound.

All these bronze axes were rather small, but it was very likely that bronze was an expensive commodity. With their skill for sharpening stone axes, craftsmen would have had no difficulty keeping a bronze axe sharp, although it may have become blunt more quickly than a dolerite stone axe. There are so many beautifully made axes of stone and bronze that the axe was almost a hallmark of the skilled craftsmen of the period. Some archaeologists suggest the better ones may have been a status symbol rather than a practical everyday tool. But the people of those days were so practical, making the best use of what they had available for everyday use, and these axes were so well made that they would have been a useful tool.

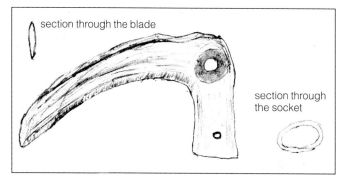

section through the blade

section through the socket

Bronze Age sickle of the type found on Longy Common in Alderney.
The crescent shape of the blade on this sickle, and the socket with a rivet hole for hafting to a handle, were quite common on bronze sickles in Britain. Some blades were ribbed along the central part of the blade to add strength to the blade.

Winged bronze mattock, a type found in France.
This drawing of a winged bronze mattock is of a type found in France. It is cast with two moulds bound together and is probably of the Middle Bronze Age. The dimensions are 6-8 in. (15-20 cm) long and the blade 3 in. (7.5 cm) wide.

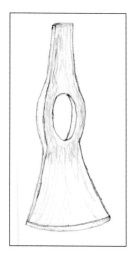

Bronze mattock with a socket.
This bronze mattock has a socket at the centre, where it has been thickened to add strength and makes a more substantial fit for the handle. The dimensions are 9-10 in. (22-5 cm) long and the socket 2 x 1 in. (5 x 2.5 cm). It is Late Bronze Age, 1100 BC, of a type found in France. It was cast using three moulds: one for the front, one for the back, and one for the socket; the three parts of the mould were assembled and bound together, after which the molten metal was poured in.

Over the centuries, the wooden ard and implement handles have rotted away in most cases, leaving only the stone and bronze pieces. Occasionally there are lucky finds such as in a peat bog in Denmark; one never knows what might be unearthed in future.

The copper industry at Villedieu-les-Poelles in Normandy is said to have started in pre Roman times, possibly Celtic. Their products became widely distributed from Ireland to southern Europe where they have been found. Tin was exported from Cornwall, all of which indicates the continuous trading and travelling between the south of England and France. Travel and movement of goods was by sea because there were no roads. The ships rarely ventured far from land but moved along the coast, and the Channel Islands were on the trade routes and would have been ports of call. No doubt Jersey benefited from this traffic, as a source of imported goods and exchange of information. In more modern times the *bachîn* that our grandparents used for making jam and black butter (apple jam) would have come from Villedieu-les-Poelles.

There was a sharp change of climate brought about quite suddenly when Mount Hekla, a volcano in Iceland, erupted in approximately 1000 BC, bringing with it a colder, wetter climate such as we experience today. The abandonment of hilltop farms as people moved down to lower levels reduced the amount of land available to arable farming and increased the amount of marginal land. It was not until the Iron Age in Britain, some 500 years later, approximately 500 BC, that any real change took place in agricultural tools and implements, so those same materials 'wood and stone, antler and bone' would continue to play an important role.

The Iron Age

The Iron Age in Britain began *c.*500 BC, extending to the Roman occupation. If the Bronze Age failed to bring about a sweeping change of materials for tools and implements, the Iron Age did, eventually making a lasting impression. The range of iron tools of the Late Iron Age and the Roman period is significant. We have only a hammer and a cleaver of the period in Jersey, but an examination of iron tools displayed in the museums in London and the south of England is remarkable for the many similarities with today's hand tools. Most notable are the mattocks, pickaxes, sickles, billhooks, pruning knives, rakes, pitchforks, field anvils, and some scythes, all very similar to any you may buy in an implement and machinery dealer's yard or garden sundries shop today. The knife coulter is instantly recognised, being almost no different in appearance from the modern knife coulter fitted on today's ploughs. The only difference between those Iron Age tools and today's is the material: today they are made of steel, although wrought iron is still used for certain items and is still used by the blacksmiths.

It was the skill of the migrating Celts which brought about that change. The flint sickle and the antler sickle could at last be discarded in favour of the new iron sickle, which was able to keep a sharp edge with the field anvil and hammer. Where available, antler and wood continued to be used for making some tools such as a two-prong hayfork and a two-prong hoe or grappin and hay rake. Wooden hay rakes were still being made in the 1950s at Pamber End in Hampshire. The stick or wood continued in use for making handles for all those tools, as it does today, and the ard continued to have a wooden frame, but with iron fittings. The carefully sculptured stone and bone shares would persist where suitable materials were available, for some time through to the Middle Ages, mostly in the north of the British Isles. The people had been making them for centuries, passing on the skills as their forebears had done for generations.

A problem with iron artefacts is that iron left outside in the open quickly becomes oxidised and rusts away, so many artefacts left out over 2,500 years will have disappeared and the condition of any that are found today will depend very much upon where they were left originally. Those that have been found were buried in wet mud in river banks, and survived remarkably well. The iron hammer and a cleaver in La Société Jersiaise's collection are thought to be from 200 BC. A hammer is a pretty solid piece of iron, which may become rusty but is less likely to rust away to dust than a thin-bladed sickle. There is plenty of pottery and several hoards of coins from the period, which indicates the Island was populated. In order for the population to feed themselves, it is safe to assume agriculture was flourishing, as in the Stone Age.

Iron Age cast-iron hammer found in Jersey. The hammer head is on the left in the picture. It measures 8.5 in. (21 cm) long and is of the 3rd or 2nd century BC. It is barely recognisable from the photograph due to the grit and other material which has adhered to the rust over the centuries, but on close examination the hammer head is remarkably well preserved; it has become peened over from hard use. The centre has a socket for a handle; the opposite end is flattened with an edge like an adze, chisel, or a pick. It is very fragile and surprisingly almost hollow, the inside having rusted away faster than the outside skin; the centre of the casting may have been softer. (La Société Jersiaise Museum at La Hougue Bie.)

Iron Age cleaver of 3rd or 2nd century BC found at Le Pinnacle (Société Jersiaise/Jersey Heritage Trust at La Hougue Bie. Courtesy of Olga Finch, curator.)

Another explanation for the lack of the iron artefacts in the Island may be that scrap iron has always been a valuable asset for blacksmiths and the iron and steel industry. It was a part of the blacksmith's stock in trade to use over again as they do today, and which was done by the bronze-smiths before them. This was probably important in Jersey; importing iron goods into the Island may have been expensive. As an example in the modern day, a sickle manufacturer at Saut du Tarn in France organised a regular supply of worn-out engineers' files with which to make the excellent sickles that are used in Jersey.

Once again we look to our neighbours on both sides of the Channel to get some idea of the tools and implements that may have been used in the Island. Hence the reference made above to the collections in the museums in London and the south of England.

As was said in 'Tillage in the Iron Age': The performance of the ard was greatly improved with the iron share and the iron knife coulter. There were three main types of iron shares. First the spear-type, or bar point share, which replaced the hardwood spear and spade types. Some spear types had a small wing to lift the soil, to assist turning, which was a step towards the modern share. Second was a simple socketed iron point to fit with a peg over the end of the wooden spear share. There is an example in a London museum. Third is a quite different type, the cast-iron asymmetrical share, sometimes with a peg hole; it was fitted with a peg to the sharebeam. Others were fitted with a wedge like the stone or bone shares which they replaced. The asymmetrical share was popular in East Anglia and what is known today as the Greater London Area.

The asymmetrical share has a similarity to some of the modern British cast-iron shares, such as those used on the general purpose plough, and fitted onto the nose of the frog with a peg (the frog being the modern-day version of the wooden sharebeam on the ard). The plough with a general purpose body turns a continuous almost unbroken furrow on heavy soils. While popular elsewhere in the British Isles, it is not used in Jersey.

The collections of iron implements in the London Museum and British Museum were found preserved in the black clay and mud banks along the River Thames in London. There are also collections of Iron Age farm tools and implements in Thetford, Reading, Devizes, and Winchester museums; they are often from known Roman sites. Because they are the nearest to us, the museums in the south of England are of interest as their collections are an indication of what might have been used here. In Wales and Scotland there are interesting items from ards and early ploughs and carefully shaped stone and bone shares which continued to be used through the Iron Age and medieval times. In the Shetlands and Orkneys, artefacts of Viking influence have been found. We have Viking names for parts of the farm and local coastal features, so the Vikings also had an influence here.

Late Iron Age craftsmen had already begun to specialise; for example in London there were knife makers making a name for themselves by stamping their names on their products. Many blacksmiths spent much of their time making nails: a hoard of a million Iron Age nails has been discovered! In the country there were ploughwrights. Roman army blacksmiths very rarely made horseshoes as we know them, but made shoes known as hippo-sandals for temporary use. They were lashed onto the horse's hoof for work on metal roads and then taken off.

Waves of Celts from Central Europe, particularly from Austria where an iron industry had been developing earlier in the Iron Age than Britain, migrated to England, bringing their skills with them. When life had settled down following the initial shock of the Roman occupation, a long period of peace ensued. This allowed innovative craftsmen among the population to devote their time to improving their skills, producing more and better tools and implements. In Britain agriculture was already under pressure to feed the Roman armies and a growing population.

In Roman and Saxon times wheat, barley, rye, oats, flax, peas, and beans were grown for both fodder and human consumption. It is reasonable to suppose they were also grown in the Island. How did people cultivate the soil? They had an exciting new range of iron hand tools to use, such as spades, mattocks, hoes, and grappins, and to harvest the crops they had iron sickles and the means to sharpen them. They had rakes with a wooden frame and iron prongs. They also had a more efficient ard, with an iron share and a knife coulter, and a new hand implement, the push plough, a variation of the cas-chrom.

The cas-chrom fitted with an iron tip in the Iron Age was pushed forward into the soil. It was then prised upwards by pushing the handle down, and the operator then pulled it back before repeating the process. The cas-chrom only broke and opened up the soil but did not turn or invert it. The push plough was pushed into the soil horizontally, by leaning the body against a T-shaped handle. The soil was turned by flipping the tool over to the same side each time. Around his waist the operator wore a belt with two boards at the front, to protect his abdomen and thighs from continually pushing on the T piece of the handle. The implement had a broad iron share, pointed to one side with a vertical piece behind it, to provide the vertical cut. The depth of work was about 2 in. (5 cm). The implement continued to be used by crofters into the late nineteenth century but like the cas-chrom, only for small areas. They may have been used in Jersey, but we have no evidence.

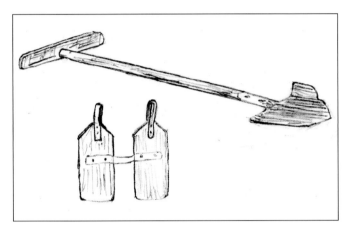

Breast plough and thigh pads.
The breast plough or push plough was used from the Iron Age to the 19th century, and possibly the early 20th. Dimensions: overall length 7 ft (200 cm), the share 1 ft (30 cm) wide and 1 ft (30 cm) long. The depth of work 2 in. (5 cm). The socketed iron share is riveted to the wooden shaft and T-crosspiece. The blade is made at a small angle to the handle to lay at a shallow angle to the ground. While it is called a breast plough, a pair of wooden pads were worn to protect the thighs; they had leather loops for the trouser belt to pass through. The most recent users were the crofters in the 19th century and smallholders in the Western Isles, the west of Ireland, Spain, and Portugal. There are no traces of it being used in Jersey but such a small, handy tool may well have been.

During the Roman occupation, developments with the ard continued. The ard was becoming more like a plough with iron shares, a knife coulter, and a very basic form of wooden mouldboard to turn the soil. It was the beginning of the mouldboard but even so, the furrow was very narrow and it was not ploughing. When the mouldboard plough came into use, no part of the soil was left unturned between furrows and the furrow was cast to one side. It would require a new method of tilling the soil, abandoning cross-tilling which had been the practice for many centuries. This major advance would lead to more efficient weed control, cleaner fields, and better crop yields.

The harrow had been used by the Egyptians for several centuries before it was used in the Roman Empire. There is little or no evidence of the harrow being used before medieval times in Western Europe and Britain. The Roman Empire included Egypt along with part of North Africa, so it does seem strange if they did not use harrows in other areas they occupied, such as Gaul and Britain.

The earliest hand harrow was simply the branch of a tree or bush or a besom broom. Whichever of these were used they were swept over the soil to cover newly sown seed. Depending on the crop to be grown, they would be used for the final preparation of a seed bed after the ard and the mattocks had first broken up the soil. On bigger areas, an early drag harrow was made by binding together a quantity of branches, which were then woven through a wooden frame. The branches were cut from a tree or a shrub; either broom or thorn were popular.

No. 3: harrow of thorn or broom; no. 4: besom broom.
No. 3 is a Roman and Saxon harrow made up of a frame with thorn or broom bushes or branches inserted through the frame. It was pulled by one or two men or an ox or horse. The dimensions of the frame are 4 ft 9 in. (130 cm) long, effective width 3 ft (100 cm). This type of implement was popular; the frames would vary from place to place according to fancy.
No. 4 is a simple besom broom with small branches bound tightly to the handle, suitable for covering seeds after sowing small plots. These implements were most effective.

The following early harrows differed in shape and size. The simplest was in the form of a V, cut from a tree where two branches divide. The tines were of a hardwood, probably oak or maple, and relatively easy to replace in the event of breakage or wear and tear. The V shape was to ensure that each tine would make its own track.

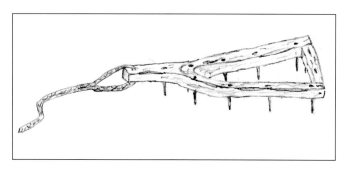

Saxon wooden V-shaped drag harrow with eleven hardwood tines.
This drag harrow was pulled by one or two men, a horse, or an ox. Dimensions: approximately 5 ft (150 cm) long overall, effective width 2 ft 6 in. (75 cm). Each leg of the V is approximately 3 ft 6 in. (110 cm) long. The tines are set at 1 ft (30 cm) centres, protruding 6 in. (15 cm), two on the back cross-member. The frame is made using the V section of a tree where it divided into two branches. When cut down they were probably prised apart and smoked to season the timber before they were bored and the tines driven through.

A bigger harrow on the same theme had four square-section timber beams arranged to fan out in an enlarged V formation. Along each beam a line of hardwood or iron tines several inches apart were driven into each beam. The tines protruded some 5-6 in. (12-15 cm). The beams were held together by two cross-members riveted to each beam with iron rivets. There were variations on the same theme, as there were with many implements, their construction influenced by local ideas to suit local conditions. Some would have looked something like our Jersey hand harrow, but probably heavier. To get the best effect, this harrow has to be drawn from the centre of the narrow end, so that no tine will follow in the track of another tine. The horse walks more quickly than an ox, so the harrow would be more effective and quicker to burst the clods of soil.

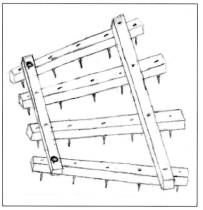

20-tine drag harrow.
This drag harrow has timber beams with iron nails and iron tines. Dimensions: the beams approximately 4 ft 6 in. (135 cm) long and the effective width 5 ft (150 cm). The tines are set at 12 in. (30 cm) centres, protruding 6 in. (15 cm). This implement would have been pulled by a horse for making a seed bed and harrowing in the seed after sowing. All these types of harrows were used in France and England.

The harvesting box cart was pushed into the crop to rip off the heads.

The harvesting box cart is a two-wheeled balanced push cart, made of wood with iron axles and fittings. It is of the Roman age—1st and 2nd centuries AD. The dimensions are approximately 5 ft (150 cm) long, 4 ft (120 cm) wide, 2 ft (60 cm) deep. The two wheels have a diameter of 3 ft (100 cm). Along the top or lip of the front board of the cart is a line of teeth: these were made of wood and occasionally of iron. The cart was so constructed that the height of the line of teeth was adjustable to be just under the heads of a standing crop of wheat. As the cart advanced into the crop, the V-shaped teeth stripped off the ears of wheat, which fell into the cart. The front board was removed for emptying. An ox, with a driver, pushed the cart. A boy may have stood in the box with a T-shaped tool, similar to a rake without the tines, to draw the heads off the teeth into the box, as the cart advanced into the crop.

An interesting implement which made its appearance at this time was the cereal harvester! It was a harvesting cart, which was used in both Britain and France in cereal-growing areas.

Recent trials with a reconstructed harvesting cart showed that it worked, but the heads were apt to accumulate along the row of teeth and had to be drawn back manually into the cart. There would have to be followers to pick up the heads that were missed and the standing straw would have been cut and harvested separately for thatching and bedding for cattle. Any remaining straw was probably burnt off. Having only the ard, it would be impossible to plough it in.

The collections of Iron Age tools in the London museums were preserved over many centuries in the London mud, along the Thames embankments. Some are remarkable for similarities to today's implements, two thousand years on!

Selection of Iron Age shares and tools.

On the left of the picture are two asymmetrical cast iron tillage shares for the ard and early ploughs. The dimensions are 12 in. (30 cm) long and 4 in. (10 cm) wide, the socket internal dimensions 3 in. (7.5 cm) wide and 4 in. (10 cm) long. Both have peg holes for fixing them with a wooden peg to the ard sharebeam. They were used in the London area across to East Anglia and continued in use to Saxon times. On the right, a combined pointed mattock and two-tine implement. In the centre are two pruning knives and the remains of a small sickle; originally the blade was twice as

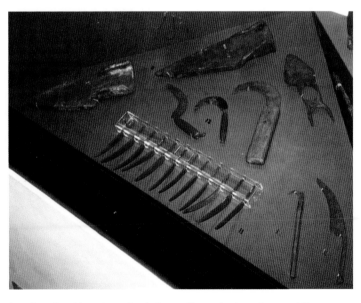

long. In the centre foreground are iron tines fitted in a clear plastic frame, illustrating how they would have been fitted in a wooden beam of a rake. A long handle would have been fitted at the centre. These are all of the 1st and 2nd centuries AD (the Roman era). They were preserved in mud and found at the Walbrook Valley site, London. All the wooden handles are replicas. (Displayed in the London Museum at London Wall; courtesy of the curator.)

Part of an iron shoe for a wooden spade.
Wooden spades were strengthened and
given a sharper edge with an iron shoe;
they were either made square like the one
illustrated or rounded. The spade shoe
above is 6 in. (15 cm) wide and is made of
wrought iron. The bottom edge is damaged
and one side rusted away. Also missing are
the straps which go up the sides and fold
over the top, to hold the shoe firmly onto
the wooden blade. Roman Iron Age of the
1st and 2nd centuries AD.

**A selection of Roman Iron Age tools found
on the Walbrook Valley excavation site.**
On the left of the picture is a mattock and
axe without the handle, behind it is a
pickaxe, and beside that a rather long
mattock. All three of these tools were useful
for digging out tree roots and bushes, etc.
At the back in the corner and on the right
are two two-tine grappins and in front of
them is a pointed mattock and a two-tine
hoe. The two sticks with iron points bound
on them are prodders used by drivers for
prodding the rump of oxen at work. All
these items are of the Iron Age (Roman, 1st
and 2nd centuries AD). They were all
preserved in mud on the Walbrook Valley
site. All the wooden handles were made by
museum staff at London Museum.
(Courtesy of the curator.)

An Iron Age spear-type share found at Silchester is illustrated and described in Chapter 3.

See caption at foot of page 65.

Roman tools and hippo-sandals in the British Museum.

At the top of this picture is a knife coulter, and standing to the right is a field anvil. Beneath the anvil are two pruning knives, one tanged and the small one with a socket. At the front on the right is a round-type spade shoe. At the back beneath the knife coulter, behind the two-prong hoe or grappin, is a socketed spear-type share. At the bottom in the foreground is a Roman hippo-sandal. The knife coulter was found in Gloucestershire, the small socketed share in London, and the field anvil at Sandy in Bedfordshire. The round-type spade shoe would have a wooden spade inserted. The socketed share was fitted over the point of a hardwood spear-type share to provide a hard-wearing point on the ard. The hippo-sandal at the bottom is a Roman innovation: they did not shoe their horses, they fitted removable shoes as a temporary measure, for working on hard metalled road surfaces. They were made by Roman military blacksmiths.

Iron Age tools in the British Museum including a two-prong grappin.

At the top left is a pickaxe, below it are axeheads, in the middle is a two-prong hoe or two-prong grappin. Below are two Roman hippo-sandals; to the right at the back is a small socketed spear-type share for the ard. The axes were found at Cammerton in Suffolk, and the remainder come from the London area. (British Museum, London Wall; courtesy of the curator.)

(Left) A further collection of Roman Iron Age tools, some of them unchanged and used today, such as the sickle and billhook.

This collection of iron tools includes a sickle at the top left and a billhook top right. Beneath the sickle are the remains of an oak beam rake and iron tines, at the bottom left are the remains of a wool comb, and on the right are four knives. These were all made by Roman-age blacksmiths and possibly earlier. The sickle is identical to the modern sickle. The rake was a solid tool with sturdy tines fitted through the oak beam and rolled over, probably for raking soil. The wool comb is double-sided for combing wool, so the fibres lay parallel to one another before spinning. Of the knives, two have a maker's name: 'Olundus' on one; the second is illegible. The big knife with a large socket may be a knife coulter; some early knife coulters had a wooden stalk for fitting to the beam of the ard, like the coulter in Winchester Museum. The sickle and knives were found in London, the wool comb in Essex, and the rake near Daventry. (British Museum, London Wall; courtesy of the curator.)

Roman-age field anvil almost identical to those used today for sickles and scythes. The field anvil is taken to the harvest field or hayfield, and hammered into the ground up to the rings on the side, to prevent it sinking further during use. It was used for beating the cutting edge of sickles and scythes in the field and was still in use in the 20th century. Up to a few years ago every farmer in Jersey would have had one. There is a more modern one on display in the Steam Museum in Jersey.

The author can remember his father and uncles using this type of anvil. They would sit on a folded sack on the ground, legs astride, beating the cutting edges of sickles and scythes prior to sharpening with a stone, to obtain a keen cutting edge. Hoe blades were often beaten on the anvil on an earth floor of a farm shed – a job for a wet day! They are all Roman-age items found on the Silchester site (Reading Museum collection; courtesy of the curator).

More Iron Age tillage items will be found in Chapter 3.

When the Romans retreated they left behind them a thriving agricultural industry in Britain, with well-established farms and farming practices. Methods of tillage had changed very little; it was still dependent mainly on the ard and the mattock, but the mouldboard, and thus the plough was in its infancy, and with the harrow would make a substantial change to tillage. By Saxon times the plough was a much more efficient and accepted implement.

Only a few centuries after the Saxons, Jersey was an attractive target for roving Vikings. Over a long period they were the cause of much anxiety, misery, and grief for Islanders. History records that growing crops and harvested crops were burnt, which implies some successful farming was going on at the time. William Longsword, the first Duke of Normandy, annexed the Channel Islands after he succeeded in colonising the Côtentin; he was the son of Rollo, the first Viking leader to settle in that part of France that is now Normandy.

The Vikings were not only good boat builders and navigators, but were skilled farmers, and they introduced a well-designed light plough to the Shetlands and Orkneys. It is reasonable to assume that a similar plough may well have been introduced into Normandy, and possibly here.

William Longsword was concerned to see that the population of his dukedom, including the Channel Islands, could feed themselves adequately. A system of land division was organised in both Normandy and in the Island, where farmers had a bouvée of arable land to grow their crops, mostly wheat. A bouvée was 24 vergées, which was considered to be an appropriate size for a man and one or two oxen to cultivate. By this time the plough and light harrow were established implements to prepare the land for planting and sowing crops. Ploughing was probably a communal activity, neighbours working together. One man was responsible for the plough, the neighbours each providing one or more oxen to make the team. The practice of ploughing with neighbours continued right up to the first half of the twentieth century.

As we consider the very slow and gradual improvement of implements, over several thousand years, one cannot help but marvel over the length of time it has taken man slowly to improve farm implements, compared with the pace of development since the Industrial Revolution. An exception was in the Iron Age, when they eventually learned how to use iron, resulting in a wide range of tools and implements coming into use, many of which have barely changed to this day, such as the modern sickle and billhook. Only the material has changed, steel rather than wrought iron. The increased pace of development of the last thirty years is breathtaking. It is a clear indication of the advantages of education, further education, and research in universities, colleges, and research institutions like Silsoe, set up by the Institution of Agricultural Engineers in the 1950s, and the West of Scotland College of Agriculture.

One has only to look at transport, the car for example, and compare its rate of development in almost one and a half human lifetimes, and we are impatient for further development. We now wait for further change in propulsion units, and in particular the fuel. The internal combustion engine that, basically, has not changed, is ripe for change, to make a dramatic improvement to pollution and the environment and reduce global warming. Much of the technology has been known for years but to bring it into use has been delayed unforgivably by the oil companies and motor manufacturers. However, development is taking place such as the fuel cell, first used on an experimental tractor by Allis-Chalmers, so change is at last on the way. Future generations, one hopes, will see a reduction of central power generators and distribution systems in favour of wind and solar generation and other systems of generating energy at the point of use.

Sources: All the drawings are the author's, with reference to *Larousse agricole: encyclopédie illustrée* and other papers.

5 Animal Draught Field Implements

Ploughs

Ploughs in Jersey, before the big plough, were the 'grain' or corn ploughs, probably ploughing a shallow furrow to a depth of 4-5 in. (10-12.6 cm), which was quite sufficient for growing cereals. The practice remained popular for autumn breezing until quite recently. It was said by Col. John Le Couteur, of Belle Vue, St. Brelade, that to plough 14 in. (35.5 cm) deep, two oxen and up to eight horses (small Cossacks, ex-Russian Army horses) were often harnessed to it. Both G. R. Balleine's *History of the Island of Jersey* (1950) and another historian, Thomas Quayle (*General View . . . of the Islands on the Coast of Normandy*, 1815), recorded trench ploughs being drawn in 1815 with mixed teams, composed of two oxen and six or eight horses. The trench plough was also known as 'la grande tchéthue', or the 'big plough'. It was quite a revolution when it was first used in the Island in the late eighteenth century. After many years of shallow ploughing, for grain crops, the open furrow of the big plough must have appeared like a vast trench! It was introduced, as previously stated, for the growing of root crops commercially. Parsnips formed a substantial part of the diet of both people and livestock, but more importantly that new crop, the potato, was becoming popular. Both crops required deep cultivation. Vraic was also a popular fertiliser for the land. Parsnips did not grow well with vraic, but it was excellent for potato growing. Exporting potatoes soon followed, as the Royal Jersey Agricultural and Horticultural Society records indicate: 30,000 tons per year were being exported in the 1830s.

At this time most of the east of the Island was covered in orchards, for making cider for export. In this century, before the apple trees were grubbed out, farmers grew early potatoes in the orchards under their apple trees. Just a few rows were planted between the rows of trees. They could not get too close to the trees, according to John Billot, of La Porte, Maufant; the 'haimes' on the horses' collars would strike the lower branches of the apple trees! Many of those orchards were probably grubbed out during the food shortages of the First World War, when there was a dwindling market for cider.

The two photographs which follow illustrate the wooden deep-digger plough, known as *la grande tchéthue* or the 'big plough'. Note the very solid wooden frame made in Jersey by a carpenter and ironwork by a blacksmith. It was probably made in the early nineteenth century, and possibly earlier, at a time when more enterprising farmers were growing parsnips and potatoes commercially. The beam, handles, stock, and frog are all of wood, the mouldboard and share of iron, and the fittings are of wrought iron. The share is 14 in. (35.5 cm) wide. The enormous, beautifully carved frog was necessary to support the relatively thin, soft metal of the abruptly curved mouldboard. The steeply curved mouldboard was so made to burst and fragment the soil, in order to make a good working tilth, in preparation of the soil for potato planting. This type of mouldboard would only work in medium to light soils, which fortunately means all over the Island. The heel has to perform as a landside (or slade) to resist the lateral pressure on the plough. It is made of wood but has a metal wearing plate under the heel, which can wear quite rapidly. A large skimmer would normally be clamped to the beam in front, to bury the top growth, farmyard manure, or seaweed. When this plough was first used the big skimmer had not yet come into being, and a light plough went ahead of the big plough. It was probably a corn plough pulled with two horses, to skim off and bury the top growth and manure.

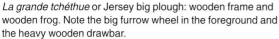

La grande tchéthue or Jersey big plough: wooden frame and wooden frog. Note the big furrow wheel in the foreground and the heavy wooden drawbar.

On the forecarriage, the crossbar, for setting depth and width of furrow, normally fitted to the two uprights on the axle, is missing (see the next picture). Also missing is the chain between the plough beam and the forecarriage. The heavy wooden drawbar is made of one piece of timber selected for its forked shape, with wrought ironwork for hitching to the bodkins (or whippletrees), which in turn are hitched to the chains, known as traces, attached to the horses' collars. The wheels are sturdy with large hubs, and have ten spokes and wrought-iron tyres. They are of unequal diameter: the furrow wheel with the bigger diameter runs in the open furrow and the smaller-diameter landwheel runs on top of the unturned soil, the purpose of which is to keep the all-important crossbar level. Red is the traditional colour for the wheels and blue or sometimes grey for the wooden beam. The plough would require a minimum of four horses and more likely six or a mix of horses and oxen. It is at present on display at the Steam Museum.

> The deep-digger plough became popular all over Jersey when potatoes were first grown for export from approximately 1820 and has remained the prime cultivating implement on the Jersey farm.

This plough is complete with a large skimmer and draw chain; the drawbar resting on a Jersey six-pot milk can shows the arrangement of the bodkins (les batchus, or whippletrees). The wooden plough here is similar to the first, but note the much deeper mouldboard, and it has a smaller 12 in. (30 cm) share. The body of this plough is made up with a deep mould-board in three parts, partly due to the limitations of materials and presses available in the Island at the time. It has a shin for the deep vertical cut of the furrow wall. The landside to take the sideways thrust is rather small, and although the long heel will also absorb some of the side thrust, its main purpose is to maintain the depth of work. It has metal wearing plates. It has a particularly large skimmer to skim off the top growth, trash, seaweed, or farmyard manure and deposit it into the bottom of the previous furrow, where it will be buried. The skimmer is almost as big as a breezing plough body and is normally set at a depth of 3-4 in. (7-9 cm); its share is 8 in. (20.3 cm) wide. The carriage has an all-metal drawbar and the draw chain to the wrought-iron hook on the beam and around the stock is in place. Also in place is the timber crossbeam with a choice of holes and all its fittings. Raising or lowering the crossbeam adjusts the height of the plough beam, which adjusts the pitch of the share relative to the soil, controlling the depth of work. Width of furrow is adjusted by moving the two tall pegs on the crossbar to one side or the other. In front of the axle the hinged drawbar has a series of adjustment holes, to which is attached a wide bodkin, and two further bodkins are hooked one at each end of the first. Those two bodkins are hooked at each end to the traces (chains) which are hooked to the collars of the horses. On the outside of the left handle there is a metal piece which might be mistaken for a hand guard; it is in fact a rest or skid. When the heavy plough is lifted out of the ground, at the end of the furrow, it is laid on its side while it is drawn along the headland to the return furrow, the rest keeping the handle clear of the ground. (The plough was the property of Mr. Le Seelleur, Cloverley, St. Martin, and is at present in the collection at Samarès Manor.)

The Jersey two-wheel forecarriage with its timber crossbeam and variety of adjustments, is almost unique in its detail. The Kent plough of the sixteenth century is much taller, but is otherwise similar with the same adjustments. Methods of attaching the draught chain to the beam do vary and it is different again on iron ploughs. The heavy loads of a deep-digging plough hauled by a team of four or six horses or oxen demand a substantial forecarriage with big wheels set wide apart to make the plough manageable.

The grain or corn plough used in Jersey, at an earlier period, was similar but ploughed a smaller furrow. It was simply a smaller plough similar to the breezing plough and hauled by one horse or two oxen. Le Cappelain, at St. Peter's Iron Works, made small wooden beam ploughs with a cast-iron frog and 15 in. (38.1 cm) wide share. The mouldboard has an abrupt upright curve but turned well over, to ensure the furrow was also well turned over. It was designed to plough between 9 and 10 in. (22.8-25.4 cm) deep.

Jean Le Boutillier's wooden potato-planting plough at Hamptonne.

In 1835 Jean Le Boutillier designed and developed the first Jersey potato-planting plough for Col. John Le Couteur of Belle Vue, St. Brelade. The planting plough makes a narrow shallow furrow, and the soil is not immediately turned over but is moved across the surface of the land and deposited on the previous furrow 18-20 in. (45.5-50.8 cm) away, so covering the planted potatoes. This design of planting plough continued in use for the next 125 years, only changing to an iron beam and iron wheels in the 1880s and 1890s. It was used by every potato grower in Jersey and is still used today, with a very light frame, on the steep early côtils such as at Rozel, St. Catherine, Gorey, and L' Étacq.

The complete plough has a light forecarriage with small-diameter wheels, the furrow wheel having a bigger diameter. The plough body has a shallow 6 in. (15.2 cm) deep mouldboard measuring 18-20 in. (45.5-50.8 cm) in length and the share is 3.5-4 in. (8-10 cm) deep and 6 in. (15.2 cm) wide. The mouldboard has an adjustment behind it with a series of holes in a bar with a peg to adjust the width between furrows; the usual choice is 18 in. (45.5 cm) and sometimes 20 in. (50.8 cm), the latter normally used to plant late potatoes. The plough is pulled by one horse.

The wooden potato-planting plough at work; the forecarriage has smaller wheels than the big plough (La Société Jersiaise photographic archive.)

Harrows and cultivators

Animal draught wooden-frame cultivator with five tines.
The very solid triangular frame cultivator has five solid 16 in. (40.6 cm) long tines, with reversible points. The points would have been a proprietary item and imported from a UK or French manufacturer. The cultivator was made locally in the middle of the 19th century, or earlier, by a local carpenter making the frame and a blacksmith producing the ironwork. Originally it had three wheels, one at the front and one at each corner at the back, but the two rear wheels are missing. All three wheel mounts would have had an adjustment to raise or lower the frame and the tines. The front wheel stalk can also turn for steering. The wheels and fittings may have been made locally or imported. One or two horses or oxen would have pulled this implement. A horse moves faster than oxen and would be more effective at bursting the soil open. This type of wooden frame cultivator was commonplace here, in Brittany and in other parts of France. This implement would not work more than 3 or 4 in. (7.6-10 cm) deep for breaking up grassland, and more deeply, up to 6 in. (15.2 cm) deep, on ploughed land. That was all that was needed for making a seed bed. The missing wheels were probably taken off to be used on another implement. This implement is at present in the Museum store at Augrès.

Horse draught light harrow, probably made by Reeves.
The harrow was probably made in the 19th century, and is very similar to the steel Reeves No. 1. The wood and iron frame has five main timber members, each with five 7 in. (17.7 cm) iron tines driven into them at approximately 10 in. (25.4 cm) centres. They are braced with steel rods riveted through the sturdier outside members and held in place by a wooden cross-member, at the back, and a light steel beam, across the front. This implement is very similar to the Jersey light hand harrows but it is larger, heavier and has longer large tines. Pulled from the corner with a *batchu* or bodkin by horses or oxen. (Courtesy of Breamore Countryside Museum collection.)

Potato diggers

Jean Le Boutillier's wooden-frame potato diggers.
In 1838, when Jean Le Boutillier made the first Jersey potato digger, he made use of the classic rectangular plough frame and wooden beam. Behind the share there is no mouldboard but a shaft with five three-prong digging forks at one end; unfortunately one fork is missing. The shaft, complete with a pinion, engaged in the cast iron 19.5 in. (48.33 cm) diameter crownwheel at one end and the forks at the other end, is rotated by the crownwheel, which is also a landwheel with eight spade lugs that rotates as the implement advances. Behind the crownwheel is a small-diameter wheel or roller that supports the crownwheel at the point where the pinion engages with it. The purpose is to ensure the crownwheel and pinion remain in mesh. The complete implement would have the usual wooden forecarriage, with two wheels, etc. (Société Jersiaise/Jersey Heritage Trust collection at Hamptonne.)

A closer picture reveals the mechanical arrangements of the digger.

The digger has an 18 in. (45.5 cm) wide iron plough share fitted to the wooden frog. As the digger advances, the soil and potatoes in the ridge or bank are lifted by the share, to be thrown off by the five spinning forks. The crownwheel has forty teeth and a circumference of 5 ft 1 in. (154.9 cm), and the pinion with ten teeth rotates four times for every revolution of the crownwheel. Assuming the normal speed of a horse, the shaft would rotate at approximately 65/70 rpm and the forks would dig every 3 in., just as they do in more modern diggers. (The digger is displayed at the Hamptonne Country Life Museum.) Two horses would be required to pull the digger which is painted in 'farm red' lead paint. One has to admire the work and ingenuity of Jean Le Boutillier.

The digger with an open-gear landwheel and two-tine forks.

The potato digger above is a slight variation of the first, similar in general appearance but not in the detail. On the spinner shaft are six two-prong digging forks. The landside is made of wood, with a wearing plate beneath the heel. The share is 20 in. (50.8 cm) wide and the crownwheel is 24 in. (61 cm) in diameter with nine lugs; it has forty teeth and a circumference of 6 ft 2.5 in. (180 cm), and the pinion has twelve teeth, so the pinion rotates at 3.3 revolutions for each revolution of the crownwheel. Thus a fork will dig every 4 in. (10 cm) approximately.

A closer view, and note the continued use of the classic rectangular plough frame

Iron implements

The big plough

Le Cappelain, at St. Peter's Iron Works, began producing iron ploughs in the 1880s and went on making them to order up to 1946. It was surprising that production went on until then because the first self-lift tractor ploughs were being manufactured before 1912 and mounted ploughs first appeared in 1937 in Jersey. Farmers everywhere were always very conservative!

La grande tchéthue , or big plough, made of iron and steel; quite often the forecarriage retains wooden wheels, hand grips and the adjustable beam or crossbar on the forecarriage.

Made by E. Slade at St. Martin where Slade had an engineering business, probably before the First World War. It is basically the same as the big wooden plough previously described. It has a cast iron frog supporting a 14 in. (35.5 cm) wide share, a deep, steeply curved mouldboard to plough 12 in. (30.4 cm) deep, a landside and heel, a skimmer with an 8 in. (20.3 cm) wide share. As usual, one of the wooden spoked wheels is smaller, and both have steel rims. The continued use of the wooden-wheeled forecarriage is probably simply making use of them when the wooden beam plough was discarded. A noticeable change with the steel plough is the hitching arrangement of the draw chains, between the beam and the forecarriage. On the iron plough, a crossbar is riveted or bolted to the beam above the share, behind the skimmer; it has curled 'pigtail' hooks at each end to attach the draught chains to the forecarriage. This has been done to avoid the chains fouling the stem of the skimmer. The drawbar is resting on a milk can to illustrate the assembly of the three batchus or bodkins, also known as whippletrees. The big plough required a minimum of four horses and often five or six were used, and it also required a large team of men: the man on the plough, one driving the horses, two men digging the ends, one at each end of the field, and someone to bring the tea! (This plough was the property of Mr. Eddie Godel, of Les Ormes, St. Lawrence.)

The Young Farmers Club horse ploughing day; the plough has steel wheels.

This event in Trinity was performed by former members of the Club, holding the plough and driving the horses. This all-steel plough is ploughing a 12 in. (30.4 cm) deep furrow, with a 13 in. (33 cm) wide share and a big 6 in. (15.2 cm) skimmer. The wheels are all steel, the furrow wheel is 3 ft 3 in. (98.4 cm) in diameter, the landwheel is 3 ft (91.5 cm) in diameter, and the rims 1.75 in. (4.5 cm) wide, and the track 3 ft 6 in. (106.7 cm) between the wheels. Although it had been a long time since these horses pulled a plough (if ever!), they worked well together; they are probably kept today for a hobby on a working farm. For regular farm work, their tails would have been much shorter to prevent them getting tangled in the traces.

Mr. McGugan's 'big plough', probably the last to be made.

The above all-steel plough was made in 1946 or 1947, which is surprising; by that time tractor ploughs had been available for many years. It was probably the last or one of the last of the 'big ploughs' to be made by Le Cappelain at St. Peter's Iron Works. The skimmer is missing although the clamp is still in place. It was made for Mr. McGugan at Le Val Vallon, Grouville, where it is cared for today by his son, Mr. Arthur McGugan.

A rare trolley for transporting the big plough when moved between fields.

This rare little triangular trolley is for supporting a 'big plough' when moving it about the farm with a horse, with a man holding the plough's handles to steady it. The point of the share's fitted into the small triangular socket at the front or apex of the frame. The landside was dropped into the space between the two uprights beside the left-hand wheel. A man would hold the handles and the plough could be wheeled between fields with one horse to pull it. It is 23 in. (58.4 cm) wide overall, and the 8 in. (20.3 cm) diameter wheels have 1.75 in. (4.5 cm) wide rims. A blacksmith would have made it to order. It was normal practice to remove the forecarriage from the plough beam and load it all onto a box cart or a farm van. (Charles Le Couteur's collection at Westlands, St. Peter.)

A delightful picture of breezing with horses—tchéthue à brîsi.

The single-furrow plough is similar to the traditional Jersey horse plough, but not a 'big plough'. The two horses are coping comfortably, the ploughman is also the driver, and nobody is digging the ends. They are ploughing 'in' the residue from a previously harvested crop at about 6 or 7 in. deep. Many farmers ploughed at this depth in the autumn and left the field fallow to the new year before ploughing with the big plough. The picture was published by the *Islander* during the German Occupation.

Autumn breezing at Samarès Manor.

The breezing plough at work. The ploughman is having difficulty burying the green grass; it would have been easier if it had been cut or grazed off first. The problem is that the grass will take root and start growing again. The plough has a 12 in. (30.4 cm) wide share and is ploughing approximately 5 in. (12.6 cm) deep.

A breezing plough turned on its side as for moving along the headland. (Made by Mr. Thérin, of Trinity).

Twin-furrow breezing plough (Samarès Manor collection).
This plough was partly made and assembled by Colbacks in the 1920s or 1930s, with Oliver mouldboards, made in the USA, and Le Cappelain legs. The two bodies have 12 in. (30.4 cm) wide forged iron shares for 5 in. (12.6 cm) deep work. The legs and frogs were sometimes cast in one piece, probably at Grandin's or in Le Cappelain's own foundry. The mouldboards are the shallow digger type to break up the soil. The under-beam clearance to share tip is 17 in. (43.11 cm). Skimmers were not always used for breezing.
Le Cappelain, in the post-First World War period, described these ploughs as self-lift ploughs. They have a lift lever at the back, handy to the ploughman who walks beside the plough while driving the horses. The same lever also sets the depth of work, having notches on the quadrant for that purpose. The lever has a rod linked to the front wheels; their stalks are fitted to a shaft that can be rotated to raise or lower the wheels. A second lever at the front adjusts the width of the front furrow. Steel wheels of this type were partly made by Le Cappelain. The spokes were delivered to Grandin's foundry at Commercial Buildings where they were assembled in a casting jig to be cast in a hub. The spokes and hubs were then returned to Le Cappelain's, where they were riveted to the rims. The landwheel has a 22 in. (55.9 cm) diameter and the furrow wheel has a 17 in. (43.11 cm) diameter. To compensate for the smaller diameter it is fitted with a longer stalk than the landwheel. The wheels and their stalks are fitted to a common axle, on top of the plough frame. This is to help the operation of the manual lift, to ensure the shares are lifted well clear of the ground while on the headland. The plough would be pulled by two horses.

The expression 'a self-lift plough' is a little confusing. Tractor ploughs are true self-lift ploughs. The tractor plough will lift itself, with a gear and quadrant on the landwheel, controlled by a trip lever operated by the tractor driver from the tractor seat.

A Le Cappelain cast-iron plough leg as described above.
These legs were often purchased by other plough makers in the Island, like Colback's, and Thérin, for assembling to their own plough frames.

Planting ploughs

 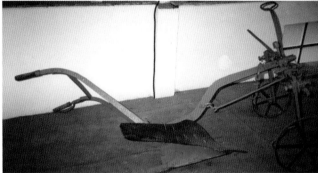

An iron potato-planting plough, with a frame similar to a light breezing plough.
The body has a small 6 in. (15.2 cm) wide share and 20 in. (50.8 cm) long mouldboard, which has an adjustment for the angle, to set the width between the rows of potatoes as described previously. The plough is pulled by one horse, in traces. The operator was both driver and ploughman, holding the reins while walking beside the plough and holding the ring handle above the landwheel. Some farmers pulled the plough with a Ransomes MG 2 tractor. It has a trip lever to tip the plough on its side to move along the headland. Almost all the Island's growers used potato-planting ploughs like this. (Steam Museum collection.)

Potato-planting plough made by Ransomes; it was originally supplied with an iron forecarriage with a trip mechanism to lay it on its side.
This plough is a model RHAJ, which means Ransomes, horse, model A type, and J for Jersey. It is fitted with a skid, or rest, on the beam for laying it on its side to move it along the headland. It is a standard model A frame used for a number of light ploughs with different bodies, probably made in the 1920s or 1930s. (Displayed at the Royal Hotel, St. Martin.)

A Melotte horse-drawn, one-way or reversible planting plough.
This Melotte one-way plough was supplied by T. Bourne, at Paramé, St. Malo. It was probably imported by a local blacksmith, with or without breezing bodies that were changed over for locally made planting bodies. The two steel wheels are equal in diameter. It has 7 in. (17.7 cm) shares. At the top is a single-screw adjustment to control depth of work. On each side are the loop handles for the operator to keep control of the plough in work. The bodies and legs are easily removed and breezing bodies fitted. It would be pulled by one horse. Le Cappelain were the local agents for Melotte's Brabant ploughs.

Iron cultivators

The cultivators which follow are for breaking up grassland before ploughing, and also for preparing a tilth after ploughing and working in guano before potato planting. After passing a cultivator over freshly ploughed land, the drag harrow would be used to prepare a fine tilth before planting.

Nine-tine horse-drawn cultivator with a lift and depth-control lever.

Horse-draught, nine-tine cultivator with solid tines, a T piece at the top, with two bolts through the beam, and reversible points. Manufactured locally, probably by St. Peter's Iron Works, in the early 20th century. The width of work is set by the two rear tines that are at 4 ft 1 in. (124.4 cm) centres. Their position behind the rear wheels is to break up the wheel marks. It was probably made locally but the reversible points will have been bought in (imported). The wheels are cast iron, diameters are 15 in. (38.1 cm) rear wheels and 12 in. (30.4 cm) front, which is steerable and designed to caster. The draught chain passes through a vertical keeper so that the front wheel may turn as the horses turn onto the headland. A lift lever on a notched quadrant raises and lowers the rear wheels by rotating the axle and through a chain link. The front wheel slides up and down the steering post. There is a locking position on the quadrant, for a transport position and a selection of working settings. Two horses would pull it. (La Société Jersiaise/Jersey Heritage Trust collection at Hamptonne.)

A similar horse-drawn, seven-tine cultivator; the legs are attached to the beam in T-shaped brackets.

This cultivator is a smaller but similar model. It has seven tines with a different fitting to the beams, using straight tines in brackets, with sockets which enable the tines to be raised or lowered. The front wheel has a bigger diameter, which would make it easier to pull. It is also allowed to caster for turning on the headland. It has the usual lift lever and notched quadrant at the back (Steam Museum collection).

Horse-drawn C-spring-tine cultivator manufactured by Walter A. Woods of Horsham, Sussex.

The spring-tine cultivator, sometimes known as a harrow, was manufactured in the early 20th century. It has seven tines with 8 in. (20.3 cm) long reversible points and width of work of 3 ft 2 in. (96.5 cm). A lever with a notched quadrant controls the depth of work to a maximum of 6-7 in. (15.2-17.7 cm) in ploughed land and 2-3 in. (5-7.6 cm) for breaking up turf. One horse in traces with a bodkin/*batchu* would pull it. They were a popular implement in their day. (Samarès Manor; courtesy of Vincent Obbard.)

Harrows

The harrow is a very useful implement with a variety of uses, in preparing a seed bed. Fertiliser and seeds sown broadcast (i.e. by hand) would be 'harrowed in'. It was used for levelling off, breaking clods, to kill off weeds on fallow land and to clean the soil for a second crop after potatoes had been lifted. Harrows were drawn by horses rather than oxen because a pair of horses walked faster, making a greater impact on clods to burst them.

Horse-drawn twenty-tine drag harrow.
This drag harrow was probably manufactured by R. & J. Reeves & Son Ltd., Bratton Iron Works, Westbury, Wiltshire, who were harrow manufacturers for many years. Almost identical to another of Reeves manufacture, type no. 1, described as 'heavy steel, coarse tines'. They were manufactured from the middle of the 19th century. It has a relatively heavy frame and measures 4 ft (122 cm) x 3 ft 7 in. (109 cm), consisting of four bars 3 ft 7 in. (109 cm) long and 14 in. (35.5 cm) apart, each bar having five tines, at 10 in. (25.4 cm) centres, and each one 7 in. (17.7 cm) long. The rectangular frame is braced with three crossbars. A draught chain is attached to a drawbar with six holes at one corner of the frame. The chain can be adjusted with the series of holes, so altering the angle of the harrow to the work and the fineness of the tilth produced. Width of work is 5 ft (152.4 cm) approximately and it may need two horses to pull it depending on soil conditions.

This type of harrow is probably a forerunner of the zigzag harrow but remained in production until 1950. The Reeves Harrow was priced in 1950 at £12. Harrows are often left out in the field so that they quickly get a coat of rust! (La Société Jersiaise/Heritage Trust collection, at present in the Augrès store.)

Medium-weight two-section zigzag drag harrow.
Medium-weight zigzag drag harrow, manufactured by Parmitter or Reeves since or before the 20th century. It is a two-section harrow with wooden whippletree. They are manufactured in 0.5 in. (1.3 cm) square-section steel. Supplied as one-, two-, three-, or four-piece sections; two were more usual with horses, three or four sections being used with tractors. They were priced in the 1940s at about £5 per section. The number of horses used would depend on the number of sections and the soil condition. There are also lightweight and heavy-weight zigzag harrows. (Shire Horse Farm collection.)

Horse-drawn rotary harrow manufactured by T. W. Ashby & Co. from 1860.
The rotary drag harrow was manufactured until the 1940s. The diameter is 4 ft (122 cm) and it has twenty-eight tines, sixteen on the outer circle, eight on the inner, and four towards the centre. At the centre of the harrow is a vertical post, about which the harrow is free to rotate; it is attached to a drawbar, and at right angles to the drawbar is an arm with a movable weight. The weight can be slid along the arm to adjust it; when it is at the appropriate position along the arm, it is clamped with a setscrew. As the harrow is drawn over the soil, the weight will have the effect of forcing the tines on that side to penetrate further into the soil than the remainder, causing the whole (*continued on facing page*)

Chain harrow originally used with horses but often used today with a tractor.
Chain harrow probably made by Parmitter, the best-known name among the manufacturers of chain harrows. The chain harrow, sometimes known as a flexible harrow, has been manufactured for over a century and is still in production. They are sometimes made with a carrying frame for use on the tractor hydraulic lift. This one is a three-section harrow with one section rolled up, as they would be, for storage and moving about the farm. It requires a long steel bodkin, or whippletree, and some have a steel wheel at each end. This three-section harrow would require at least two horses; a single section could be hauled by one horse. Chain harrows are usually used to invigorate and aerate pasture, and also to clean up pasture after cattle and other livestock have grazed on it, to disperse the droppings and spread the molehills, etc. (Shire Horse Farm collection.)

Rollers

The horse-drawn roller was probably used on every farm in the Island for rolling when preparing a seed bed, for example when a seed drill, such as a Planet, is to be used for sowing a rowcrop of maize or kale and root crops such as mangels or turnips. It is also useful to roll immediately after ploughing, to keep the moisture in the soil in drying weather conditions. Some wooden rollers had only a single, one-piece roll and a diameter of 14 in. (35.5 cm). While some rollers have 12 in. (30.4 cm) cast-iron transport wheels, not all rollers have transport wheels. If the roller has to be transported some distance, then the pin holding the shafts in their sockets beside the platform can be withdrawn and the shafts taken out of their sockets. The roller and shafts would be loaded onto a box cart or in the farm van. Not all of them had a platform for the driver; if one is needed a plank of wood may be placed on the frame to serve the purpose.

Horse-drawn flat roller, with a wooden roll in two sections; made in Jersey.
This 5 ft. (152 cm) long roller is in two parts, each of 15 in. (38.1 cm) diameter with metal bands around the ends, which will make turning easier and is less likely to make the soil build up when turning short, which can be a problem with a one-piece roll. For transport it has two 15 in. (38.1 cm) diameter cast iron wheels that can be lowered to raise the roller off the ground. The shafts with iron fittings, for a horse in cart harness, are fitted into sockets with locking pins each side of the platform. The driver stands or sits on the platform and it may carry extra weight, such as sacks of soil, when breaking clods of soil. This roller has iron V frames to support the plain bearings but many had wooden V frames with iron bearings. It is a standard local design, with slight variations, and they were made to order, by a local carpenter and blacksmith. They were made any time in the first half of the 20th century or earlier. One horse would pull the roller. (Shire Horse Farm collection.)

(*continued from facing page*) harrow to rotate about the centreas it is dragged along. The rotary action imparts a swifter movement to the tines to pulverise clods, and they are self-cleaning, pushing aside small weeds, etc. They could be used in pairs, with a coupling frame and two horses in traces with bodkin. The tines on this one are worn, indicating it has been used. One unit could be pulled with one horse. (La Société Jersiaise/Jersey Heritage Trust collection at Hamptonne.)

Potato scarifiers and bankers

Potato scarifier.
Single-row horse-drawn potato scarifier, for scarifying between the rows of early potatoes. These were made locally and every potato grower would have one. The first were probably made in the last decades of the 19th century; previously they were made of wood with iron fittings. A light triangular steel frame with handles and a single iron wheel at the front, three solid cultivating tines with no replaceable points. One tine was clamped at the front, centre, with an 'arrowhead' point; behind it on the right was a tine with half an arrowhead; the fluke on its left side towards the centre; and on the opposite side, slightly staggered, was the third tine, also with half an arrowhead, and its fluke on its right side toward the centre.
The tines are set at an overall cultivating width of only 8 or 9 in. (20.3 or 22.8 cm). Right at the back is a crumbler, or knife roller, 9 in. (22.8 cm) long and 8 in. (20.3 cm) in diameter. The knives are spaced about 1.5 in. (3.8 cm) apart. Depth of work was approximately 2 in. (6.3 cm) and adjustable by raising or lowering each individual tine and adjusting the height of the rear knife roller. The cast-iron front wheel is 14 in. (35.5 cm) in diameter, some others being 12 in. (30.4 cm). The overall width would be 12-14 in. (30.4-35.5 cm). The crumbler may differ from one machine to another; some may be 10 in. (25.4 cm) in diameter and 11 in. (8 cm) wide. It is pulled by one horse, carefully selected to walk placing its hooves one before the other in the 18 in. space between the rows of potato plants. This was to ensure the hooves did not cut or tread on the tender young shoots. The horse was usually led by somebody holding the bridle, the second person holding the scarifier. The knife roller or crumbler broke up any clods and chopped up any weeds; the crop always looked very neat and clean after scarifying. The frames can be altered when scarifying is finished, removing the tines and roller. A light triangular frame is fitted to carry three potato bankers to push up earth around the growing potato plant. Each banker body is curving roundly and measures 12 in. (30.4 cm) across from wing to wing; it is beautifully formed to mould the soil into well-shaped banks rising to a pointed ridge. (La Société Jersiaise/Heritage Trust Collection at Hamptonne.)

The author recalls that on the way home from school, in the 1930s, towards the end of the Easter term, everybody appeared to be scarifying their potatoes. The author spent many Easter holidays scarifying potatoes, leading the horse, looking down all the time to make sure the horse's hooves missed the plants. Darkie was a lovely chestnut-brown mare, and she knew she must not touch the plants, which made the job easier. The author's father held the cultivator. It was a slow, tedious business, scarifying row by row from one side of the field to the other. To a youngster, the beauty of banking after the scarifying was done was simply that three rows were banked at a time and each field was soon finished. It meant this daily job was coming to an end and maybe there would be one or two days of the holidays left, before returning to school!

Potato cultivator with banking bodies for banking up the potatoes.
The potato scarifier set up with banking bodies for earthing up early potatoes. This one has two wheels; very often they have only one wheel, as in the previous illustration. The banking bodies are unique in Jersey as each one is made with a single piece of pressed steel. They are fitted to a stalk on a toolbar and adjustable to equalise the depth of work and set the width on all three bankers. One horse would pull this implement. (Steam Museum collection.)

Horse hoe

In the seventeenth century Jethro Tull, farming in East Anglia, perfected a horse-drawn hoe, for killing weeds in root crops sown in rows, known as 'rowcrops'.

Planet JR horse-drawn rowcrop hoe, model no. 8.
The no. 8 hoe has three hoe blades, one 18 in. (45.5 cm) V- and two 8 in. (20.3 cm) L-shaped blades mounted on a steel frame. Earlier implements had wooden handles, but by the late 1940s the handles and grips were made of metal. The frame can be set narrow or expanded, adjusting the width of work from 22 in. (55.9 cm) to 34 in. (86.3 cm), with a lever adjustment. A second lever will adjust the depth of work; it is usually an inch for young weeds and more for older, bigger weeds. It has one wheel at the front with an adjustment to control depth of work; and is pulled by one horse. The operator, using long reins, walked behind the implement. A local supplier was the Country Gentlemen's Association (CGA), a business which once operated on the Esplanade. They were used for weed control in tomatoes and to maintain a tilth in the wider spaces between pairs of rows of tomato plants. If these spaces were left unattended the soil became hard from the traffic as people passed up and down attending to the crop, weeding between the plants in the rows and tying and 'side shooting', as it was known. If ever the ground became too hard the implement could be difficult to keep in the soil. They were used in many rowcrops and brassicas in particular. (Steam Museum collection.)

Titbits

In the heavy, sticky soils of the Vale of Evesham, in damp conditions, the soil will stick to the mouldboard of a plough and will not slide off. It will stick to boots; each foot quickly becomes as big as a football. A two-prong fork has to be used for digging. Wooden mouldboards were found to work better than metal, as the sticky soil would slide more easily over a timber board. Other ideas include mouldboards made with a number of bars or strips of flat steel so curved as to resemble as closely as possible the curve of a mouldboard.

In general terms, the plough body is basically the same today as it was 180 years ago; only the supporting frame, materials, and means of draught have changed. Increased power allows more and more bodies per plough to be added. Today a four-furrow reversible plough is not an uncommon sight in the Island and there is a five-furrow reversible plough at a farm near Rozel. Eight-furrow, semi-mounted, reversible ploughs are working in the UK.

Four- and five-furrow one-way ploughs are not new; they were in use 160 years ago, hauled by cable with steam ploughing engines with winches under the boiler. They were used on the great plains of Eastern Europe, Russia, Egypt, Australia, and Canada, and on big estates in England.

Both plough and ploughing engine were manufactured by Ransomes of Ipswich and John Fowler of Leeds, who led the world with this equipment, exporting them worldwide. Quite a remarkable achievement given that transport was still by sailing ship and draught animal, and when roads were just rough tracks in many parts of the world.

6 Horse-Drawn Machinery

The nineteenth century

The nineteenth century was to be an exciting one, when life would change as never before. The days when the horse set the pace of life on land and the wind set the pace at sea were coming to an end. The new engineering processes and the brilliant engineers of the period introduced new products and procedures: people like Brunel and his work on transport, producing railways, tunnels, bridges, and steamships; Stevenson's steam railway engine; Obed Hussey producing the first reciprocating mower, and McCormick producing it almost on a mass-production basis; Ransome's ploughs, steam traction engines, and threshing machines; John Fowler's steam ploughing engines; and lastly, Dr. Otto with the four-cycle internal combustion engine. These were men with vision and foresight. The common material in all this work was iron and steel; even the tunnels and bridges could not be constructed without it.

In agriculture, although steam engines were driving threshing machines for many agricultural contractors and farmers, and steam ploughing engines were pulling multifurrow ploughs on big estates, the horse and the ox were still a main source of power on most farms, as they had been for centuries and would continue to be to the middle of the twentieth century. Before the steam engine there were the horse engines, driven by one, two, four, or six horses, the idea going back many hundreds if not thousands of years when the earliest engines were made with wooden gears and wooden components. Details of horse engines will be found in Chapter 7.

Harvesting machinery

A harvest scene in a field in Jersey, showing a reaper/mower with the team to make the sheaves and stand them in stooks to dry out.

In 1826 Patrick Bell designed the first reciprocating mowing blade that moved over a line of fixed blades, and which became the basis for the successful reapers that were to follow. Cyrus. H. McCormick is often reputed to have invented the reciprocating mower and demonstrated it in July 1831; however, a second claimant for this honour was one Obed Hussey, who demonstrated his reaper in public in 1833 in Cincinnati. Hussey received his patent in 1833 and McCormick received his in 1834. Obed Hussey was an interesting individual, a Quaker who first went to sea in whaling ships before coming ashore to become a draughtsman. He designed a number of successful farm machines, including mills for processing sugar cane, maize cobs, etc., and designed the horse engine for each one. Finally he designed and built a reaper with a cutter bar that basically remained unchanged for over a hundred years. The reaper had the potential for cutting the cost of harvesting, which in turn would reduce the cost of man's basic food – bread. Although it was quite an arduous undertaking at a time in a vast country without good roads, Obed Hussey travelled widely throughout the United States to demonstrate his reaper, and he also visited the UK. The demonstrations were successful but, with cheap black farm labour in the USA so readily available, he was never taken seriously. A few years later in the Midwest of the USA a desperate need became apparent for mechanising the harvesting of the wheat crop. Like all cereal-growing areas the world over, sickles and scythes were the only alternative. It was 1847 before McCormick finally got his reaper into production in Chicago. They sold in vast numbers; many could not afford to pay for them and failed to do so! However, the company survived, and together with Deering later formed the International Harvester Company. International reapers were sold in Jersey; the author's family shared one between the two family farms, at La Porte and Beau Désert, both in St. Saviour.

Woods reaper and gathering tray, horse pole removed.
Reaper and sweeper tray manufactured by Walter A. Woods, Hoosick Falls, New York, and at Horsham in Sussex, in the mid-19th century. It has a 4 ft 3 in. (129 cm) cutter bar with a reciprocating knife (which has been removed). The knife is made up of triangular blade sections, riveted with two rivets to a steel bar that passes over ledger plates in each pointed finger, the two performing like blades of a pair of scissors. It is mounted on two cast-iron wheels and is drawn by two horses harnessed to a pole. The reciprocating motion is delivered via a long wooden con-rod fitted to the knife at one end, and a balanced crank wheel at the other, driven through a gearbox by the near-side landwheel. The machine illustrated has two seats: when mowing hay, only the driver's seat is occupied, but when reaping cereals, the second seat over the wheel beside the cutter bar is also occupied. The second man would gather the crop into a sheaf, as it fell on the slatted platform, and then push it off the back, using a specially angled sweep. The mower with reaper attachment in the Steam Museum was last used during the Occupation, but many continued to be used after the war and were adapted to be pulled with a tractor. A spare knife was kept ready in the field, together with a box of new sections and rivets. A man was kept busy sharpening the knife and replacing broken sections, which were frequently damaged by stones and large twigs.

The Walter A. Woods company established a branch in the UK in 1852 at Horsham, Sussex. In the USA the company was eventually bought by Daniel Massey in 1861 (later Massey Harris then Massey Ferguson). In the same year, Kansas joined the Union as a state.

Hornsby reaper, complete with horse pole and bodkins, and a sweep.
Horse-drawn mower/reaper, manufactured by Hornsby of Grantham, Lincolnshire, before the Second World War. It has a 4 ft (122 cm) cutter bar with reciprocating knife passing through pointed fingers. Mounted on two cast-iron wheels, which drive a shaft to the gearbox. It has a pole, with bodkins, etc. for two horses. Lying beside the pole is a sweep, for use when the mower is converted with two seats and the collection tray, behind the cutter bar. (Shire Horse Farm collection.)

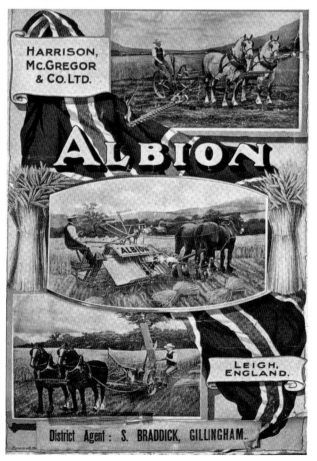

Harrison McGregor's Albion range of reapers and binders.
This colourful old poster advertises Albion harvesting machinery, manufactured by Harrison, McGregor & Co. Ltd. It was produced for their dealers such as Messrs. S. Braddick of Gillingham. At the top is a hay mower, in the middle is a binder, and at the bottom is a reaper, with sweeps that deposit the cut crop in bunches for making sheaves. This does away with the second man. Albion equipment was used in the Island, as were Bamlett mowers, Bamford's equipment, and other British-made harvesting machines.

Potato diggers

Potato digger at work in the 1920s, digging the famous Jersey Royals near La Hougue Bie.

In the days before the mechanical potato digger, potatoes were dug by hand with a team of three people known in Jersey French as a *tâch'ron*, or a 'potato fork', or 'fork'. A *tâch'ron* is composed of a man, who was the digger, with a five-prong potato fork, digging the potatoes, followed by two people, often women in the days of the Breton diggers, one of whom shakes the potato tops (the green foliage) and arranges the potatoes for the picker. The picker follows behind with two baskets, one for the ware, the bigger potatoes, and the other for the smaller potatoes, known as 'mids'.

Mechanical potato diggers first appeared in Jersey in the nineteenth century with the machine designed by Jean Le Boutillier in 1838, when he made the first Jersey potato digger. It is described in detail in Chapter 5. Iron potato diggers, like Browne's Big Marvel, Pollock's Perfect, and Bamford's first Jersey Lily, were manufactured in England and Scotland and first appeared in Jersey before the turn of the nineteenth and twentieth centuries. They were all mounted on two iron wheels, with spade lugs around the iron tyre to provide a grip or traction, to drive the digging mechanism through a gearbox to a star/spoke wheel, fitted with forks and a share beneath to lift the crop. They were basically the same technology as Mr. Le Boutillier's innovation some sixty years before, but were more advanced. More mechanical potato diggers came into the Island during the First World War due to the absence of men who had joined the forces. The second occasion was in the 1930s, when unemployed English and Welsh men who were unskilled with the fork came to the Island for the potato season, replacing the Breton *tâch'ron*. The new circumstances forced the farmers to buy mechanical potato diggers.

Browne's Big Marvel potato digger.
A Big Marvel spinner-type potato digger restored and maintained.
Manufactured by Browne of Leighton Buzzard at about the turn of the 19th and 20th centuries, it has five two-prong forks, mounted on a five-point curved cast-iron starwheel. The share is 15 in. (38.1 cm) wide. The two large-diameter all-steel wheels were fitted with spade lugs, using the single holes in the rims. The spade lugs were necessary to obtain a better grip to drive the digger forks. Two horses were used, one between the shafts and the second in traces in front. The wooden 'handles', held almost vertically in the ring above the spinner, ensured the tines on each fork were held at the appropriate angle for digging. (Shire Horse Farm collection.)
Pollock's Perfect potato digger is almost identical. The design was popular in the Island for very many years in the first half of the 20th century.

The 'handles' were always the source of amusement to the author when he was a schoolboy, because they appeared to dance as the forks spun round in work.

The Perchard family digging Jersey Royal potatoes at La Hambie in 1928.

Pollock's Perfect spinner-type potato digger.
Manufactured in the early 20th century. Note the similarity to the Marvel! With a curved five-point starwheel with two-tine forks and wooden poles/handles removed but lying beside the wheel. The gearbox had a wooden cover, which has rotted away, exposing the crownwheel and pinion gears and the simple dog clutch for disengaging the transmission. The sloping surfaces are a safety device, allowing the clutch to slip in the event of a fork striking a root or rock while in work. The sloping surfaces slide over each other working against a coil spring, that normally holds them together. However, on a horse-drawn machine, very often the horse will stop first! A very good safety device! The big steel wheels have the spade lugs removed. This digger was converted, the horse shafts removed, and a drawbar fitted for hitching to a tractor. This practice was commonplace in the 1950s, as horses disappeared from the farm.

Bamford's no. 2, the Jersey Lily potato digger manufactured in the 1930s.
Bamford no. 2 Jersey Lily potato digger (second generation), serial no. 9228, manufactured in the early years of the 20th century. It has two steel wheels, with spade lugs on the driving wheel, with a ratchet in the hub to drive

through a dog clutch, to engage the transmission of chain and gear system to operate the digging forks. The parallel motion wheel at the back maintains the three-prong forks upright. A lever and notched quadrant raised the machine in and out of work and set the depth. A spinner mounted at the side, part of which is missing, cast the haulms aside, leaving the potatoes clear for the picker. Imprinted on each casting is the part number. Two horses were required to pull it, but the horse shafts have been removed and a drawbar fitted to it for tractor draught. A seat fitted on top was never used, the horses being led by the bridle or driven with rein. All the remaining examples of these machines have been converted for tractors. The first generation of the Lilies had a wooden pole fitted to each fork, like the Pollock and the Marvel. The local supplier was thought to be Le Cappelain, St. Peter's Iron Works. (Steam Museum collection.)

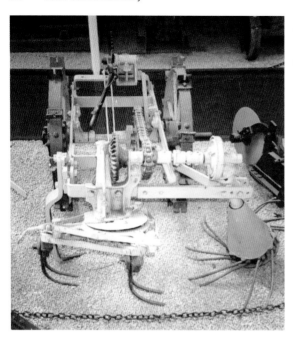

Lister Blackstone potato digger.
This potato digger was manufactured by Lister Blackstone in the 1930s, probably supplied by the CGA on the Esplanade in Jersey. The axle has a dog clutch to engage the chain and sprocket transmission. A lever and notched quadrant raised and lowered the share in and out of work. It has two wheels with spade lugs and a ratchet, to allow the wheels to turn independently. The machines had a narrow road band that fitted in the slots on the lugs and could be left on, because the lugs provided sufficient traction with them on. Some of the tines are missing from the side spinner that removed the haulms, casting them aside. The horse shafts have been removed. When they are fitted, the nearside (left) shaft has a divider that looks like a large hook. The hook was pivoted at the front and carried on a small hook on the shaft when lifted out of work. When it was lowered into work, it passed between two rows to separate the foliage. Mr. Francis Billot had the same model at Beau Désert in St. Saviour. (Steam Museum collection.)

Mr. Billot bought his when unemployed men from the UK were brought over to dig potatoes. It became clear very quickly that these chaps were no use with the Jersey potato fork. They were damaging so many potatoes, by pushing the prongs of the fork into the crops. The Bretons before them were born with a fork in their hands; many of them brought a potato fork with them, in the old days. As the saying used to be: 'Arriving in Jersey off the French boat with a fork over his shoulder.'

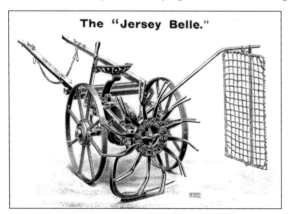

Ransomes Jersey Belle potato digger.
Ransomes potato digger manufactured in the 1920s and 1930s. Development trials were conducted in Jersey: output was 3 vergées an hour. Lightness and strength was a particular aim in the development. It has two wheels, normally fitted with spade lugs. Pulled by two horses, one in the shafts and one in traces in front. The pre-war Jersey agent was T. W. Le Blancq, 5 Beresford Street, St. Helier. (Courtesy of Reading Museum.)

After 1945 there was full employment in the UK, leading to a shortage of some seasonal workers for the potato and tomato seasons in Jersey. So once again Breton labour was employed for each season's work. After a few years the economy began to improve in Brittany and France as a whole, and as a consequence the Bretons were finding work at home and were reluctant to come to Jersey. This left Jersey short of farm labour, and so the mechanical potato digger became a must for many farms. Mr. Clem. Le Breuilly, who had cleverly designed the first mounted one-way plough, imported the Lanz potato digger from Germany. They were available either for horse or tractor draught, and those he ordered sold quickly. In 1956 Mr. Le Breuilly, by then established at his premises at La Rocque, imported twenty-four machines in one consignment. Again they all sold quickly, so he ordered a further consignment.

The Lanz potato digger.
Horse-drawn potato digger manufactured by Lanz of Germany. The forks are driven by a landwheel through a gearbox similar to the Pollock and Big Marvel, but manufactured much later. Both wheels are fitted with spade lugs and road bands and would work well with the bands in place. The adjusting handle and quadrant can be seen for raising and lowering the machine in and out of work. The hook on the left under the nearside horse shaft was lowered to divide the foliage, to untangle it between the rows. The arm on the right would carry a piece of canvas, or more often an old sack, which hung down like a curtain to prevent the potatoes being thrown too far. The digger was pulled by two horses. (Shire Horse Farm collection.)

Fertiliser distributors

Fertiliser distributors before 1940 were mostly made with a long wooden box and lid, fitted between two big steel wheels. The floor of the box was fitted with various mechanisms to control the distribution of the fertiliser. Some have a number of narrow perforated steel plates, along the length of the box, that reciprocated along the bottom; the stroke of one is adjustable to increase or decrease the size of the apertures, so adjusting the flow of fertiliser to be distributed. Above them is an agitator, which will reciprocate or rotate, depending on type, to keep the fertiliser moving and make it flow. One of the landwheels operates a mechanism to the reciprocating parts, which can be disengaged to close the apertures, to stop the machine from functioning when turning at the headland or manœuvring. At the end of the season, the reciprocating plates had to be dismantled and cleaned after use and stored in an oil bath, to prevent rust.

Later designs had a quite different system. Under the box was a line of shallow, dished round plates, the size of a dinner plate, with gear teeth around the circumference that engaged with a small worm wheel, to drive and rotate them. Above each plate is an adjustable aperture through which the fertiliser will flow at a controlled rate onto the revolving plates. Above the plates is a shaft with a small flicker wheel which is clamped to the shaft; each flicker wheel has little arms only an inch or so long that plunge into the fertiliser on the plate and flick it off. These machines were manufactured by Nicholson's, in the East Midlands, and others by Twose and Bunce in the West Country. When the cone-shaped tank and the spinning plate came into use, in the second half of the twentieth century, the long box type went out of fashion.

Twose fertiliser distributor.
Fertiliser distributor manufactured by E. V. Twose of Tiverton in the 1930 and 1940s. It has a wide box with reciprocating plates; one of the wheels drives a connecting rod to the plates. A hand lever on a quadrant adjusts the flow of material and shuts it off. (Shire Horse Farm collection.) Twose fertiliser distributor (*right*). Rear view of the Twose machine. In this view, the back of the spreader can be seen, the driving gear beside the wheel on the right and the control lever at the centre.

A fertiliser spreader manufactured by A. W. Bunce.
A distributor manufactured by A. W. Bunce & Son in Somerset. It has the long box, in the bottom of which is a roller. The gears driven off the landwheel turn a roller with indents which fill up with fertiliser as they pass through the bottom of the hopper, and it falls to the ground as the roller with its filled indents rotates. The application rate is adjusted by changing gears to alter the rpm of the roller. Pulled by one horse. (Shire Horse Farm collection.)

Drilling machines

The first seed drill is thought to have been used by the Chinese in 3000 BC. The Italians had a drill in AD 1600. Jethro Tull perfected a seed drill in Norfolk in 1601 and they came into more general use in England by the middle of the century.

During the German Occupation, the German forces imported three Cougis Auneau seed drills from France. They were supplied to certain farmers, on the understanding they would have horses available to drill seed for any farmer in the Island. The recipients were Mr. Jack A'Court of Jubilee Hill, St. Peter, Mr. Ozouf, of Highstead, St. Saviour, and the third went to Guernsey. After the German Occupation Jack A'Court sold his drill to Mr. John Perrée for £25. Mr Perrée continued to use it with horses but later converted it to tractor draught, using an Allis Chalmers model B tractor to tow it. One winter, in his busiest year, he drilled 300 vergées (133 acres) for customers.

A Cougis Auneau seed drill for drilling cereals or grass seed; one of three imported from France during the German Occupation.
The Cougis Auneau drill was manufactured in the 1940s. It is 6 ft (1.82 m) wide and has thirteen drill spouts and coulters. The seed box is made of wood; seed is delivered to the iron spouts and coulters by the fluted force-feed system and driven by the landwheels through ratchets in the wheels. Delivery of seed to the spouts is controlled overall with sliding shutters and individual shutters for each spout. The rate of sowing is adjusted by changing over the exposed gearwheels. The wheels have steel spokes in cast-iron hubs with a steel rim and wooden tyre. The drills were operated by one man, driving a pair of horses with reins; he walked behind the drill, where he could watch the coulters for blockages. In the event of a blockage, the spouts could be lifted out of work individually to clear them, and each one could be locked out for short turns. The driver also raised or lowered the machine in and out of work with the hand lever.
(*right*) Front view of the Cougis Auneau drill converted for tractor draught.
All trace of the horses' pole was removed when a substantial tractor drawbar was fitted. To operate the drill with a tractor, the driver would have to dismount from the tractor to operate the control levers and check the spouts for blockages.

Machines manufactured later for tractors are wider and faster and had a footboard behind the drill for one man to stand on and move about as he attended to the blocked coulters. Even later drills were manufactured with two hoppers of almost equal size, one in front of the other; one was for fertiliser, which was laid in a band alongside the seeds in a separate spout, and the second for the seed.

Cereal drill manufactured by Bickman & Huffman in the USA.
This drill has also been converted. It had a pole for two horses working side by side and was later converted to tractor draught with an A frame for the hydraulic lift. Beneath the frame, two spring cultivating tines have been fitted on each side to remove the tractor wheel tracks. The drill was manufactured by Bickman & Huffman of Macedon, New York, on 18 June 1899. These details were painted on the back of the seed box; the model is named The Farmer's Favourite, serial no. 1201 & 1200, and the patent numbers and dates from 1870 to 1899 are printed inside the lid of the seed box. It has ten coulters and seed spouts and uses the internal force-feed system. The wheels have wooden spokes and felloes with iron tyres. The first owner was Mr. J. Le Masurier, of Greystones; it was last used in the 1990s and is now in Mr. Charles Le Couteur's collection at Westlands. Similar seed drills to those illustrated have six seed spouts and coulters set at 2 ft (61 cm) centres or five spouts set at 1 ft 3 in. (38.1 cm) centres for drilling rowcrops, such as kale, roots, and maize. Walter A. Wood bought this business, and in due course manufactured a similar drill, but with improved disc coulters, under their Climax brand.

Spraying machines

This type of sprayer was popular in Jersey in the first half of the 20th century for spraying against blight. This horse-drawn sprayer was manufactured by P. Berthoud, of Belleville, Rhône, in France. It is the Toboggan type, serial no. 51T.8073, and is thought to have been made in 1951. The cylindrical copper tank has a capacity of 35 gallons (160 l). Previously, these machines were on two iron wheels with large hubs containing ratchets to drive a pump under the tank. The pump is driven by two triangular cams, mounted on a live axle, the cams to push alternately on two pushrods. The pushrods push on a pair of diaphragms, with a pressure vessel, to stabilise the pressure from the pulses emanating from the pump to provide a steady pressure at the nozzles. The hoses were made of rubber reinforced with woven cotton. They were inclined to buckle and perish as they got old. It has two booms, each with four nozzles at 18 in. (45.5 cm) centres and two on the centre section, making a total of ten. The length of boom is 15 ft (457 cm), giving a spraying width of 18 ft (548 cm). The earlier machines had nozzles at 16 in. (40.6 cm) centres, giving a reduced spraying width. The booms were hinged for lifting in the vertical position, for transport, and lowered to rest horizontally, on either side of the machine, for spraying. The height of the booms is adjustable, to suit the height of the crop. In the picture, Mr. Charles Le Couteur, of Westlands, has the booms set low, to spray weeds and docks. One horse pulls the machine quite comfortably.

Other owners were Mr. Hedley Le Quesne of La Retraite (his sprayer was manufactured in 1930, no. 30T 838), and Mr. Francis Billot at Beau Desert, St. Saviour, used a 1925 model for many years before the Second World War. Both machines sprayed potatoes and tomatoes against blight. Mr. Billot used big wooden casks on the headlands, to mix the copper sulphate crystals into bright blue liquid spray. It could be a messy job, particularly in tomatoes, when the booms were set high to clear the bamboo canes to which the plants were tied. A slight breeze could carry the spray over both horse and operator. In the post-war years the machine was used to spray against Colorado beetle. The machine illustrated is in Mr. Charles Le Couteur's collection at Westlands and is still being used. A second machine is in the Jersey Museum's collection in the store at Augrès. Messrs. A. T. Jeune on the corner of James Street and Burrard Street were importers of French spraying machines.

In 1911 Sir Jesse Boot, of Boots the Chemists, a Jersey resident and a great benefactor to the Island, donated ten horse-drawn spraying machines to the Royal Jersey Agricultural and Horticultural Society. They were to be used for spraying potatoes and tomatoes against blight.

Mr. Shepard, the secretary of the Society for many years at its first office in Mulcaster Street, placed an announcement in the Society's year book. (shown right.)

SPRAYING OF POTATOES.

THROUGH the generosity of Sir Jesse Boot, Bt., 10 Horse Spraying Machines have been presented to the Society to enable farmers to spray their crops.

These Machines can do 5 to 6 vergees per hour and the charge will probably be 2/0 per hour, including attendant (non-members of the Department 3/0 per hour); farmers providing their own spray and horses.

Members who wish to avail themselves of these Machines are requested, **without delay,** to notify the Secretary, **in writing,** of the number of vergees (and where situated) that they intend to spray. Applications will be considered in the order in which they are received.

H. G. SHEPARD,
Secretary.

3, Mulcaster Street,
Jersey.

Haymaking machinery

Hay tedders

Hay tedder.

This horse-drawn hay tedder was manufactured in the late 19th or very early 20th century. The driver's seat on this machine has been removed, probably when it was altered to tractor draught. It has six forks, each with four tines, mounted on a crankshaft. Each one is held by a rod, extending forward and attached to a bar in front of the axle, to hold them at the appropriate angle as the crankshaft rotates. The crankshaft is driven by chain and sprocket, through ratchets in each wheel and a dog clutch. The operating width was 6 ft 8 in. (203 cm) overall. The driver sat on a seat, where there is a foot-operated trip which lowered the machine into work and engaged the dog clutch. A lever lifted the machine out of work; on some machines the lifting action was assisted by a linkage to a foot pedal beside the driver. The motion of the forks kicks the mown hay into the air, and it falls loosely, allowing sun and air to aid drying. It has two steel-spoked wheels, 4 ft 6 in. (137 cm) in diameter, with ratchets in the hub, to drive a live axle, and to drive a chain to the crankshaft. It is pulled by one horse. The horse shafts have been removed to be replaced with a drawbar for tractor draught. Hay tedders like these were manufactured by Massey Harris, Walter A. Wood, International Harvester, and others. Although only used during haymaking very few times a year, they were quick and labour-saving, doing in a couple of hours or so what a team of men and women with hay forks would take all day to do. (Steam Museum collection.)

Horse-drawn hay tedder manufactured by International Harvester in the USA (La Société Jersiaise/Jersey Heritage Trust collection at Hamptonne Museum).

The hay tedder in this picture was manufactured by International Harvester, like the previous tedder in the late 19th or early 20th century. 'IH', their trademark, is instantly recognised on some of the castings. Unfortunately the machine has been neglected, one of the steel-spoked wheels having rusted through. While it still has the driver's seat, the horse shafts have been removed.

Hay rakes

Hay rake at work at La Porte, Maufant, in the 1920s.

The horse-drawn hay rake at work with Mr. John Billot driving at La Porte. It was probably a McCormick rake (part of International Harvester). It has sixteen-spoke steel wheels, 4 ft 6 in. (137 cm) in diameter. The photographer was probably Mr. Francis R. Billot, the author's father and the brother of the driver, using his new camera in 1920 or 1921. Mr. Billot had a dark room and developed and printed his own films for several years.

Ransomes of Ipswich were awarded the Royal Agricultural Society of England prize for the first horse-drawn hay rake in 1869. Very soon after, they were being made, with only slight variations, by many of the big names in the farm machinery business: Massey Harris, Walter A. Wood, International Harvester, J. & F. Howard.

Horse rake.
This rake was probably made by J. E. Howard. It is composed of twenty-four C-spring tines fitted 3 in. (7.6 cm) apart, giving an overall working width of 6 ft 6 in. (198 cm.). Hay raking is done after tedding has dried the crop. In work, the rake collects the hay, and when it is full, it is released with a foot-operated lift, driven by gearing in the wheel hubs. The release mechanism raises the rake against four rods, which helps to push the hay off the rake and drop the hay. The rake has to be held up, long enough to clear the collected hay, before dropping back into work. The operator or driver will time the lifting of the rake, to be alongside a previous drop of hay to form a line of collected hay, called a windrow. The rake can also be raised with a hand lever, and a second foot pedal is operated to lock the tines in the lifted position for transport. It has two eighteen-spoke steel wheels of 4 ft 6 in. (137 cm) diameter and 2 in. (5 cm) wide steel rims. One horse will pull it. (Shire Horse Farm collection.)

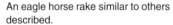

An eagle horse rake similar to others described.
A hay rake manufactured in the late 19th or early 20th century. It has twenty-four C tines. This view of the rake shows the four 'push-off' rods. The horses' shafts have been removed to take up less space when not in use. (Mr. Obbard's collection on one of the threshing days at Samarès Manor.)

The author recalls working overtime in the evening with a horse and hay rake, during school holidays, in the summer of 1941.

Binders

The Romans made an early attempt at harvesting cereal crops with a cart that was pushed into the crop. The details are in Chapter 4. The idea was repeated centuries later by the French. In 1786 a more sophisticated machine, consisting of a similar cart, with a revolving cylinder with rows of teeth, cut the heads off the standing crop, depositing the heads in the cart.

Binders may only be used when the crop is thoroughly dry. If the canvases get damp they will tighten up and breakages will occur; the knotter will bind the sheaves too tightly, and as a result they do not dry out. The canvases must be slackened off if they are to be left out overnight, and covered with a tarpaulin. In the morning the dew must be allowed to evaporate off the crop and to dry out before attempting to start cutting. It is better to spend the waiting time going around the machine with the grease gun and oil can, making sure the spare knife is sharp and in good order and that no blades are bent on the knife and no fingers bent on the cutter bar.

While the stooks stand for three Sundays one hopes and prays that the weather remains dry, before the crop is carried to the rick yard or the threshing machine.

Albion 6 ft cut binder at Reading Museum.

Albion cereal binder manufactured in 1930 by Harrison McGregor & Co., model no. 5.

It has a 6 ft (182 cm) wide cutter bar; the crop falls on a canvas conveyor, and is delivered to the elevator canvases. The elevator canvases, which are not easy to see clearly, are one above the other; the crop is carried up, sandwiched between them, to the knotter table. Behind the name board is the red-painted cylindrical box for the binder twine. The binder is displayed on its transport wheels. (Reading University collection, Museum of English Rural Life.)

In operation, the horses pull the machine, which turns the landwheel that provides the power to operate the machine and drive the connecting rod to the reciprocating knife, the canvases, the knotter, and so forth.

As the crop is cut, it falls on the battened canvas conveyor, which delivers it to the elevator canvas, delivering the crop to the knotter table. The packers push the crop onto the table to form a sheaf; when sufficient has been delivered, a needle, driven by a cam, passes up through the table, delivering one end of the binder twine to the open beaks of the knotter; the beaks then close and rotate, making the knot. Three arms rotate, to push the sheaf off the table, which tightens the knot and pulls the twine off the knotter. The sheaf then falls to the ground, to wait for the team of stookers, who take it and build a stook, usually of six sheaves propped up with the butts on the ground.

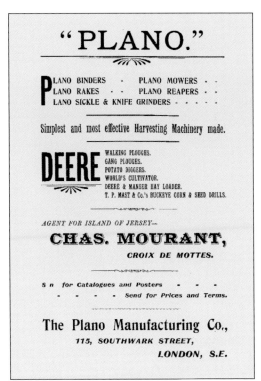

An advertisement in 1903 for Plano and Deere, known today as John Deere.

7 Horse Engines, Steam Engines, and Threshing Machines

Horse engines

Before the steam engine there were horse engines, driven by one, two, four, or six horses. Engines of this type go back thousands of years and not only with horses and oxen, but with men. The earliest engines were made with wooden gears and wooden components, to drive pumps to raise water from wells, lakes, and rivers for irrigation and human consumption, and to operate mills for making flour. The Jersey stone apple crushers for making cider are a variation on the same idea. The horse engine on the farm in the eighteenth and nineteenth centuries was constructed either in a farm building or in the farmyard, adjacent to a farm building containing a variety of machines to be driven by the engine. Such machines might be a small threshing machine, a winnowing machine, the chaff cutter, root crusher, a rolling mill for rolling oats or for preparing cattle food.

Horse engines were manufactured in England by all the well-known names: Hunts at Earls Colne, Ransomes of Ipswich, R. A. Lister in Gloucestershire, etc., all working on much the same principle with horses walking around in a circle, each drawing a pole, attached to a spur gear or crownwheel at the hub. Engines constructed in the farmyard had a circular walkway for the horses, with a specially hardened surface. Some were paved with large stone slabs. On some installations, the driven shaft was underground, which gave the horses a level path all the way round; alternatively, the shaft was just above the ground and the walkway, raised with a ramp, over the shaft, which passed through a short tunnel to the gearbox at the side.

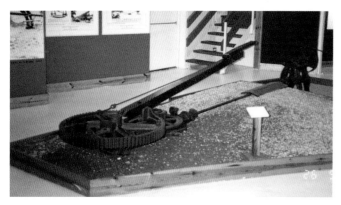

One of Hunt's horse engines for one horse manufactured in 1846.
The horse engine consisted of an assembly with a vertical shaft and up to six poles arranged like the spokes of a wheel approximately 1 ft (35 cm) or 18 in. (45.5 cm) above the ground. Each pole was attached to a central hub and the horses were harnessed to the outer end of each pole. As the horses walked clockwise, in a circle, they drove a set of gears at the hub, which in turn drove a shaft which was located just below ground level and delivered power to an open-frame gearbox, which increased the revolutions per minute (the rpm). The open gearbox was either in the shed or in the yard, the driven shaft from the engine going through the wall. In the building would be an arrangement of pulleys and shafts to drive the barn machinery.

Some manufacturers offered an overhead engine, with a substantial vertical shaft at the hub, supporting a 5 ft (152 cm) or 6 ft (184 cm) diameter gearwheel or crownwheel. The poles, either one, two, or four, were all mounted at the top of the shaft, fitted to the underside of the crownwheel. The driven shaft from the crownwheel would be carried in bearings attached to the underside of a floor beam. At least two overhead engines were made in Jersey and installed in the building, with the barn machinery, the horses circulating on the ground floor and the driven machinery on the floor above.

The 'engine' illustrated here, manufactured in 1846 by R. Hunt & Co. at Earls Colne, is driven by one horse, but this model is able to take two poles at 180 degrees apart for two horses. Some of the central cast iron hubs were made to accept up to six poles, enabling up to six horses to be harnessed to it. Spur gears are used throughout; they may be the noisiest gears but they are the most efficient for transmitting power, and as these will rotate slowly, noise is not a problem. The length of the pole is 10 ft (304.8 cm), the central spur gearwheel is 3 ft 3 in. (99 cm) in diameter, and the driven gearwheel 9 in. (22.8 cm) in diameter. Below it and integral with it is a crownwheel 2 ft (61 cm) in diameter that drives a pinion on a shaft, with (continued on facing page)

The gearing at the centre of the horse engine.
The illustration shows the detail of the gearing at the centre of the Hunt horse engine and the attachment of the pole. Behind it is a steel bracing rod, supporting the pole. Beneath it is the driven crownwheel and pinion to drive the shaft, through a universal joint, to the open gearbox. (Acknowledgement to Reading University, Museum of English Rural Life.) Miss Jean Arthur and Mr. Stephen Arthur remember a horse engine similar to the engine illustrated above. It was in the yard at the family farm at La Pompe, St. Mary. It had only one pole for one horse, to provide the power to drive a chaff cutter and probably one or two other machines in the loft of a shed alongside. A flat belt from the gearbox, beside the engine, went at an angle upward through a door in the wall of the loft and onto a flat belt pulley. It was dismantled sometime in the 1940s.

Of two overhead engines made in Jersey, one was assembled in a building at Beau Désert and another at La Ferrière, both in St. Saviour. Some components still exist from the engine at La Ferrière. If the engine was likely to drive more than one machine, a flat belt from the gear box pulley would drive an overhead shaft, fitted with a number of pulleys of appropriate size, to drive the different machines. There would only be sufficient power from the horse engine to drive one machine at a time.

An overhead two-horse engine above an apple crusher from Beau Désert being reassembled at Samarès Manor Museum.
This horse engine was taken out of a shed at Beau Désert Farm in St. Saviour, where it was originally erected over an apple crusher. Unfortunately it was already partly dismantled and some components are missing. The cast-iron gearwheel or crownwheel is 5 ft (152 cm) in diameter and has eight spokes; the wooden beam or draught pole appears to be rather short at 12 ft (381 cm) long, but it had two iron bars which could be slid out to extend the draw pole at both ends and vertical ends for harnessing to a horse. One of the extension bars is missing, along with the driven pinion and the driven horizontal shaft, but these items have been replaced by parts which have been adapted.

The wooden pole or beam is 6.5 in. (16.5 cm) wide and bevelled and 9 in. (22.8 cm) deep at the centre, tapering to 6.5 in. (16.5 cm) at the ends with an iron collar on each end, with various fittings for the extensions. It was pulled round by two horses, harnessed to the ends of the extensions, one at each end of the beam. The pole/beam is a little off-centre. The eight-sided vertical iron shaft is 8 ft 4 in. (255.5 cm), long and has four bearings, each measuring 4.5 in. (11 cm) in diameter. The draught pole for the stone wheel of the apple crusher could be slid in, to be out of the way of the two horses operating the engine. It was an interesting and ingenious space-saving installation.

The crownwheel was fairly close up under a beam (part of the building structure), carrying the top bearing. The bottom bearing is set in a stone block on the floor. A shaft with a spur gear pinion engaged with the teeth around the top of the periphery of the crownwheel. Originally the shaft was carried in two bearings, fitted to the underside of a beam stretching across the shed. At one end, the shaft passed through a hole in a wall. On the end of the shaft would have been a pulley or a gearwheel, to drive any one of a number of barn machines. The 5 ft (152 cm) diameter crownwheel was probably cast in a local foundry. The new installation at Samarès is mounted along the top of a beam and drives a root crusher, a mill, and a chaff cutter.

(*continued from facing page*) a universal joint at each end, to drive an open-frame gearbox. The gearbox increases the rpm to drive a 15 in. (38.1 cm) diameter pulley. The horses will make 2.5 circuits a minute, rotating the shaft at 80 rpm. The open-frame 'gearbox' at the side will increase the revolutions to 400 rpm at the pulley. The shaft is above ground, passing through a short tunnel, which the horses would have to walk over.

Mr. Perchard had a foundry in Seale Street, where the Town Hall is today; he made the 6 ft-diameter gearwheel/crownwheel installed at La Ferrière, so he was able to make this smaller one at Beau Désert, although this has not been confirmed. That engine was probably installed in the 1840s, at about the same time as the one at La Ferrière. There are no illustrations or drawings surviving of either engine, but they were broadly similar.

There is a detailed description of the engine at La Ferrière, in a document and letter dated 1951, at the library of La Société Jersiaise. It is written by one G. S. Knocker to a Mr. Mourant, probably a descendant of a previous owner, Mr. Jean Mourant, who sold the property in the late 1840s to Mr. Jean Guiton. The horse engine and machinery were installed at about the same time, so it is uncertain who ordered it. It may have been installed for Mr. Guiton, for his newly acquired property. The installation was completed in a building with a threshing machine, a winnowing machine, a chaff cutter, and an apple crusher. According to the date stone over the door, it was built in 1841.

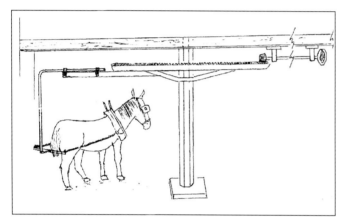

An overhead horse engine pulled by a horse harnessed in traces and a bodkin.

The horse engine at La Ferrière was a four-horse engine, with the four poles immediately under the beams of the floor above. The horses circulated on the ground floor, each one pulling a pole fitted to the underside of the overhead crownwheel. The shed was 21 ft 9 in. (6.62 m) wide, and the poles were made with an overall diameter of 21 ft (6.38 m) to clear the walls by 4.5 in. (11.4 cm). It had a vertical shaft at the hub with a bearing bedded in a block set in the floor of the shed; the top bearing was set in a beam specially constructed under the floor above. Above the central shaft is the crownwheel, 6 ft 10 in. (210 cm) in diameter, with bevelled spur teeth around the periphery. It was fairly close to the beams supporting the floor above. The four horizontal draw poles were fitted to the vertical shaft and under the crownwheel. At the end of each pole is an iron collar with a bracket to carry the ironwork for attaching to the horse.

The bevelled spur gear around the periphery of the crownwheel is meshed with two pinions on the ends of two horizontal square-section shafts, mounted 180 degrees apart on opposite sides, and carried in bearings fitted under the floor beams. Each of the horizontal shafts had a dog clutch, so that either shaft could be disengaged when not in use, to reduce the load and the friction of the bearings. Part of the way along one of the shafts, a pulley was keyed on to drive a chaff cutter or the winnowing machine, and at the end was a 6 ft (184 cm) diameter gearwheel. This big gearwheel engaged with a small gearwheel to drive the threshing machine. On the end of the opposite shaft was a gearwheel to drive an apple crusher, which is described in Chapter 8.

The big-diameter crownwheel and the 6 ft (184 cm) gearwheel served the same purpose as an open-frame gearbox to increase the rpm. To cast a large 6 ft diameter crownwheel successfully required the utmost skill.

When Mr. Perchard died, his business, including the patterns and other materials, was acquired by Messrs. Grandin, the foundrymen at Commercial Buildings. The patterns were held in their pattern store, where they remained in the 1930s after Mr. Gallichan acquired the Grandin business. Mr. Pullam, who was employed in engineering in the Island before the Second World War and up to the 1940s, remembered seeing them there. They were then a hundred years old! From photographs, he was able to confirm that the crownwheel at La Ferrière was cast from the pattern he remembers seeing in the pattern store at A. F. Gallichan & Co. More recently Gallichan's business was taken over by Nichols Garage, which changed hands again to become a part of the Norman Group of companies.

There is evidence of a low-level horse engine having been constructed at Ponterrin Mill, below Victoria Village. Sadly the mill is now a ruin, but in the yard beside the mill is the circular paving of what is thought to have been part of a horse engine. It was probably used in a dry summer, when there was insufficient flow of water in the mill stream. At a much later stage an internal combustion engine was installed at the mill. There were other mills with horse engines in the Island.

The horse engine on a farm was a source of power available for use at a time of the farmer's choosing, to run any one of several machines in his shed. When the steam engine and large threshing machine came along, a farmer could only use it when the contractor could fix a date between his commitments.

Threshing machines

A Garvie threshing machine would have been installed in a farm shed or loft and driven by a horse engine.
This little threshing machine manufactured by Garvie of Aberdeen, model NS, serial no. 76346, is a good example of the type of threshing machine installed in a loft at La Ferrière. It has a 2 ft (60.8 cm) wide peg-type drum, 23 in. (58.3 cm) in diameter, which seemed to be favoured north of the border, rather than the more common rasp bar. On the end of the drum shaft is an 8 in. (20.30 cm) diameter flat belt pulley, with a free-wheeling pulley beside it, to enable the operator to stop the machine quickly, in the event of a problem such as a blockage. The peg drum breaks up the straw, which no doubt has certain advantages on the farm, such as bedding for livestock. Unusually it has no cover over the three straw walkers, so it is clearly intended for use in a shed or loft. Any breeze would blow the straw about. (Steam Museum collection.)

Taskers portable threshing machine.
An early portable threshing drum, manufactured by Taskers, with horse shafts, and light enough to be hauled by one horse. Probably driven by a horse engine originally, and later by steam engine. Like the Garvie, it is not as sophisticated as the bigger threshing machines; it has only one delivery spout for bagging off the grain beside the elevator, at the side. The sieving and sorting was simple, as it had only a chaff sieve. Chaff and cavings (the rubbish of broken short straw, husk, and weeds) would be deposited with the straw, off the four straw walkers. The walkers and the crankshaft to which they are fitted are clearly visible. It was probably at first driven by a portable horse engine, which would have been mounted on a base plate, pegged to the ground, and moved from site to site with a horse and van or horse and cart. In later years it was probably driven by a portable steam engine.

Taskers threshing machine has a 3 ft 4 in. (101.5 cm) wide drum, with rasp bars and a wooden frame, but with steel hangers for the sieves. The above view shows the grain elevator, the grain bagging-off spout, and the cast-iron spoked wheels. Taskers, like Garvie, are well-known manufacturers and were still in business in recent years. Taskers also built steam traction engines. (Displayed at La Société Jersiaise/Heritage Trust Museum at Hamptonne.)

The word threshing is more often spelt with an 'e' but Ransomes were alone in always spelling it with an 'a'. The peg drum was popular in America, whereas the drum with the rasp bars has always been more popular in the UK and Europe.

The straw walkers and crankshaft can be seen in this view; the straw and chaff are discharged here and fall to the ground.
The horse's shafts are lifted for storage and removed when operating the machine.

Steam threshing sets

The steam threshing set comprises the steam engine, the threshing machine, and a baler (or more often a trusser), which packs and ties the straw into a handy bundle. It may include a water cart.

The earliest steam engines resulted from James Watt's experiments in the 1750s, when condensing engines were simple reciprocating engines. Many were built to pump water out of mines. There was no rotating crankshaft; it had not yet been invented. It took some time to develop the conversion of reciprocating motion to rotating motion with a crankshaft and connecting rod. When it was invented, it was patented, limiting its use and further development for some years. When the crankshaft and connecting rod were invented, steam engines with the big-diameter, low-rpm flywheels became popular in the industrial world.

An early stationary steam engine, made by Trevithick, was installed for Sir Christopher Hawkins, on his farm in Cornwall, to drive a threshing machine in 1811. The next big step forward was in 1841, when Ransomes of Ipswich manufactured a portable steam engine and a threshing machine, to be known as a 'threshing set'. It was exhibited at a meeting of the Royal Agricultural Society of England, for which they were awarded the RASE prize in 1842. Regular manufacture of portable steam engines and threshing machines commenced and the development of the steam traction engine soon followed.

Many steam engines and steam traction engines were produced by the manufacturers of threshing machines, to provide the power to tow their threshing drums from farm to farm and drive them on the site. These were manufacturers such as Ransomes of Ipswich, Clayton and Shuttleworth, Marshalls of Gainsborough, Taskers, and several others. They were not only concerned with the home market but with the export potential of traction engines and threshing machines. Many thousands were soon being shipped all over the world, to Europe, Russia, the Middle East, South America, Australia, and the Far East. Other manufacturers, like John Fowler of Leeds, concentrated their efforts on large, powerful traction engines, with winches under the boiler, for hauling seven-furrow reversible ploughs across large areas of land by cable, which while interesting, were quite unsuitable for Jersey.

The first rasp bar threshing drum was built by a Scotsman in 1786. The rasp bar became the popular choice for threshing machines and later combined harvesters, the second choice being the peg bar; but it has the disadvantage that it tears the straw into short lengths, which absorbs more power and renders the straw useless for thatching but useful for bedding for horses and cattle. In the days when ricks were common, straw was used for thatching the ricks, to keep the rain out.

Portable steam engine and driver near La Hougue Bie in 1927 (probably one of Le Cappelain's).
(*right*) Placing the engine on blocks, to stand level before work can start.
Before a portable steam engine can be started, it must stand level and be lined up accurately with the threshing machine, otherwise the flat driving belt between the engine and thrashing machine will be thrown off! On the right of the picture can be seen the horse's shafts. The men's clothing is indicative of the period: men in waistcoats, the man in the foreground with twine tied around his trousers below the knees—this was often done by labourers in the fields.

In 1873 a large group of farmers made a presentation to Mr. Le Cappelain, of St. Peter's Iron Works, for introducing the threshing sets into the Island. The advertisement below indicates that St. Peter's Iron Works were a well-established business, and as we have seen, British steam engines had been available for some twenty-five years and received worldwide acclaim at the Great Exhibition of 1851 at Crystal Palace. So one can reasonably assume the threshing tackle offered for sale and hire by Mr. Le Cappelain had been available in the Island for several years previously. The business soon had five machines, stationed in different parishes around the Island, and one in Guernsey and another in Carteret in Normandy, all of which indicates a big demand for steam-powered threshing. They also offered tillage implements of their own manufacture.

During a conversation with the late Don Pallot, the author asked if he could recall anything about threshing machines in his youth. He remembered the Le Cappelain machines and several other threshing sets in the Island. Mr. Jean Richard, of Old St. John's Manor, had two Merlin portable steam engines made in France; one was bigger and more powerful than the other. Just after the First World War Mr. Richard had a Rivière threshing machine and a Calabis low-density baler.

Don Pallot recalled a threshing set that threshed in one of Mr. Peredé's fields at Fairview Farm, adjacent to La Hougue Bie, in the summers of 1947 and 1948, and this was confirmed by Trevor Le Cappelain, who could remember the family talking about it. It remained there

Theophile Le Cappelain's advertisement in the Royal Jersey Agricultural and Horticultural Society's journal in 1875.

for several weeks while everybody in the district gathered in the harvest and took it to the machine to be threshed. But by this time, the thresher was driven by an International tractor, rather than a portable steam engine.

In 1919 Mr. Cabot, of Le Câtel, Trinity (former Constable Roy Cabot's grandfather), had a Ransomes threshing machine, with a Hornsby trusser fitted behind the straw walkers. The trusser was driven by chain and sprocket from the drum. A Ransomes portable steam engine provided the power.

This machine was sold in 1973 to two farmers in Sark, Mr. Philip Purrée, of Duval Farm, Little Sark, and Mr. Frank Perchard of Mon Plaisir. Moving it around Sark was straightforward but La Coupee is a narrow road over a narrow isthmus with steep cliffs each side. They had to use two tractors to cross it, one in front to tow the machine and the second behind, also hitched to the threshing machine, to hold it back, because the machine had no brakes and there was a fear that the weight of the machine might push the tractor in front, making it difficult to control. The thresher was fifty-four years old and spare parts were difficult to obtain.

George Le Cappelain, of St. Peter's Iron Works, had several Marshall threshing machines and portable engines, with Hornsby trussers on wheels. The trussers were placed behind the threshing box, under the straw walkers, and driven by a flat belt and pulley from the drum. One was still in use after the Second World War, but by this time it was tractor-driven. The author has only a childhood memory of seeing a portable steam engine and threshing machine, both being hauled by horses, passing along the back of St. Saviour's School and onto the Bagatelle Road, early in the 1930s. Thereafter he can only recall tractors being used for that purpose.

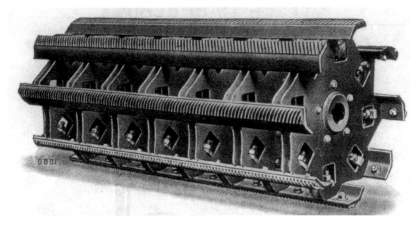

A Ransomes threshing cylinder or drum, illustrating the rasp bars.

The rasp bar-type beater bars, on a Ransomes threshing cylinder or drum, are used in threshing machines and combined harvesters. The alternative is the peg drum already mentioned. The threshing cylinder is the central feature of the threshing machine, the principal task of which is the removal of the grain from the husk; the machine will then separate the grain from the husk and straw and deliver a clean sample of grain or seed. The rasp bar would produce clean unbroken straw, much favoured by thatchers, for thatching hay and corn ricks, to keep out the weather.

The drums of different diameters depend on the size of the machine: 20 in. (50.6 cm), 22 in. (55.7 cm), and 24 in. (60.8 cm) diameters. The 22 in. (55.7 cm) diameter and 54 in. (153 cm) wide drum or cylinder is the most popular. Some machines had two drums, such as clover hullers for special crops with very fine seeds or grains, and were often exported, as were the bigger machines, 66 in. (200 cm) wide with 24 in. (60.8 cm) diameter drums.

The operating speed of the 22 in. (55.7 cm) diameter drum was 6,000 ft (1,846 m) per minute, at the periphery of the beaters, or 1,050 rpm. This was achieved, in practice, with a flywheel pulley of 4 ft (122 cm) diameter rotating at 175 rpm at the steam engine. The driven flat belt pulley was always on the cylinder shaft; it had to have a diameter seven times the thickness of the belt, which at a belt thickness just less than 0.25 in. (0.6 cm) meant a pulley diameter of 7.5 in. (19 cm). The standard pulley size was 8 in. (20.30 cm) diameter, with a flange on the inside. The shaft was mounted in plummer blocks, with bronze bearings and oiling rings, but in due course ball bearings were used.

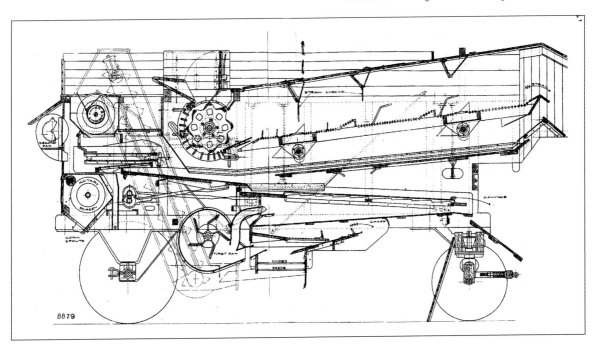

A drawing of a Ransomes threshing machineillustrating the inner working components of the machine.
The cylinder can be seen to the left of centre, partially surrounded by the concave; the clearance between the cylinder and concave is critical. It is adjusted at the top, towards the centre, and at the end just past the bottom. It is set more open at the top, tapering to close, at the bottom. If it is too close the grain will be chipped; if it is too open, the grains are not cleared out of the husk. The operator will stand in the box, to the left of the cylinder, slowly feeding each sheaf into the machine, allowing it to fall between the cylinder and the concave. As it passes through, the grains will fall through the concave, onto a shaker beneath, and the straw will pass onto the straw walkers. There it is gently shaken to make any grains fall into the channels in the bottom of the walkers, and the straw will move along them to the right and out of the machine.

Any grain falling from the walkers will drop onto a coarse sieve on the first shoe, which rocks back and forward on its hangers, driven by a small crankshaft. There, the grain is separated from the cavings, chaff, and husk with the aid of a blast of air from the first fan. The cavings are carried right away, by the current of air, to fall to the ground in front of the wheels on the right.

The grain and remaining chaff fall onto a board, over which the grains will roll downward, and the chaff will be blown away, by the winnowing effect of a blast of wind from the first fan. The grain will pass through two more fine sieves and be carried through to the elevator, to the left of the first fan, and on up to the top of the machine, to be delivered to the awner and chobber, which removes the awns on barley seed and any other unwanted material. Then it passes onto the final cleaning shoe, which has two more sieves and, with the aid of a blast from the second fan, will remove any remaining unwanted small material. Finally the grain passes through a rotary screen, which is rather like coils of wire stretched out to form a cylinder, with a gap between each coil. The gap is wider at one end and is adjustable for different crops and seeds, to allow the good grains to be separated from the poor ones. At last the grain is delivered to the corn spouts, with a sack attached to bag it. Every now and then the farmer and engine driver will gather a handful of grain from the spout, to examine the sample. This enables them to see that the machine is properly adjusted to produce a good clean sample. The straw and cavings will also be examined, to be sure that all the grain has been separated.

As can be seen, the threshing machine is a complex, sophisticated machine, which performs a thorough job of threshing out the grain or seeds of different crops.

A 56-year-old French threshing machine imported during the Occupation at work at Samarès Manor during an Open Threshing Day in 1997.

The French threshing machine was manufactured in 1941 by Société Français Veirzon (Cher). It belonged to Mr. Jean Richard of Trinity, who operated it on two sites in the parish. Model Unis Français has a 5 ft 2 in. (125.2 cm) long cylinder with rasp bars fitted with countersunk flat-top bolts mounted in a conventional concave. (On a British cylinder, the bolt heads will have a rasp ridge across them, to match up with the ridges on the rasp bar.) This machine has no straw walkers but has a single large shaker. It is on cast iron spoked wheels, with 4.75 in. (12 cm) wide rims. While basically the same as British threshing machines, it differs in detail such as the arrangement of elevators and sieves, but mainly in having a shaker and no straw walkers. The shaker was used on many trailed combined harvesters which appeared during and after the war. Almost all the large self-propelled combined harvesters have straw walkers.

Mr. Charles Le Couteur feeds a sheaf of oats into the drum.

The sheaf of oats is drawn off the feeding table. This operation requires careful attention to feed the crop in steadily and continually; if it were simply thrown in by the sheaf, the drum would jam and the drive belt between the drum and the steam engine would be thrown off.

A threshing set might comprise more than a steam engine, threshing machine, and a baler or trusser. Another piece of equipment needed will be a water cart, and in England a set might include the driver's living van, if he was far from home. Threshing machines were also known as drums, or threshing boxes, because the machine is really contained in a wooden or metal box on wheels. They may have a wooden or steel frame; the last Marshall machines, for example, were all steel.

The French machine was imported during the German Occupation by the States Purchasing Commission, in 1941, for the Essential Commodities Committee. They sent a buying commission to Occupied France to purchase essential items. It is now part of the Steam Museum's collection.

Portable steam engines

The portable steam engines, like the threshing machines, had to be towed to the site by a team of horses. The traction engines were, of course, self-propelled, and would also haul the threshing drum from site to site. In Jersey, because the distances were short, the threshing contractors favoured the portable engine, although one or two used traction engines. When tractors arrived in the Island after the First World War all this changed, as the tractors were used to both tow and drive the threshing machine.

The power of the steam engine was measured as nominal horsepower, or nhp. It was arrived at simply by the size of the circumference of the cylinder or, in the case of the compound engine, adding the circumference of both cylinders together. A circumference of 10 in. (25.4 cm) or a diameter of 3.125 in. was equal to one nominal horsepower. It was not very accurate because it did not take into account anything else, such as steam pressure. The brake horsepower, or bhp at the flywheel was usually four or five times greater than the nhp, so that a 6 nhp engine was more likely to have 24 to 30 bhp at the flywheel.

One horsepower was calculated by James Watt to measure the power of steam engines. A horse and weights were used, to establish the unit of measurement. One horsepower is equal to one horse lifting 33,000 lb through one foot in one minute, i.e. 33,000 foot-pounds a minute. An apparatus was devised in the early days of steam to apply a known load to an engine, which was equivalent to the engine lifting a given weight. The apparatus was a friction brake, or dynamometer; water brakes and wind-fan brakes were later designed to measure the power of engines. A textbook on the subject illustrated the method with the drawing (possibly by Claude Culpin) of a horse in traces, with a bodkin which was hooked to a chain, which passed over a sheave descending into a pit. At the end of the chain was a plate upon which the weights were placed. At the top of the pit, one man stood with a stopwatch gazing at a board on the ground marked off in feet; at the bottom another man placed the weights on the lifting plate, while a third man led the horse.

Compound engines, used mostly on traction engines, made more efficient use of the steam pressure, first driving the high-pressure cylinder, followed by the bigger-diameter low-pressure cylinder. There was no loss of steam from the high-pressure cylinder, it being added to the low-pressure cylinder, so increasing its output. The engine ran more smoothly and exhaust pressure was reduced, all adding up to a greater economy with more power. Less fuel and water was consumed by the engine, which was important when travelling, apart from the economy during threshing. But they were more expensive and heavier.

The single-cylinder engine producing a continuous 20 bhp would consume 6 cwt of coal and 500 gallons of water over eight hours, whereas a compound engine would consume 4.5 cwt of coal and 360 gallons of water for the same number of hours of operation.

On the road, a traction engine would travel at two speeds, 1.5 or 2.5 miles per hour, hauling a threshing machine and baler. A distance of 5 or 6 miles could be made between stops for taking on water by suction from a wayside stream through a length of suction hose, which always formed part of a steam engine's kit and which was the general rule.

Wheels on the portable engine were smaller and of lighter construction than on the traction engine. Hubs were cast-iron, with steel spokes set in the hubs and riveted at the rim. The diameter of the wheels on the traction engine was usually 6 ft (184 cm), for rear wheels, frequently referred to as 'hind wheels'. The rim widths varied between 1 ft 4 in. (40.5 cm) and 1 ft 6 in. (45.5 cm), whereas front wheels were 4 ft (122 cm), 4 ft 3 in. (130 cm), and 4 ft 6 in. (137 cm) in diameter and rims were 9 in. (22.8 cm) wide on smaller wheels and 8 in. (20 cm) on bigger wheels.

Some traction engines were fitted with winding gear (or winch) and a steel wire to enable the engine to remain static on firm ground while it hauled the drum or baler, or both over soft-going or rough terrain.

The list of tools supplied with a traction engine throws some light on the driver's task: a set of spanners, a hammer and chisel, piston clip, governor belt, and drum pin; two shovels, one with a long handle and one short; a poker and coal rake; a tank gauge rod; a tun dish (large funnel); oil can and rags (usually cotton waste in those days); two buckets and suction hose; wire rope for winding gear; a mud rake and mudhole rings; spuds, bolts, and cotters, sixteen of each; forty frost pins and a set of chocks; and quite a list of spare parts. In addition to these he would have to be sure his lamps front and back were fitted, filled with fuel and the wicks trimmed, and his drawbar pins were in place in the jaw hitches at the front and back.

A Merlin portable steam engine at the Steam Museum. The Merlin is a good example of a portable steam threshing engine. It was restored in 1984 and can often be found running in the Steam Museum. It is thought to be the only working portable steam engine in the British Isles. The attractive curved spokes of the flywheel were designed because spokes in cast-iron wheels were notoriously difficult to make, often snapping as they contracted during cooling; the curve absorbed the tension in the spokes and allowed the metal to cool without snapping. The portable steam engine in this picture was manufactured in France by Merlin et Cie. Vierzon in 1924. It is a 6 nhp single-cylinder engine, burning wood or coal. It is on steel-spoked wheels and has a cast-iron spoked flywheel, polished bronze boiler, and copper pipework.

When driving a threshing machine, the power required may vary, so a governor is necessary to control the engine speed, or rpm. It is above the engine and can be seen as a small frame with two balls set on either side of a vertical shaft. The governor is driven by a shaft and gearwheels from the crankshaft. The two balls are free to move in or out according to the engine speed; as speed increases, the balls move out, closing the steam valve via a linkage. As the speed decreases, the steam valve opens, to allow the engine speed to increase. It is vital that the water level in the boiler does not fall below a certain level. In order for the engineman/driver to monitor the level, a specially toughened glass gauge is fitted to the side of the boiler. (Note the engineer's vice on a stand on the right.)

The engine has a belt-driven, James Watt-designed, two-ball governor to control the engine speed, as the load varies. The engine has a winding drum (winch) to haul any load over a soft muddy surface or tree roots, etc. The engine was used for operating a threshing machine but was last used in the 1950s, for steam-sterilising soil in glasshouses, before being abandoned. When the engine is not being used it is on view at the Steam Museum.

Ransomes steam traction engine at the Steam Museum.

The view from the top of the threshing machine as the driver, Mr. Bomford, opens the steam valve slowly and gradually the drum rotates and gathers speed The steam traction engine was manufactured by Ransomes Sims & Jefferies Ltd. of Ipswich in 1904, serial no. 15740. It is a single-cylinder 7-nhp wood or coal engine. This engine was purchased and rescued in 1962 by Mr. Don Pallot, who restored it. It is on forged, steel-spoked wheels on solid tyres. The valve gear on the engine is Stephenson's link motion driving a slide valve, enabling the engine to be run forward or backward. Exhaust steam and smoke are carried up the chimney, the smoke running through fire tubes, through the water in the boiler, having the effect of drawing up the fire. So the harder the engine works, the more steam is generated to meet the demand for more power. Ransomes produced steam engines for one hundred years from 1842 to 1942.

Balers and trussers

Low-density balers and trussers were often of continental manufacture The bales, or trusses, weighed 60 lb and were approximately 3 ft 6 in. (175 cm) wide; they were tied with binder twine, by a pair of knotters similar to the knotter on a binder. Trusses, not being as firm as high-density bales, were not so convenient for stacking and took up more space, but were a handy size for a man to pick up and carry about. Before 1939 bales of hay and straw were delivered by sea to Jersey; they were high-density, wire-tied bales.

Trussers were sometimes attached to the back of the threshing machine, under the straw walkers, to catch the straw and truss it. The drive was taken from a pulley on the threshing machine. Other trussers were a separate machine, which were placed under the straw walkers, taking the drive in the same way.

Tullos threshing machine and Lanz trusser at the Steam Museum, 1996.

The trusser was manufactured by Lanz of Germany and imported into the UK by Messrs. H. Leverton & Co. Ltd. of Spalding. The drive is taken from a pulley on the drum shaft of the threshing machine and operates at 350 rpm. The straw from the threshing machine falls from the straw walkers into the straw hopper, where the packers compress it. When sufficient straw has been packed to form a truss, a cam brings two needles up through the straw, delivering the binder twine to the two knotters, which in turn tie the knots. The finished truss is pushed from under the knotters and onto two wooden rails. The density of the trusses does depend on the number of trusses lying on the two rails, the action of the packers pushing the trusses along the rails, compressing them together, and in particular the truss about to be knotted. When they reach the top they are lifted off and stacked on a farm van or tractor trailer. When starting up, the first few trusses are always slack until sufficient trusses have accumulated along the rails. At the point when they become denser and firmer, the first trusses will have the twine cut and removed and are thrown back into the baler's hopper. For transport, the two rails will be removed and a pair of horse shafts fitted; very often it is simply hitched to the back of the thresher and hauled along behind. The flywheel for the packers and knotters can be seen beside the driven pulley. The Lanz trusser is on cast-iron wheels. (Steam Museum Threshing Day, 24 August 1996.)

The Tullos threshing machine serial no. C 428 has three spirit levels fitted to the frame, to help to set it level, ready for work; sacks are hooked to the grain spouts.

The threshing machine was manufactured in 1950/1 by Messrs. Tullos of Aberdeen. It is a full-size box, with a 54 in. (153 cm) wide cylinder. The operating speed is 900/1,000 rpm approximately. It has modern pneumatic-tyred wheels. This machine was imported by Mr. J. F. Pirouet, of La Hambie, St. Saviour, together with a Jones Panther high-density baler from Coodes Engineering, Royston, Hertfordshire. The baler later went to Mr. Percy Le Masurier, of La Pointe, St. Ouen, and the threshing machine to Mr. Len Pipon. (Steam Museum Open Day; here it is threshing oats.)

(*Insert*) one spirit level can be seen in the centre of the picture

Albion low-density straw and hay trusser.
Albion low-density trusser manufactured by Harrison McGregor & Co. Ltd., probably pre-war or early post-war. The two iron wheels are for transport. The two knotters can be seen almost side by side, towards the centre of the machine. The machine's operation is similar to the Lanz described above. The machine will be driven off the threshing machine, operating at a low speed of 300 or 350 rpm. (Shire Horse Farm collection.)

Jones high-density baler, converted to be driven by a stationary engine, mounted in the frame.

The AT model Panther high-density, stationary baler was manufactured by Jones Balers in Wales in 1950 or 1951. It is on pneumatic-tyred wheels. The baler was normally driven by a flat belt from the pulley on the threshing machine but at the suggestion of Mr. Edwin Carré, of St. Ouen, who had an engineering business, Mr. Le Masurier agreed to have a stationary engine mounted in the frame. This enabled the baler to be used on its own, and our picture shows it at work in a hayfield, with hay being pitched into the hopper with hay forks from a line of haycocks. It is being towed along the windrow by a Ferguson tractor.

Balers were used like the trusser with threshing machines, to make high-density bales with the straw and for baling hay at haymaking time. High-density balers, like the Jones baler illustrated below, produce bales weighing approximately 1 cwt. The rams were of cast iron running on four iron wheels on rails; the stroke was nearly 3 ft. The bale chamber was made of substantial angle steel and channel-section steel, measuring 17 in. (43 cm) wide by 22 in. (56 cm) deep, and the extension was up to 7 ft (213 cm) long. Wire was used for tying the bale. Boards were pushed across the bale chamber to separate the bales and to facilitate feeding the wire across and knotted with a twisting tool, but as often as not with a pair of pliers. Some balers used baler twine, similar to, but thicker and stronger than, binder twine.

The way things were: lines of haycocks wait to be collected.
These haycocks at La Pointe, St. Ouen, are waiting to be baled. Haycocks were a common sight in the countryside during haymaking, before they were carried to the hay loft by the horse and van. This is a sight unlikely to be seen again, the 'pick-up' baler making this task unnecessary.

During the German Occupation, there was a wire-tying baler in use in the Island, thought to have been of French manufacture. It would be one man's job to feed the wire into the bale chamber, the knot probably being tied with a tool which twisted the ends tightly.

A Ross Crofter stationary baler; it has no knotters; Mr. Vincent Obbard ties the knots by hand with baler twine.

The Crofter model high-density, stationary baler was manufactured in 1948, by Messrs. Ross in Scotland; it is on two pneumatic-tyred road wheels. The baler is driven by a stationary engine. To separate the bales, a board is placed into the bale chamber manually from the side, every so many feet, and a pair of needles, on a frame, are threaded with baler twine and thrust into two grooves in the board. In the picture, Mr. Vincent Obbard, sitting beside the bale chamber, inserts the board and the needles. The loose ends of twine are joined from the previous board and knotted, while the straw is still compressed. The twine tightens up when the bale is released. It is a small machine and cannot keep up with the output from the threshing machine. The hopper is also rather small and cannot be lined up with the walkers so straw is forked in. The A frame above the machine is the plunger, in the raised position, at the top of its stroke; as it falls it pushes straw into the bale chamber. It is raised and lowered by a pair of connecting rods, on a crankshaft at each end of the drive shaft, which also operates the ram that pushes and compresses the straw in the chamber. It can be seen at work on the open threshing days at Samarès Manor where it is part of the Samarès Manor collection. The original owner was the late Mr. Emile Pallot, of Petit Ménage Farm, Bagot.

In the days when neighbour worked with neighbour, they helped to collect each other's crop of cereals, mostly wheat and oats and sometimes barley, and took it to be threshed. After the war, at Beau Désert the author worked with his father and with the neighbours: Mr. Hedley Le Quesne, at La Retraite, next door to Beau Désert, Mr. Le Gallais at Roselands; Mr. Le Gros, at Patier Farm, in Patier Road; Mr. Georgelin, at Welton Farm, Prince's Tower Road, Five Oaks; and the author's uncles at La Porte at Maufant. They would take the loads of cereals in convoy on the vans, trailers, and lorries to wait their turn at the threshing machine and, in turn, load the straw and bags of grain to take back home again. Then they would move on to the next farm. The farmer whose crop was being carried on a particular day provided lunch for all. Tables were pushed together, tablecloths and cutlery laid. Farmers' wives had helpers, usually the other farmers' wives, having spent the previous days cooking in preparation for the great day.

Unfortunately those days could not be repeated today, not simply because of farm mechanisation but because of the changes to the countryside, as farms get fewer and more town folk seek the country life and occupy the farm and farmhouse. Beau Désert was later farmed with La Retraite as one farm by Mr. Hedley Le Quesne's son, Nicholas; Mr. John Le Gallais still has his farm at Roselands; but Patier Farm, a pretty little farmhouse and farmyard in a hollow at the side of Patier Road, has been demolished to make way for urban housing, namely Le Clos de Patier. The farmland opposite was bought by compulsory purchase and is now Le Jardin à Pommier, a housing estate. At Five Oaks, Welton Farm has gone, being until recently the Redwood Hotel and Twigs Restaurant. The farmland has mostly been built on, with housing estates.

So the country has become more urban and, far from experiencing country life, these folk are living in large housing estates, with pavements and streetlights, etc.: all completely foreign to the countryside. Their inhabitants, far from knowing or accepting and enjoying the country life, often complain about country smells, which the countryman takes for granted and barely gives a second thought to. Pumping the liquid manure from the cistern and carting it to spread on the field was a smelly operation, but folk did not complain, and would probably have been laughed at if they did. It is true though, that those smells have changed: farmyard manure and liquid manure have been replaced by slurry. It has a lot of water in it, from washing down, and has a particularly foul, pungent smell, compared with the equally pungent, but more acceptable, smell of farmyard manure or liquid manure of earlier times.

Neighbours working together, in those days, added to the spirit of community. Today, unless you have business with your neighbour, you rarely see him, preferring to whiz past shut in your 'tin carriage'.

While harvesting and threshing was a neighbourly practice in Jersey, in England, when farmers gathered in the harvest, it was sometimes threshed immediately in a field, on the farm. Often it was stored in a Dutch barn or stacked in a rickyard. Sometime later it was threshed by a contractor's threshing set, in the winter, so providing work for the farm labour in slack months. Wire-tied bales were in use before the Second World War.

The author's father regularly bought imported straw and hay from England. The hay was always green, beautifully made, and wire-tied. The cowman, Mr. Tom Keen, carefully folded the wire from the bales and placed it outside the side stable door at Beau Désert. There it accumulated into a rusting heap. It was one of those silly little things the author can remember thinking about when he was away, during those long years of the war and Occupation. He had a little bet with himself that the heap would still be there after the war. Within a day or so of returning home on his first leave in September 1945, after six years of war, he went to see if it was there and yes, there it was! He knew he was home at last. Not everything had changed.

It was exciting working around a threshing machine, an experience the author quite enjoyed when working on farms in school holidays in England during the war, but it was serious stuff; no neighbours and party atmosphere there! If there were Land Army girls present, then one might have a giggle, as the author recalls. There was always so much going on, many busy people about, the engine driver, someone on the load or rick forking sheaves onto the threshing machine while another picked them up, to put them onto the feeding table and cut the twine around the sheaves, carefully collecting the twine and putting it aside. Then the feeder would gather the sheaf and let it run in a stream down his outstretched arm into the gaping hole above the spinning drum. Meanwhile, two people looked after the grain bags, changing them as they filled, then weighing and tying the sacks with used binder twine. Meanwhile, another person had the job of raking away the heap of cavings, the husk and chaff that accumulated under the threshing box: a dusty and uncomfortable task, as a slight breeze would catch the cavings and blow them everywhere. It was another man's task to take the trussed or baled straw, before it fell from the baler, and place it on an elevator. There the bales were carried up and dropped on top of the straw rick, to be stacked carefully by an experienced rick builder, or onto a trailer. There yet another skill was necessary, to build a high load between the hay ladders on the wagon or trailer. Meanwhile, more high loads of sheaves of wheat, barley, or oats would arrive straight from the field.

In Jersey, there were often many people about during threshing, as loads joined the 'string' or queue and farmers or farmworkers waited with their loads to be threshed. The loads were on a variety of different farm vehicles, horses and vans, lorries and tractor trailers. Farmers who had threshed were departing with their sacks of grain and loads of baled or trussed straw.

The successful operation of the threshing machine requires considerable skills. The critical setting of the clearance between the beaters/rasp bars on the drum and the concave has been explained earlier. Set it too close and some of the grain will be chipped and skinned, set it too open and grain will remain in the husk. Selecting the correct sieve size is also critical, and another problem is to line up the engine, to get the flat-belt pulleys perfectly in line so the belt will run true, then move the engine back to get the correct tension on the belt. The aim is not to tighten it, but to have the biggest arc of contact between the belt and pulleys where it passes over them. This is achieved by having the belt hang slightly between the pulleys. Starting the machine, getting the heavy drum rotating, the elevators and straw walkers and the trusser all moving together, requires considerable care and attention to avoid the belt being thrown off as the engine takes up the load.

As said previously, feeding the machine is critical; it is no use an enthusiast feeding in the sheaves as fast as he can, cutting the twine and just letting it all go. The twine must be set aside and the sheaf placed along the opening and held so it flows in a steady stream off his forearm and hand or is drawn off the feed table into the drum, at a speed the drum can take it. Woe betide the man who does not heed this advice. If the machine is fed too fast, it will be overloaded and the cylinder will jam and, as the drum locks up, the pulley stops turning, and if the flat belt does not break, it is thrown off the pulley and work stops. The jam in the drum has to be cleared, using a handle placed on the end of the drum shaft, and strong men will try to turn it backwards to free it. In a severe case, considerable force has to be used, with crowbars, and the danger is that impatience or carelessness at this point will break something. After some time the jam will be cleared. If the overload has snapped the belt, sometimes at the join, then it will have to be rejoined and riveted by the engine driver. With the drum free and the belt on the pulleys the driver will then have to go through his careful starting procedure again, everybody breathes a sigh of relief and work starts once more!

While threshing proceeds, the engine driver has to keep his steam engine running smoothly, keeping an eye on the steam pressure and the water levels in the boiler, and keeping his fire burning, which requires a steady supply of water and coal or wood.

One of the last threshing drums to be imported was manufactured by Ransomes soon after 1945. It was purchased by Mr. Clarence R. Priaulx, Les Corvées, St. Ouen, for contracting; it was on iron wheels. Mr. Priaulx towed the machine with a tractor from job to job, mostly in St. Mary and sometimes in St. Ouen. He was frustrated by the Planning Department in his attempts to build a shed to house it. To add insult to injury, people would frequently steal the tarpaulin cover. The sad remains are where it was last used, in the 1960s, beside Rue de La Cour, near St. Ouen's Church. This threshing machine is included here simply because so many people got in touch with the author about it. Unfortunately, it is well beyond restoration.

The next threshing machine to be brought into the Island would be the combined harvester.

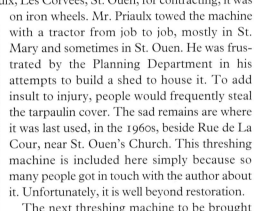
Ransomes threshing machine, sales literature.

Maufant, 1920, a happy threshing 'party' complete with decorated horse, in the days when neighbours worked together.

Threshing from a rick; note the second rick, behind the portable steam engine and the water cask. The cask has been rolled up a wooden ramp, to keep the water topped up in the steam engine. Mr. Elias Billot senior is holding the decorated horse's bridle, Mr. Francis Billot (the author's father) is sitting at the back in the centre of the group in the van, and his brother Mr. John Billot is sitting second from the left.

The sight of a rickyard with the chickens scratching for grain, once so much a part of the farmstead and often a subject for artists, has disappeared completely along with the binder, the threshing machine, and the farm horse.

8 Cider Crushers and Presses

Cider, crushers, and presses

Cider exports were a very important industry for the Island, becoming popular with farmers in the seventeenth century and expanding in the eighteenth, then declining in the late nineteenth and twentieth centuries. It was said that St. Saviour had many more orchards than any other parish in the Island. Cider crushers existed on almost every Jersey farm and are dear to the heart of every Jersey countryman and woman. There must have been money to be made with cider, as the stone crusher and press were two expensive pieces of equipment to purchase and install. Although there were many in the Island, they were not unique to Jersey. The author was pleasantly surprised when he discovered one on a farm in the little hamlet of Flyford Flavell, in Worcestershire, where there were many orchards. In the spring each year the AA marked out a Blossom Tour Route for tourists to view the blossom.

In Jersey, there remain excellent sets of crushers and presses that have been preserved. A farmhouse in Trinity has been modernised and extended into the presshouse, complete with crusher and press. Both have been cleaned, varnished, and polished to make a feature in a 'gentleman's study'! There are sets that are maintained in working order, for use in the autumn on special visiting days, at Les Prés Manor in Grouville, Samarès Manor in St. Clement, and at Hamptonne in St. Lawrence, the last operated by the Museum Service.

At La Porte, Maufant, as on many farms, there is a building called the 'presshouse', or *le preinseu*, that once housed both a crusher and press on an earth floor. The press went many years ago and the crusher was sold in the 1950s, no doubt to decorate somebody's garden and make room for other purposes on the farm. Only the vertical centre post, with an annular groove where the beam for the stone wheel was fitted, remains, and a hollowed-out space in the wall, to allow the horse to pass through, between the crusher trough and wall, as it hauled the stone wheel around the trough.

The apple crusher in the presshouse at Le Prés Manor, Grouville.
This crusher, and the beam press pictured on the following page, are brought into use once a year, when the Le Maistre family hold an annual fete at Les Prés Manor farm in the summer.

The beam press.

The vertical pole winch.
The rope on the vertical pole winch is tied to the lever on the screw of the beam press, to obtain an extra turn of the screw to apply a few extra pounds pressure, after the press has been screwed down as far as possible with the standard lever.

One of the last farmers making cider commercially with a stone crusher and press was George Boléat in the 1970s at Valley Farm, St. Saviour. In fact he imported apples from France as local supplies became fewer and fewer. Mr. Blayney in St. Mary crushed apples in recent years to make apple brandy. This activity still goes on with frequent appeals for apples in the autumn.

The apple crusher at Samarès Manor in operation.
Mrs. Obbard leads the horse.
Mr. Obbard at Samarès Manor, St. Clement, has the stone apple crusher in the middle of the yard with a flower bed in the centre! An old Jersey press was recently acquired and brought into use again, on an open day in the summer of 1998. A museum collection of old farm machinery and farm vehicles is housed in the farm sheds around the yard.

A cider press manufactured by E. Boule, St Brieuc, Brittany.
The Boule cider press is described as a type A, beautifully made and well looked after. It has a slatted barrel and two cast-iron handwheels to apply pressure to the pressure plate. The apple juice runs into the square trough at the bottom and then into the wooden tub. It has been installed by Vincent Obbard in the former dairy at Samarès Manor, and has been used in the autumn open days at Samarès.

(*right*) Crushing apples with a stone wheel and stone trough at Hamptonne
The stone crushers in Jersey are often made of Chausey granite. They were made and assembled during the years of cider production and exporting in the 18th and 19th centuries and earlier, when many orchards were planted all over the Island, particularly in the east.

The trough is composed of six perfectly matching pieces of blue granite. It has an outside diameter of 14 ft (431 cm), the channel measures 18 in. (45.5 cm) across the top, the outside wall of the trough measures 4 ins. (10 cm) across the top, and the inside surface slopes toward the centre to reduce width across the bottom to 14 in. (35.5 cm). The inner wall side is vertical, also 4 in. (10 cm) across the top, and the trough is 12 in. (30.4 cm) deep. The best shape was no doubt learned over many years of experience, to accommodate the stone wheel circling round inside the trough and to help keep the pulp in place at the bottom before it is lifted out with wooden shovels and placed in the press. The wooden shovel on the right is being used to scrape the pulp to the centre of the trough, and the wooden scraper pulled behind the stone wheel also moves the pulp to the centre of the trough.

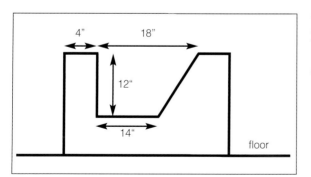

Cross-section drawing of the circular stone trough and dimensions.
The blue granite crushing wheel is 9 in. (22.8 cm) wide and 43 in. (110 cm) in diameter. The wheel is hauled round by a horse and requires at least two people to operate it.

The cider press, or *le preinseu* , at Hamptonne is a two-screw beam press.

The dimensions of this two-screw beam press are massive. The bed measures 8 ft x 4 ft (246 x 123 cm) supporting a 6 ft (182 cm) square base upon which rests the 4 ft (121 cm) square container. The vertical screws are 9 in. (22.8 cm) in diameter, the threaded length is 65 in. (164 cm) pitch at 11 threads to 21 in. (53 cm). The bases of the screws are 4 ft 6 in. (138 cm) long and each supports a 30 in. (76 cm) diameter windlass ring. The heavy wooden beam is 11 ft 3 in. (345.5 cm) long, 17 in. (43 cm) wide, and 14 in. (35.5 cm) deep at the screws and 18 in. (45.5 cm) at the centre. A vertical pole winch behind the press is obscured from view. It is 12 ft (365 cm) high, from the floor to the overhead beam. It provides the extra leverage to turn the two screws that extra bit more, similar to the smaller one at Les Prés Manor. The press was made and assembled locally but the threads of the vertical screws are thought to have been cut in France. It is difficult to date when it was made, because cider was being made in the 17th century and became a busy industry, continuing through the 18th and 19th centuries. Two men operate the press, one on each screw. (La Société Jersiaise/Jersey Heritage Trust collection at Hamptonne.)

It was in late autumn on many farms when the Island exported thousands of gallons of cider. These days this equipment at Hamptonne is used every autumn, when a cider-making day is held. Many thousands of people over many centuries drank cider produced with this type of equipment; when freshly made it is a delightfully refreshing fruit juice. Today, cider produced with this equipment is considered by the Public Health Department to be unfit for sale for human consumption but it can be given away! So the Société Jersiaise and the Jersey Heritage Trust cannot sell it to provide valuable revenue. Today, we live in a crazy world!

Small lightweight crushers and presses

As time went on, design and manufacturing of machinery advanced, and in the nineteenth century new forms of cider-making machinery became available. Smaller and lighter apple crushers and presses were developed. The press made by E. Boule of St. Brieuc, at Samarès Manor is an example.

The feed hopper has been removed on this crusher to reveal the two rolls.

Within the sturdy wooden frame are the two wooden rollers of equal length and diameter: 11.5 in. (29 cm) long and 9 in. (22.8 cm) in diameter with iron wedge-shaped pointed tines 1.25 in. (3 cm) long in each roller. As the rollers rotate, the points penetrate a hole in the exact opposite position in the neighbouring roller. The rollers are mounted on axles located in bearings that are adjustable, to vary the gap between the rollers. The rotating wooden rollers crush the apples into a pulp which then falls onto a pair of large 15 in. (38 cm) diameter stone rolls that are 16 in. (40.5 cm) long.

There are two 15 in. diameter stone rollers; one can be seen here beneath the two wooden rollers.

The stone rollers are also mounted in bearings that are adjustable to vary the gap between the rollers. The apple juice and pulp falls into a removable pulp box underneath. The box can be seen at the rear of the picture on the left. The machine is mounted on four cast-iron wheels, on steel axles, and is operated by two crank handles and two men, one on each side of the machine. The machine was manufactured by the Bristol Wagon Company in the late 19th century. (La Société Jersiaise and Heritage Trust collection at the Augrés store.)

(*right*) Another crusher with the hopper removed to reveal the crushing mechanism of two rotors with curved teeth; it was manufactured by E. Boule of St. Brieuc.

This apple crusher manufactured in the late 19th or early 20th century has two cast iron rotors, each with deeply fluted and curved teeth. The rotors are mounted in adjustable bearings. The machine has been dismantled and the rotors are out of their plain wooden bearings and resting on the bearing blocks. The distance between the rotors is adjustable and set by two setscrews, with locknuts, in the foreground, all mounted in a stout wooden frame. The rotor with the long shaft is turned with a handwheel; the second rotor is an idler, meshed like a gearwheel with its neighbour and rotating with it. A wooden feed hopper fits over the rotors and a collecting box for the pulp is placed underneath. (La Société Jersiaise and Heritage Trust collection at the Augrés store.)

General purpose fruit crusher, manufactured by Dening & Co. of Chard in Somerset.

This general purpose fruit crusher also has twin rolls. It is more modern than the machines described previously and is thought to have been built between the wars. In the varnished wooden box under the hopper is a spiral of knives, which while in operation rotate, passing through a comb; beneath are two stone rollers. Through the space between them the pulp is further crushed, before falling into a wooden collecting box underneath. The machine is driven by a 4 or 5 hp engine and flat belt to a large-diameter pulley. It has also been fitted with a V pulley, probably for use with an electric motor, to drive it at between 100 or 200 rpm. The twin rollers are similar in operation to those in some old mills for crushing oats, etc. It is interesting that two machines from the West Country (Chard and Bristol), use large-diameter stone rollers in the process, as compared to the Breton machine, which has none. (Steam Museum collection.)

Another but smaller barrel fruit press, by E. Boule of St. Brieuc.
This small, slatted, barrel-type fruit press was made by E. Boule of St. Brieuc before the First World War. It is a similar type to the larger barrel-type press at Samarès Manor but has only one handwheel, on the top, to turn the screw, fitted through a solid wooden crossbeam, to apply pressure onto the pressure plate. The barrel is composed of wooden slats, held in place with stout metal hoops. Beneath the platform is a wooden trough to collect the fruit juice. It may have been used by a small producer, together with the small crusher manufactured by Dening of Chard described above. This press was last used during the German Occupation, for pressing sugar beet to make sugar. (Steam Museum collection.)

The cooper

A cooper repairing cider casks at Hamptonne.
The cooper is repairing the metal hoops for cider casks at Hamptonne on a cider-making open day. The hoops' ends are riveted together and they have to be made slightly conical, to fit the shape of the barrel.

9 Tractors before 1945

The early years

The word 'tractor' did not come into use until the First World War in 1914. Before that there were various names, including 'motor plough' and 'agricultural motor'. In Jersey the first reference to the motor power on the land was in the *Evening Post* in January 1904, when the paper announced that an agricultural motor would be introduced into the Island shortly and suggested it would enable the Jersey farmer not only to dispense with the trouble and risk of keeping so many horses but also to do his work more cheaply at about half the cost of horses! However, it was a two-wheel tractor which first appeared, in 1913, according to the *Chronique de Jersey*. It was manufactured by John Fowler of Leeds and would cost about £300.

Dr. Otto developed and built the first four-cycle, internal combustion engine in 1876. By the time problems with patents had been overcome, the 'Otto Cycle' technology was well understood, resulting in a scramble by many manufacturers to get into production with stationary engines. It is thought the first petrol-engined 'tractor' to be built was in Illinois in 1889. On those early tractors, a stationary engine was mounted on a frame or chassis, making use of components from traction engine transmissions to drive the rear wheels. Only the boiler, firebox, and the steam engine were removed. Very often, having cleared out the boiler, the petrol engine was mounted in the shell. Threshing machine manufacturers were among the first to do this, converting their traction engines to tow and operate their threshing machines. They were not manufactured to haul field implements.

The change to manufacture tractors for tillage came later, in about 1895, due to pressure from farmers on the Great Plains to replace horses. These tractors had either single- or two-cylinder engines and stronger transmission systems, to haul multifurrow ploughs. Most burnt petrol but the Advance Rumely Thresher Co. Inc., of La Porte, Indiana, were the first in the USA to pioneer using kerosene in a tractor engine in their Oil Pull tractor manufactured in 1898. They were beaten to it by two years when England scored a first with the giant Ackroyd Hornsby tractor, with its single-cylinder hot bulb paraffin engine. They were all big and heavy, only suitable for the wide open spaces. J. I. Case are credited with building probably the first real tractor but they were dissatisfied with the ignition system, which plagued all early petrol engines. They were highly successful steam engine manufacturers and decided to wait for a more efficient ignition system before manufacturing tractors with oil engines.

The Rumely Oil Pull tractor was an early success in America. It still resembled a steam engine, with the big iron rear wheels and a large-diameter flywheel, but otherwise it was a vastly different machine. It had a twin-cylinder horizontal engine, cylinder heads towards the driver, which were oil-cooled, enabling them to run at a higher temperature and so burn the kerosene more efficiently. The 'box' stack at the front contained the oil-cooling heat exchangers, which were cooled by cold air induced into the bottom of the box by the exhaust gases entering near the top of the box and exiting through the short stack above. The tractors were used in many parts of the world, including Australia.

Rumely Oil Pull paraffin tractor, type H, model 16-30, serial no. 2628.
The Rumely tractor developed 30 bhp at 530 rpm at the pulley and 16 hp at the drawbar. These tractors were first produced in 1898 and were so successful that they remained in production with little change up to 1931, when the company was taken over by Allis Chalmers. (Courtesy of the Jondaryan Woolshed, Vintage Tractor Collection, Queensland.)

On many American tractors, two pairs of numerals, e.g. 16-30, are used to indicate model numbers. They indicate the engine bhp at the flat-belt pulley, followed by the drawbar hp. By 1902 in the USA, other makers were Hart Parr, Twin City, Case, International. The British companies such as Ransomes, Scott, and Saunderson were making smaller tractors, but farmers in the British Isles were very reluctant to change from horses, so some companies including Ransomes ceased production.

The first to win universal approval in the UK was the Ivel, designed, developed, and manufactured by Dan Albone of Bedfordshire in 1903. This three-wheel tractor, with a twin-cylinder, horizontally opposed, water-cooled petrol engine developing 18 hp at 850 rpm, weighed 1,500 lb. It was small and light enough to be attractive to UK farmers and was exported to many countries, including the USA. It remained in production until the First World War and was the precursor of the modern farm tractor. There is no evidence of an Ivel in Jersey.

The Ivel agricultural motor/tractor won approval from British farmers and many were exported.
It is thought to have been made by Payne & Co. of Coventry, for Mr. Albone. The ignition was by trembler coil that was replaced with a magneto in 1910. The engine cooling water circulated through a 44 gallon (200 l) water tank with an expansion pipe above. Transmission is via two cone clutches, one for forward and the second for reverse. One drove to a toothed chain and a large-diameter sprocket and the second to a gearwheel and then to two large-diameter rear wheels. Speeds were 2.5 and 5 mph. Steering was by steering wheel and a sprocket and chain, to two rods, to two arms on a single front wheel. The tractor weighs 28 cwt.

The American response was the Allis Chalmers 10-18, which was very similar to the Ivel but used a radiator for the cooling water. Many manufacturers were experimenting with tractors, J. I. Case, Wallis and Henry Ford among them. Henry Ford was brought up on a farm and had built his first tractor at Dearborn in 1907. By 1914 in USA tractor manufacture was well established; on average, one tractor replaced nine horses. International Harvester was the biggest producer.

The First World War had a significant effect on agriculture, the farm tractor and farm mechanisation. The Allied armies' demand for men and horses created a shortage of both on British, French, and American farms and, as we see in the year books of the Royal Jersey Agricultural and Horticultural Society, Jersey was seriously affected. Tractors and machinery became an essential requirement for food production, against the onslaught of the German U-boat campaign. Demand for tractors went up on both sides of the Atlantic.

A popular American tractor was the Waterloo Boy, rebranded Overtime in England; it was manufactured in Iowa and purchased by John Deere in 1918. A Waterloo Boy distributor in Ireland was Harry Ferguson. The most popular British tractor in England in 1918 was the Saunderson. The British Government went as far as fitting lights to farm tractors, so that ploughing could continue through the night; this also happened in France and the USA.

In 1917, after ten years of development, Henry Ford went into production with the Fordson F tractor, at half the price of many tractors on the market!

After four years of war and U-boat activity, the UK faced starvation, unless something was done to speed up food production. The British Government sent Henry Ford an urgent message, requesting a supply of tractors in large numbers, as soon as possible. Two model X prototype tractors were sent over to England for testing and proved highly successful. The intention was to produce the tractors in England, but continued Zeppelin raids over England led to a change of plan; the factory that was to be used instead produced the famous Camel fighter plane. Henry Ford, to his great credit, responded by shipping the first 6,000 model F tractors produced to England. Deliveries began in 1917 and 7,000 had arrived by the end of 1919. Production exceeded the ability of the convoy system to ship them!

On early tractors, the words 'Henry Ford and Son' were painted on the radiator. Henry Ford and his son were financing this enterprise themselves; the Ford Motor Company was not involved.

The model F tractor was manufactured from 1917 to 1929 in the USA. Tractors were produced in Cork, Ireland, in 1919 for three or four years. They were marked on the ends of the fuel tank 'Cork Ireland', and, according to Mr. Jack Le Sueur, some of them came to Jersey. In 1929 the new model N was produced in Cork, before being transferred to Ford's new complex at Dagenham in 1930/1. After further improvements, the model N was manufactured in quantity.

Was the Fordson model F the first tractor in Jersey? Research shows that tractors were beginning to come into the Island towards the end of the First World War and included a small number of those first 6,000 Fordson model F tractors. Unfortunately, a search through Jersey Customs Department's archives for 1916-19 revealed nothing helpful; no tractors were listed.

The earliest of the 6,000 model F tractors were at work in England in 1918, so it is reasonable to assume that a few of them were imported into Jersey in the same year, or early 1919. It was closely followed by the International Junior 8-16 HC series. Although production began in 1917, the first shipments of Juniors did not arrive in England until the improved HC series was available. It had a large aircleaner and a two-bearing crankshaft and went into production in 1919. Fortunately, people in the farming community with long memories can help us. The late Pat Gruchy said that his uncle A. W. Blampied, at the Hawthorns, St. John, told him that he purchased his Fordson model F in 1917 or 1918. He may well have ordered the tractor in 1917, direct from the Ford Motor Company, in time to take delivery and start ploughing with it early in 1918.

Hedley Maillard's father bought a new Fordson F from Bougourd Brothers, the agents, in 1919. Mr. Charles Perchard, who became a successful farmer, recalls seeing his first tractor, a Fordson, beside St. Martin's Church while on his way home from Mr. Silk's school in 1920. The Fordson tractor belonged to Smith & Coles, who farmed at Wrentham Hall, St. Martin. This was confirmed by Mr. Jack Le Sueur, of Clairval, and he recalls Mr. Philip Le Riche of La Retraite, St. Lawrence, having one. He thought it was one of the Cork-built tractors.

The earliest Fordson F tractor had a radiator with an open-ladder-type, side casting and twelve-spoke rear wheels. We have an early photograph of Mr. Blampied's model F Fordson at work. Unfortunately Mr. Morvan is leaning against the radiator, so we cannot see whether the words 'Henry Ford and Son' were painted on it. Fortunately we can see the rear wheels, which have twelve spokes, so we know it was manufactured in 1917 and was one of the first 6,000 tractors. Later models had fourteen spokes and solid radiator sides; some were built in 1918. Mr. Blampied's tractor is unusual for an early model F: it has fenders between the driver and the rear wheels. Early model F tractors were not produced with fenders, so presumably these were made and fitted locally, which was done frequently.

Mr. Blampied's Fordson model F tractor manufactured in 1917.
The model F developed 25 hp, 20 hp at the belt pulley, and 10 hp at the drawbar. It had four cylinders with side valves and it burned kerosene, with a vaporiser, but with petrol to start the engine and warm up. It had low-tension spark ignition, with flywheel trembler coils and water-bath air filter. It had all-steel, fabricated, twelve-spoke rear wheels with angled cleats. The flat belt pulley is fitted beside the gearbox on the offside. All the Fordson F tractors were painted grey. The supplier may have been Bougourd Bros., of Guernsey, or it was ordered directly from the Ford Motor Company. The owner was Mr. A. W. Blampied, of the Hawthorns, St. Lawrence. The tractor was hand started with a crank handle. Half the horsepower was lost driving the worm and wheel final drive.

Whenever one started an engine with a crank handle, one never put the thumb over the handle itself; all the fingers and thumb were placed on the same side, because if the tractor backfired you broke your thumb!

Ransomes of Ipswich and Oliver in the USA, and others, were manufacturing tractor ploughs. On all of them, the controls were brought forward, to be in reach of the tractor driver from his seat. They were lifted out of work at the headland by a simple trip lever, operated by the tractor driver from the seat. These arrangements dispensed with the need for a man at the plough. However, some Jersey farmers continued to use the horse plough, requiring two men, while others purchased tractor ploughs with their tractors and saved labour.

Mr. Blampied's son is holding the plough and Mr. Le Riche is driving the tractor.
In this picture Mr. A. W. Blampied's son is holding the handles of the 'big plough' and Mr. Stanley Le Riche, of Le Bannelais, Trinity, is driving the tractor. Leaning against the front of the tractor is a neighbour, Mr. Morvan, grandfather of the former Senator and Constable, Bill Morvan. The three of them worked their farms together.

Mr. A. W. Blampied of the Hawthorns, St. John, who may have been the first farmer to buy a Fordson F tractor.

Mr. Eddy Buesnel with his Fordson model F pulling a binder in 1928.
The picture illustrates the ladder-like side of the tractor's radiator and the twelve-spoke rear wheel of the 1917 production. It has the road bands over the cleats on the rear wheel. The ground was firm enough to provide sufficient grip to tow the binder.

Mr. Blampied was a go-ahead, technically minded farmer. It is surprising he did not have a tractor plough, so one man instead of two could do the ploughing. Mechanisation did not result in any labour-saving in this instance. Mr. Blampied had installed a stationary engine and electric generator and wired his house and farm buildings for electricity before 1920. The same engine provided the power for his mangel cutter/crusher, chaff cutter, and his butter churn. Apart from farming, he was the Deputy for St. John. He also built a radio receiver. These were available as kits in those days; the author's father had one in the 1920s. They were powered with an accumulator, which was a rechargeable battery. They were commonplace in the 1920s and 1930s.

The only model F left in the Island; it belonged to Mr. Frank Le Brun of Pond. View, St. Ouen. It was last used in 1939, when Mr. Le Brun retired.
The tractor was manufactured in 1923, in Detroit, with the serial no. 310705. The supplier was Bougourd Bros., Guernsey, and it was sold through a local dealer in Jersey. The distinguishing features between the Fordson F and the later N are the wheels. The F has fabricated, spoked front wheels and angled cleats on the rear wheels; the N has cast-iron front wheels and spade lugs on the rear wheels.

The tractor was acquired by the late Mr. R. E. Kirwan, of Cambrai, Bellozanne, who hoped to restore it. He was apprehensive about getting the low-tension ignition system working, to have the engine running. It is now in the hands of Mr. Lyndon Pallot and is on display in the Steam Museum.

Miss Beryl Mourant, who knew the author as a small boy in Boulivot, told him that her father Mr. John Ernest Mourant, who farmed at Boulivot, ran a business with showrooms in Bath Street, next door to West's Cinema, now Wests Centre. He imported International Harvester equipment, mowing machines, cultivators, and Welsh ponies! Quite a mix of products! In 1918

International Harvester began production of the 8-16 Junior HC model tractor; it was noteworthy for having a power take-off, with an operating speed of 540 rpm. That speed eventually became the world standard for the tractor power take-off, or PTO. Many of the HC series with a large air filter on the nearside were imported into England from 1919. Beryl recalls her father proudly looking at the new International Harvester tractor in the farmyard at Boulivot, when it was delivered. She also remembers quite a lot of the detail, as it looked very different from the Fordson. Sadly Mr. Mourant died relatively young, on 1 January 1921. The date is significant. We can conclude that the first International tractors came into the Island in 1919, when the first shipments arrived in the UK, or at the latest, 1920. Mr. Mourant's widow continued to run the business for a time, but eventually sold it to Mr. Richmond, who continued to import International Harvester tractors and lorries through the 1920s and 1930s.

Mr. Eddy Buesnel ploughing at La Hougue, St. Saviour, with an International Junior, 8-16 HC series, in 1928 (courtesy of Mr. Donald Le Boutillier).
The International Junior tractor was manufactured in Chicago from mid-1919 to 1922. Under the old RAC rating, the horsepower was 25. It had four cylinders with replaceable liners and a two-bearing crankshaft. The engine was started on petrol, and when the it was warm it was switched over to paraffin; a magneto provided the ignition. Transmission was by chain and sprocket at final drive, it had steel rear wheels with angled cleats, and the drawbar pull was 8 hp. Like the Fordson, the colour was grey. There were binders being manufactured for the power take-off (PTO), no doubt by International Harvester! The tractor also had a belt pulley, which was standard equipment on American tractors. The radiator on the Junior is mounted behind the engine to protect it against damage. The HC type of 1919 is identified by the large aircleaner on the near side; the first model had no aircleaner.

Mr. Buesnel's tractor is probably one of the three Mr. Mourant imported. One of them went to Sark and only recently it was acquired by a purchaser in Kent for an agricultural museum. The price in the UK in 1919 was £325. By 1922 the price of the International Junior had dropped to as low as £275, probably due to Henry Ford's pricing policy, which forced many manufacturers to reduce their prices. Some did not survive but International Harvester, who suffered more than most in lost sales, were an old-established company even then, with a big line of implements and machines, enabling them to survive.

Mr. Buesnel had served as aircrew in the Royal Flying Corps during the First World War and later became an agricultural contractor, operating his business at Carrefour au Clerq, Grouville. He also had a Fordson F, as previously illustrated cutting wheat with a binder. Mr. John Perrée told the author that his father was a customer of Mr. Buesnel, for harvesting with a binder in St. Mary.

Case tractors were also among the first tractors in Jersey. Mr. Maurice Jeanne, of Les Hougues, Trinity, recalls his father talking of a demonstration of a Case tractor at Beau Désert in the field opposite St. Saviour's school. The demonstration was for Mr. Charles Le Quesne, the builder, who bought Beau Désert just after the First World War. The tractor was also used at the neighbouring farm, La Retraite. Mr. Jack Le Sueur of Clairval, St. Saviour, says that sometime later Mr. Aubin Peredes, of La Croix Cattelain, bought the tractor. Jack also remembers a Mr. L'Amy, of Les Arches, St. Clement, having a Case tractor, which was notable for the exposed spur gear, pinions, and gearwheels of the final drive to the rear wheels. These could be seen through the spokes of the rear wheels. Research suggests that the tractor demonstrated at Beau Désert was probably a Case 15-27 and that Mr. L'Amy's was smaller, most likely the 10-18.

Just to add to the confusion of researching this history, there were then two J. I. Case companies. They were both in Racine, Wisconsin, and of the same family, both producing tractors, and both using spur gear, pinions, and gearwheel final drives visible through the spokes of the rear wheels!

The Nilson tractor hauling a binder in France; it is on steel wheels with pyramid lugs on the rear wheels. (courtesy of Larousse agricole: encyclopédie illustrée, Librairie Larousse, Paris.)

The Nilson Farm Machinery Co. moved from Minneapolis to Waukesha in Minnesota in 1916. It did not survive when Ford cut their prices, and failed sometime after 1918. A number were imported into England and France.

Mr. Le Sueur recalls in the 1920s a Nilson tractor being imported into the Island by a Dr. Stapleton, of Oak Lane, The Oak Walk, St. Peter. Like all tractors at the time, it was on steel wheels with lugs on the rear wheels. The doctor evidently used it for hauling materials up the hill to his property. But due to the damage the lugs did to the road surface, he was stopped from using it until road bands were fitted.

The first tractor in Jersey

Summing up, it seems that the first tractor in the Island was the Fordson model F in 1917/18, followed closely by the International Junior, probably in 1919, and the Nilson, followed by the Case, in 1920. The British response to Fordson was the Austin tractor, one of a crop of British tractors to appear in 1918; it looked very much like the Fordson. Mr. Gordon Bennett of the Paragon Garage held a public demonstration of the Austin tractor on 20 December 1928 at Enderby, Longueville, the home of Capt. A. H. Brayn. Several appear to have been imported into the Island. Mr. Hedley Maillard remembers them and Mr. Louis Rondel remembers an Austin tractor owned by Mr. Frank Luce, of Highcliff, St. John, and another by Mr. Arthur of St. Mary, which was confirmed by Mr. Neville George.

This Galloway/Garner tractor belonged to Mr. Alfred Surcouf in Jersey in the 1920s (Courtesy of Mr. Brian Surcouf).
An early tractor imported into England by Henry Garner, a garage proprietor in Birmingham, was the Galloway; Mr. Surcouf bought one. It was first manufactured in 1918 by William Galloway in the United States and rebranded as the Garner for sale in the UK. It was demonstrated at the Lincoln Tractor Trials in 1920. It is thought the company was unable to survive after Henry Ford reduced his prices in the 1920s. The tractor had a 27-8 hp four-cylinder petrol/paraffin engine and a three-speed gearbox. It could travel at 5 mph in the high gear. They were priced at £385.

The 25 hp Austin tractor; it was more expensive than the Fordson. Because the Austin tractor was more expensive than the Fordson F, it only survived when it was manufactured in northern France by Société Anonyme Austin, at Liancourt, Oise, where it benefited from French government subsidies. (Courtesy of *Larousse agricole: encyclopédie illustrée*.)

The 1930s

In 1929 the Fordson F tractor had run its course; as more modern tractors were coming on the market, Henry Ford decided it was time to cease production and he would concentrate on cars and commercial vehicles. However, under pressure from Britain and Ireland, it was decided to transfer production to Cork. All the tooling, moulds for the castings, etc. were shipped over to Cork. Production commenced in 1929 and continued to 1932. The Ford Company constructed a factory with its own iron foundry and steelworks at Dagenham, complete with its own pier and railhead. After completion, a much modified and improved Fordson N tractor went into production, commencing in 1935.

Fordson model N manufactured in 1935 at Dagenham; it has a 27 hp engine.

The N engine speed was controlled by adjusting the governor, which in turn controls the throttle, to set the engine rpm steady, as the load changes. It had splash lubrication for the three main bearings and the big and little end bearings and a down-draught exhaust pipe. The Fordson model N had a more powerful engine, improved ignition, with a high-tension magneto. Other improvements were water bath, aircleaner, cooling water pump, stronger transmission, modified front axle, with heavy cast-iron front wheels, adding weight to the front, to keep the front end down. Production began in Dagenham in 1935. Later the Standard Fordson N had further improvements: rear wheels with spade lugs, an oil bath aircleaner, and worm- and sector-steering.

The factory at Dagenham built Fordsons for the UK; they were painted navy blue and orange for the USA. That policy changed again in 1937, when they were all painted orange. White- or red-dot models distinguished a different gear ratio on first and second gears.

A lot of power was lost in the transmission, reducing horsepower to 10-11 at the drawbar. It has a four-cylinder side valve engine with petrol for starting and switching over to paraffin. known as tractor vaporising oil, (TVO) when the engine and vaporiser had warmed up. A primary aircleaner was at the top of the steering column through which the air was drawn to the large water-bath aircleaner; it can be seen as a large casting behind the engine. Hand starting was with a cranking handle and there is a clip at the bottom of the radiator to stow it upright. The fuel is carried in a two-section fuel tank, TVO at the front and petrol in the small rear tank. Ignition is by high-tension magneto and impulse starter to provide a good spark to start the engine. The governor can be seen beside the engine behind and towards the bottom of the radiator. Steel rear wheels with spade lugs; road bands with strengthening pieces between the lugs are necessary for road work. (The road bands had strengthening pieces between the spade lugs, which were important. Some locally made road bands would eventually flatten between the lugs, making for a very bumpy ride for the driver!) The cast-iron front wheels are on a shallow V-shaped front axle. The transmission is via a multiplate clutch driving a 'worm and wheel' final drive to the back axle. The clutch and brake are operated with a single foot pedal and there is no handbrake; a hook on the foot plate is placed over the pedal to hold the brake on. The brake operates on the transmission to the rear wheels. There is no PTO or hydraulic system; a pulley was an extra fitted to the side of the gearbox. The tractor was supplied through Bougourd Bros., of Guernsey and La Motte Street, Jersey. The owner was Mr. Thomas Cabot, of Trinity (Displayed at the Steam Museum.)

The red Fordson model N was manufactured in 1938, to the same specification except for the aircleaner. It had a separate inlet pipe on the opposite side, to the upswept exhaust pipe. The inlet pipe led to an oil bath aircleaner replacing the water cleaner. Steering was changed to a worm and segment. It was originally painted orange. It was supplied by the main Ford dealer, La Motte Street Garage, to Mr. H. Le Brocq, of St. Ouen.

The Fordson tractor engine had to have an oil change every fifty hours; the unburnt fuel (paraffin/TVO) would run down the cylinders and dilute the engine oil. Vigzol oil was the popular choice of the Ford dealers in those pre-war and early post-war years. The Fordson N was better known to many people as the Standard Fordson. In the late 1930s it was offered on steel wheels with spade lugs, or on rubber-tyred wheels, which eventually became standard practice.

La Motte Street Garage, the main Ford dealer, was formed in the 1930s. The previous dealers were in financial difficulties with the tractor business. Mr. Bill Sutton was the Fordson tractor representative for the south of England; he came over to see what could be done and discussed the problem with the Ford main dealer in the Southampton area. Between them they arranged for Mr. Sutton to take over the Ford main dealership for Jersey and the Sutton family remained in control until quite recently, when the late Mr. Colin Sutton retired. During the German Occupation, Mr. Sutton travelled to France for the Essential Commodities Committee of the States of Jersey, to purchase supplies and equipment necessary for the Island to keep functioning.

A 1935 Fordson N tractor, serial no. 793135, beautifully restored by Raoul Le Mière (in the green overalls).
The Fordson N tractor has been restored in the navy blue of the early post-war tractors and some pre-war tractors; it was previously owned by Mr. Bill Sarre. In the background is a Ransomes steam traction engine driving a Tullos threshing machine. The red tractor is a Nuffield built by Morris Cars.

The Nuffield was not imported into Jersey for farming purposes but recently by an enthusiast. It is driving the pick-up baler, to bale the straw from the threshing machine. Like the Fordson Major, the Nuffield tractors were considered to be too big for Jersey. The present generation of farmers seem to overlook the problems caused by big, heavy tractors and equipment on the land!

International W12 tractor, serial no. WS 2682, manufactured in 1936.
International Harvester Co. manufactured tractors in Chicago, Illinois. The tractor develops 12 hp at 1,800 rpm maximum. On the serial number plate is a warning not to overload the engine. The four-cylinder overhead valve (OHV) engine has a magneto and is hand-started; it runs on TVO, starting with petrol until warm before switching over to TVO. It is on steel wheels with spade lugs on the rear wheels, with road bands. External transmission brakes were fitted on either side of the gearbox and could be operated independently with a hand lever: one lever to one brake on one rear wheel, and a second lever to the other brake and wheel. In rowcrop work this enabled the tractor to turn or spin round within its own length on the headland, preparatory to going down the next rows, when weeding between the rows. It has a pulley behind the back axle; in some cases this is removable, exposing a splined PTO shaft. In front of the radiator, at the bottom, is a rolled-up canvas dust

screen to prevent dust and debris clogging up the radiator in dusty conditions. The paint is the original International Harvester red. The owner was Mr. Reg Quérée, of St. Ouen, and J. E. Colback, of Saville Street, in St. Helier, supplied the tractor. This tractor is displayed at the Steam Museum.

International Harvester tractors imported into the Island were the W12 and W14 and the Farmall F12 and F14; they were all petrol/paraffin models.

It is not surprising that Henry Ford ceased production of the Fordson F in 1929, when tractors of the above specification were being developed.

International Farmall model F14; rowcrop tractor manufactured in 1937.

This rowcrop tractor was originally fitted with fenders over the rear wheels and had a sheet-metal bonnet over the engine. Unfortunately these items were lost before restoration. It has chassis-type beams along each side, drilled out to accept mid-mounted rowcrop implements. It is powered by a four-cylinder OHV engine, burning petrol to start and TVO when warm; ignition is by magneto and it has an oil-bath aircleaner. Steel, rowcrop, rear wheels are adjustable for track width by sliding along and clamping to the back axle. The front axle length can also be adjusted to move the front wheels in or out, to match the track of the back wheels. It has a PTO and a shaft for a pulley fitted externally, at the side of the gearbox, and it has independent rear wheel brakes. The radiator has a mechanical slatted blind, operated from the tractor seat. While it has no hydraulic lift, it is very likely that a mechanically operated lift would have been an option. The steering column is horizontal, over the engine, to a steering gearbox with a worm and wheel. The tractor could also be converted to a single front wheel, for rowcrop work. No three-wheel tractors seem to have come into the Island but many American tractors were produced with three wheels. The colour is International red. The owner farmed in St. John and the supplier was Richmond, of Bath Street, St. Helier. (Displayed at the Steam Museum.)

International W14 tractor, serial no. W 84596, manufactured by International Harvester in 1939.

The W14 tractor has a four-cylinder OHV TVO/petrol engine, developing 18 hp at 1,800 rpm. The silver and black magneto stands out clearly among the filters on the side of the engine. It has independent rear wheel brakes and steel wheels, with spade lugs. It is fitted with well-designed road bands, with an internal flange, to prevent flattening between the lugs. It was supplied by Messrs Richmond of Bath Street, to Mr. Peter Allo, who farmed at Hamptonne, St. Lawrence, Les Landes, in St Ouen, and Trinity. It has been beautifully restored by Mr. Robert Allo, at Greenwood, Trinity. The tractor was recently moved to the Steam Museum, where it is on display.

Harry Ferguson was not the only tractor manufacturer to concern himself with weight. Both International Harvester and Allis Chalmers designed and built lightweight tractors for arable work: the Allis Chalmers model B, with a very slim transmission tube behind the clutch, and the International model FAA Cultivision. Both were rowcrop tractors. Details of the model B are given towards the end of this chapter.

The International Harvester Co. Farmall Cultivision rowcrop tractor, model A, serial no. FAA 7974; the independent rear wheel brake pedals can be clearly seenbeneath the steering column.

The model A was manufactured in 1939 and develops 16 hp at 1,540 rpm. It has a four-cylinder engine burning TVO and petrol to start; ignition is by magneto. It has pneumatic tyres on all wheels; they are adjustable for track width, to suit the crop row widths, etc. It is designed with an offset engine to improve vision for mid-mounted rowcrop implements such as hoeing between the rows. Complete with mechanical lift, PTO, and pulley attachments. The supplier was Colback's Garage. The tractor was acquired, beautifully restored, and painted International red by a farmer, Mr. Peter Hamon. He uses it for transporting and operating a milking bucket in the field, the vacuum being provided by the engine inlet manifold. More recently a pump was fitted to operate a second bucket.

The author recalls a tractor demonstration on a neighbour's farm in his schooldays. The tractors demonstrated were an American John Deere, imported by Le Cappelain, of St. Peter's Iron Works, and a Ransomes MG2. One of the first of the John Deere tractors and one of the first little MG2 tractors in the Island were demonstrated to Mr. Cotrel at La Retraite, above Swiss Valley, St. Saviour, in 1936. The John Deere performed well, deep ploughing, with a Jersey big plough, or *la grande tchéthue*, normally pulled by a team of four or six horses. Having seen the John Deere demonstrated, it was decided to demonstrate the MG2 pulling the big plough! It is the usual practice when ploughing with wheeled tractors to put the front and rear wheel on the furrow side in the open furrow. The MG2 was driven with one track in the open furrow and reversed up to the plough. Because of the narrow track width and the 12 in. (30.5 cm) deep furrow, the little tractor was angled over very steeply and when it attempted to pull the plough it was not very successful. The MG2 had a single-cylinder 5-6 hp engine compared to the John Deere, with a 27 hp engine and 15 hp at the drawbar. Hardly a fair comparison; the result of the demonstration was a foregone conclusion! The MG2 was never designed for ploughing with a big plough! Jack Cotrell told the author recently that his father kept the John Deere.

John Deere model B 10-20, serial no. 332148, manufactured in 1941 and supplied to the UK under wartime 'lend lease' agreement with the USA.

This John Deere model B is similar to those used in Jersey, where only one, in a sorry state, survives. The four-stroke engine was unusual, having two horizontal cylinders. The cylinder heads were towards the front of the tractor. As one piston reached top dead centre (tdc), the second was at bottom dead centre. The power stroke of one was followed immediately by the power stroke of the second, and the next down strokes were both suction strokes, resulting in uneven power strokes and the engine running with an uneven sound. It had a large-diameter cast-iron flywheel on the crankshaft at the side of the tractor to even out the power transmitted. No starting handle was used; there were instead a line of finger-grip holes on the inside of the flywheel rim. To start the engine the fingers were placed in the finger holes and the flywheel was pulled round. The engine was started on petrol, and it was when warm the petrol was turned off and the paraffin turned on. The John Deere model D tractor's great virtue was that the unusual 27 hp engine was very economical to run. The tractor illustrated is displayed at the Breamore Countryside Museum at Breamore Manor House near, Fordingbridge, in Hampshire.

There were three John Deere model B tractors in the Island: one was sold to Mr. Binet of La Maison du Buisson, at Maufant, St. Saviour, the second going to Mr. Cotrel, at La Retraite, St Saviour. They must have been sold at approximately the same time because Mr. Binet and Mr. Cotrel each claim they had the first one! A third one went to Mr. Hedley Egré, of Oakdale, St. Peter, and a fourth, a smaller model L, manufactured in 1939, on rubber tyres, went to Mr. Gotel, at Trinity Manor. The model L is an exception for John Deere, as it had an upright twin-cylinder engine and was on rubber tyres.

Mr. Binet used a Midland self-lift trailed plough with his. After the war the plough was considerably altered, having the wheels removed and a tripod fitted with a crossbar, etc. for the three-point linkage system of a Ferguson tractor. This was done to many pre-war trailed tractor ploughs.

This is the sorry-looking model B and only surviving John Deere tractor in the Island (courtesy of Lyndon Pallot). This John Deere model B 15/27, serial no. 326393, has 15 hp at the drawbar and 27 bhp at the pulley, and was manufactured in 1936. Like all model B tractors, it has a two-cylinder horizontal engine, with a big exposed flywheel on the crankshaft with finger holes for starting. It is a petrol/paraffin TVO engine with ignition by magneto and has a reputation for very economical fuel consumption. It has a pulley but no hydraulic lift system. It was originally painted in John Deere green with yellow wheels. The rubber tyres and wheels are not original; originally they were steel wheels on spade lugs. The present rear wheels have been made up using Ferguson wheel centres. The supplier was Le Cappelain, of St. Peter's Iron Works. It was purchased second-hand by Mr. Philip Cotillard of La Commune, Victoria Village, St. Saviour, who used it for contracting. He fitted a winch on the side of the engine for ploughing côtils and later sold it to Mr. Ken Godel, of Bel Air, St. John. The model B is about to be put into Mr. Lyndon Pallot's workshop at Sous les Bois, St. Brelade, to be stripped down and rebuilt. Mr. Pallot has made an excellent job of restoring many old agricultural machines and stationary engines, so we can expect to see this tractor looking in much better shape in due course.

Ransomes MG2 is a relatively small tractor, which came on the market in the mid-1930s, becoming a popular tractor with potato growers. The first of these was ordered direct from Ransomes in 1936 at a price of £135 by A. W. Blampied of the Hawthorns, St. John (see above, p. 000), who saw it advertised in an agricultural journal. It replaced the horse for many potato growers in Jersey, hauling the planting plough, scarifying, and banking early potatoes. A second one went at the same time to Mr. C. W. Arthur, at Fauvic Villa, to be followed by more up to the Occupation and again after the war.

Pat Gruchy driving Mr. Blampied's Ransomes MG2 tractor, pulling a potato-planting plough; the two steering handles can be seen, one on each side of the upright inlet filter (the planting plough is a horse-drawn plough). Ransomes model MG2 tracklaying light tractor, manufactured in 1936 at a price of £135. It has a Sturmey Archer-Raleigh single-cylinder, 6 hp, 600 cc air-cooled petrol engine, developing 600-lb pull at the drawbar. Ignition is by magneto, with an impulse starter for starting the engine with a starting handle. The gearbox has only one forward and one reverse gear; a centrifugal clutch engages as the engine speed increases. It has a speed of 2.5 mph. The rubber-jointed tracks were designed by Roadless Traction Ltd., Hounslow, Middlesex, who also made the rubber joints; the track plates were (continued on facing page)

Ransomes MG2 tractor displayed at the Steam Museum, serial no. 3162 Mk. 11, manufactured in 1948 (courtesy of the Steam Museum)

In 1935 the Bristol tractor, a small, light, tracklayer, was demonstrated at the RJA & HS summer show at Springfield and again at La Hougue Bie; here it is ploughing with a Jersey big plough normally used with horses.

The Bristol tractor was manufactured by Bristol Tractors Ltd. The tracks were made by Roadless Traction Ltd. of Hounslow. The width between the tracks is 35.5 in. (90 cm) and was adjustable out to 55 in. (140 cm); the width of each individual track is 7 in. (17.8 cm). The petrol engine is a 7-hp, two-cylinder Jowett. It has three forward gears and a reverse. Drawbar pull in first gear is 2,000 lb and 1,400 lbs. in second gear. The PTO ran at 500 rpm and the pulley at 750 rpm. Steering by clutch and brake with a single tiller. Ground pressure was 4.5 lb/sq. in. and the colour was green. The supplier was Sion Garage. Later a Coventry Victor 10-hp diesel engine was offered, and after the Second World War two steering levers replaced the tiller. (Courtesy of Mr. Don Le Boutillier.)

(*continued from facing page*) made in Ransomes' foundry in Ipswich. Ground pressure is 4 lb/sq in. The track width is adjustable in 3 in. (7.6 cm) steps, from 2 ft 4 in. to 2 ft 7 in. and 2 ft 10 in. centres (71, 78.7, and 86.4 cm). It has a PTO running at 400 rpm and a choice of pulley sizes, to fit over the PTO. There is no hydraulic lift but it has a mechanical hand lift. The tracks were driven by the front sprockets so compressing the rubber-jointed tracks in work, rather than pulling and stretching the rubber joints. First models had a swinging drawbar, and a hand-operated mechanical lift. The owner was Mr. A. J. Blampied, of the Hawthorns, St. John (who had the first Fordson F). It is seen here in a field beside Grouville mill. (Courtesy of the late Pat Gruchy.)

Roadless Traction Ltd. produced a rubber-jointed track that was used by both Bristol and Ransomes, hence the similar appearance of track arrangements on the two makes of tractors. Roadless rubber-jointed tracks were designed to be driven by a front sprocket, which kept the rubber joint blocks in compression during operation; normally, tracklayers with all-steel tracks are driven by sprockets at the back. The power unit was a Jowett water-cooled engine, with twin, horizontally opposed cylinders, a perfectly balanced engine. The tractor design originated in the Tank Engineering Works, where the First World War tanks were developed and produced. After the war they turned their attention to agricultural applications. Development was continued by Douglas Motorcycles in Bristol, using the Douglas twin-cylinder, horizontally opposed, air-cooled engine, until the business was acquired by Jowett.

The author driving a Bristol tractor at the Royal Jersey Agricultural and Horticultural Show at Springfield in 1935.
There was nothing the author enjoyed more at those RJA & HS summer shows, in the 1930s, than spending the morning going around the trade stands, where he collected the odd leaflet of vehicles, tractors, and machines to take home and read. While examining the Bristol tractor in 1935 he was invited to drive it, and leapt at the chance. He was not quite 10 years old, and still wearing short trousers! The engine was started and he climbed over the tracks and into the seat. He was given instructions how to operate the clutch, engage a gear, and steer the tractor. He was then asked to drive round in a circle, then stop. Having done that he was invited to be back at 4 o'clock to drive it again. That time a cameraman was there and the result is above. Little did he know that the cameraman was an Evening Post photographer! The next evening the photograph was in the local paper. Fame indeed; he was on the front page, much to his surprise and that of his startled parents!

A poster advertising the virtues of the Bristol tractor, at present displayed at the Hamptonne Museum.

The Ferguson tractor

A restored model A Ferguson tractor, serial no. 1147, manufactured in 1937; like so many early tractors, it has no rear wheel fenders.

Ferguson tractors were built for Harry Ferguson Ltd. by the David Brown Company of Huddersfield and are sometimes known as Ferguson Brown, to distinguish them from later production arrangements. The Coventry Climax four-cylinder petrol/paraffin engine develops 18 hp. The ignition is by magneto and is started by hand, with a crank handle. It is on steel wheels with spade lugs; there was no track-width adjustment. There is no PTO or pulley but it did have that great Ferguson innovation, a hydraulic three-point lift system and a pump, driven by the back axle. Because the back axle drove the hydraulic pump, it only operated the three-point lift and hitching system when the tractor was moving forwards or backwards. The David Brown Company was an old and well-established firm of gear cutters in Huddersfield. They supplied the gears for the famous pre-production 'black' tractor in 1933. They were also implement manufacturers and developed a trailed plough for the Bristol tractor. The Ferguson is painted battleship grey. The supplier was St. Helier Garages. (Displayed at the Steam Museum.)

Harry Ferguson's tractor marked a revolution in tractor design; it was to be copied within twenty-five years by every tractor maker worldwide.

The back of a Ferguson model A tractor, serial no. 108, showing the three-point hydraulic lift system that was to become so famous; the U frame and drawbar across the back is not a standard fitting. Ferguson supplied a drawbar that fitted between the two lower links for use when towing a trailer.

Ferguson tractor: the top link arm is missing, it being fitted between the lugs above the back axle. The hand screw adjustment, at the top of the lifting rod on the right, is for adjusting the level of the implement especially the plough. The supplier was St. Helier Garages at First Tower and the owner was Mr. P. M. Laurens, of St. Lawrence.

Born in 1884, Harry Ferguson was brought up on his father's farm in Northern Ireland under a regime of work on the farm when not at school. On leaving school at about the turn of the century he continued to work on the farm and leapt at the chance when his older brother invited him to join him as an apprentice in his garage in Belfast. To promote the business he took part in motor sport, winning various events with motorcycles and cars, and was the first person in the British Isles to build and fly his own aeroplane. In 1911 he established his own garage business. He ran the business meticulously, selling French Darracq and Vauxhall cars. In those days they were both high-quality and high-performance fast cars. The business was successful, as a result of his having gathered a skilled team of people to run his workshop, especially William Sands who later conducted most of the experimental work in the field for the new tractor. War was looming in 1914 and the loss of men and horses from the farms to the army put pressure on the authorities to promote the use of tractors. Harry Ferguson began to sell the Overtime tractor, known in the USA as the Waterloo Boy, one of the successful girder frame designs. It attracted the attention of the John Deere Company, who took it over. Harry Ferguson demonstrated it extensively in Ireland, but very often only to be laughed at, as farmers remained reluctant to change from horses.

The Government was under severe pressure to mechanise farming. However, farmers still resisted, in spite of being pressed to plough up more grassland for home-produced food. In the spring of 1917, Harry Ferguson was asked by the Government authorities in Ireland to undertake a tour of the whole country to demonstrate, inspect, and where possible improve the standard of tractor ploughing. William Sands accompanied Ferguson and they worked together on many different makes of ploughs and tractors as they toured the country. They discovered a variety of problems, largely to do with the hitching arrangements between the plough and tractor. Some were bad and some were dangerous!

Harry Ferguson resolved to design a plough and a system to attach the plough or implement to the tractor. His concept was a well-designed, integrated tractor and implement that must be a lightweight unit. The Ford Eros tractor was a converted model T Ford car, using a kit manufactured in Minnesota. The kits were fitted quickly, and were quickly removed to return the car to normal. They sold quite well, including in Britain. More important to Harry Ferguson, the tractor was light in weight and suitable for his design, of a two-furrow plough, with his system of hitching under the belly of the tractor, in front of the back axle. In that position, when the load came on as the plough entered the soil, it tended to pull the tractor down onto its wheels, increasing the traction; the plough has no need for wheels. The next step was to design such a plough for the Fordson F tractor. Ferguson's new Duplex plough had no wheels but two hitch points, one beneath the final drive-housing of the tractor and the second above it. The plough was close coupled, making both tractor and plough a single unit, and when ploughing, the weight of the plough was transferred to the back axle of the tractor, increasing the traction.

Back in Belfast developments were proceeding with a hydraulic system. Harry Ferguson was frustrated for a second time when, in 1929, production of the Fordson tractor ceased, and he began to think of building his own tractor. It would incorporate his ideas and a hydraulic system. This took time and resulted in the famous 'black' tractor being built in 1933. The rest of the story is well known. Harry Ferguson now had a light tractor with a simple three-point hitch. A small lever beside the driver's seat controlled the hydraulic lift, to raise the lower linkage arms, so raising the implement to be carried by the tractor. His tractors were highly successful but were slow to take off. A few of the first 100 Ferguson tractors produced were delivered to Jersey. The low serial numbers indicate just how quick some Jersey farmers were to see the suitability of this remarkable tractor to Island farming.

The Ferguson Brown tractor with a three-point linkage system was replaced by the Ford Ferguson, as a result of the famous 'handshake' agreement between Harry Ferguson and Henry Ford. Some of these tractors came to Jersey just before the Second World War and were sold by La Motte Street Garage, the Ford dealers. Post-war, this tractor was followed by the TE20, built at Coventry by Standard Motor Co. and sold in Jersey by St. Helier Garages at First Tower.

Returning from school, Mr. Maurice Le Quirot recalls passing Beau Désert and seeing a Ferguson Brown tractor for the first time. The author's father was driving it; he was particularly tall and had long legs. Maurice recalls seeing the driver's feet could reach the ground, from the tractor seat, to get on and off! He could not believe what he was seeing! Implements were specially manufactured to fit the three-point hitch and Ferguson offered a a range of them. Jersey blacksmiths quickly learnt how to get the geometry of the hitching tripod right, to make suitable implements. They were mostly ploughs and cultivators in those early days. The late Mr. Clem Le Breuilly excelled himself by being the first to produce a quarter-turn, one-way, mounted plough.

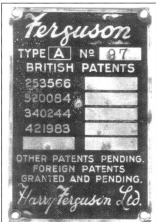

Mr. Donald Le Boutillier was aware of the significance of the low serial number on his Ferguson tractor and saved the serial plate when he disposed of the tractor.

Ferguson Dearborn or Ford-Ferguson Ford 9-N, serial no. PN8725, manufactured in 1938/9 (courtesy of the Steam Museum). The Ford-Ferguson has a side valve, petrol or petrol/TVO engine, with coil ignition producing 15-16 hp. It has a three-speed gearbox, giving a maximum speed of 6 mph. It was one of the first tractors to have a battery and self-starter. All four wheels have pneumatic tyres. The tractor, of course, has the three-point hydraulic lift and a 540-rpm splined PTO shaft. The pump for the hydraulic lift uses the transmission oil and is mounted in the bottom of the gearbox and driven off the input shaft to the gearbox. Whenever the engine runs, the hydraulic three-point linkage could be raised and lowered. A small lever, on the left side of the gearbox, engages or disengages the hydraulic pump and also puts the PTO shaft in or out of gear. A pulley attachment can be fitted over the PTO spline. The tractor has fixed foot rests and two foot pedals, one on each side, to operate the independent rear wheel brakes. All four wheels could be adjusted for track width. The front wheels are extended by extending the axle and the back wheels by altering the wheel rim position, on the central wheel disc. The local supplier was La Motte Street Garage, the Ford dealers.

View of the back of the Ford-Ferguson; unfortunately the three-point lift is not complete: the right lift rod and top link are missing and the PTO cover is also missing.

The Ford-Ferguson or Ferguson-Dearborn on pneumatic tyres has a battery and self-starter. The live lift pump and PTO marked a significant step forward for the Ferguson tractor. The PTO cover has been removed to reveal the splined PTO shaft.

In this back view the tractor is not complete; as in the model A, above, the top link rod is missing, the left-hand lift rod between the short lift arm and the lower link is also missing, and the restraining chain is detached. This link rod is adjustable for length, with a crank handle, at the top and a small gearbox as on the Ferguson Brown illustrated above. The splined PTO is exposed; it would normally have a threaded cap screwed on to cover it when not in use.

Henry Ford was a gentleman of the old school and would not have broken the famous handshake agreement. However, the next generation did not feel obliged to stick with an agreement to which they had not been a party. The agreement was perhaps rather lacking in detail. After the Second World War, when the new management wanted to build their own Ford tractor, they continued to make them with the Ferguson system, contrary to the verbal agreement. Harry Ferguson sued Ford for using his patents concerning the hydraulic system and in particular the draught-control system. Ford were producing and selling tractors through their dealerships and cutting out Ferguson. The case went to court and went on for several years, on both sides of the Atlantic, costing millions. While Ford lost the use of the patent following an agreement settled out of court, Ferguson lost financially. As we shall see, Ford engineers eventually developed a successful system of their own.

Allis Chalmers

Harry Ferguson was not alone in being concerned with lightweight tractors but he dealt with the problem in a systematic manner, having the hydraulic three-point lift. Below is another example of a light tractor, the Allis Chalmers model B.

Allis-Chalmers model B light rowcrop tractor, manufactured in 1938.
The Allis-Chalmers B has a four-cylinder petrol/TVO engine with ignition by magneto; it develops 19 hp. It is on pneumatic tyres and has a 540-rpm PTO, and a pulley is an option for fitting over the splined PTO. Painted in Allis Chalmers orange. The supplier was Le Cappelain, St. Peter's Iron Works, and the owner Mr. Lyndon Bichard. It is displayed here at the Steam Museum, Trinity.

Nothing is ever quite as new as you may think and not all ideas catch on at once!

In 1903 a tractor with a power-driven cultivator with vertical rotating tines was working experimentally.

In 1906 a tractor with a power take-off (PTO) was driving a binder.

In 1917 a tractor with a mechanical rear lift operated with a four-furrow plough.

In 1920 a tractor with a four-cylinder engine had sixteen overhead valves.

Finally, one that did catch on quickly: in 1932 an Allis Chalmers tractor in the USA was used to experiment with low-pressure aircraft tyres – and we know the result.

The resistance of farmers to buy tractors before and after the First World War produced some interesting arguments and stories.

Against the tractor:

Tractors compress the soil, ruining its texture and productive capacity.

A tractor does not produce a foal each year!

In favour of tractors:

A horse requires a minimum of 6 acres or 12 vergées of land to feed for one year.

A horse is expensive in time and labour when it is not working as it has to be housed and bedded, fed and watered, and groomed every day all the year. A tractor cost nothing when idle.

The big plough needs six horses and two men, a tractor with a tractor plough needs only one man and ploughs the same area in less than half the time.

At a demonstration held in the Midlands before the First World War, an enterprising tractor manufacturer entertained the visiting public by harvesting a ripe crop of wheat reaped with a tractor and binder. The same tractor was then coupled to a threshing machine and threshed the newly harvested wheat. The grain was milled in a mill, driven by the same tractor, and a baker, using a field oven, baked bread with the flour in the afternoon. Meanwhile the tractor ploughed in the stubble and, with a corn drill, proceeded to drill in the next year's crop. Then they celebrated their day's work in a marquee with a meal, eating the bread baked by the baker from wheat harvested that morning.

The economics of neighbours working together was not as simple as it may seem at first. The sharing of horses with neighbours, for ploughing with the big plough, was a necessity before tractors. There was a financial saving, as capital was invested in only one big plough, shared between the participating farmers, who provided the horses. If they each buy a tractor, they will each need a plough.

The problem with the Ferguson tractor was that it needed a new set of implements, to fit the three-point linkage mounting system, which added to the expense of changing over from trailed implements to mounted implements. Many local farmers ordered implements from their blacksmith, asking them to make a single-furrow deep-digger plough, a twin-furrow breezing plough, and a C-spring-tine cultivator, with a star roller on the back to crumble the lumps and level off. The author's father and uncles and some neighbours had their implements made by Jack Marett in his forge at Five Oaks, where the Five Oaks pub is today. It was a very busy forge in its day, employing several blacksmiths.

The big advantage when the new TE20 on pneumatic tyres came along was the convenience. It made so many operations so much quicker. A tractor and trailer on pneumatic tyres could travel quicker over the roads, around the farm, and over the fields than a horse and van, or horse and box cart or a tractor on steel wheels. The author recalls his father getting on the new TE20 simply to drive to the other end of the farm to go and see the state of the crops; previously he would have walked!

10 Tractors after 1945

Ferguson

The post-Second World War years were exciting times in the farm machinery world: the release and relief from thinking about the 'war effort' to thinking of more useful things, and in Jersey the knowledge that the German Occupation was over. Engineers were coming forward with so many new ideas. The chief difference between pre- and post-war tractors was that the tractor was no longer a slow-moving simple tug on steel wheels, to which an implement was attached by a drawbar or chain and pin, to the jaw of the tractor drawbar. We began to see the change in the 1930s, with mid-mounted rowcrop implements and Harry Ferguson's hydraulically operated, three-point linkage, in which the implement became an integral part of the tractor. This was quickly followed by the power take-off, the 'PTO', a splined shaft behind the back axle of the tractor. It would provide power to drive the machinery of the implement attached to the tractor, such as harvesting machines. At the same time a hydraulic connection on the tractor was provided, to operate an external ram or rams, which led to the introduction of the front loader and the tipping trailer and other machines.

Most of the leading British tractor manufacturers were offering the hydraulic three-point lift and PTO either as standard, as on the Ferguson TE20 and the David Brown VAK, or as an option, as on the Fordson Major, a tractor considered to be too big for Jersey. In the 1950s and early 1960s Ferguson, Ford, David Brown, and later Nuffield were supreme and were exported worldwide. British tractors and agricultural machinery combined were among the first five high export earners in the UK, on one or two occasions in the 1950s beating the aircraft industry. New farm machinery and equipment was being designed and coming onto the market. The author enjoyed being a part of it and experienced driving a new Ferguson TE20 tractor, ordered by his father from Jones's Garage at Five Oaks for the farm. The old Ferguson Brown went to a new owner. The new tractor was on rubber tyres and had a pressed steel bonnet over the engine. It was started with an electric starter and had fenders over the rear wheels. It was more like driving a car than a tractor on steel wheels!

The author driving the new Ferguson TE20 tractor in 1947.
Harry Ferguson's own design of hydraulic pump is mounted on the floor of the transmission casing, driven by a shaft that also drives the PTO. The hydraulic control valve, with a control lever to the right of the tractor seat, raises and lowers the three-point hitch and sets the depth of work. It was possible to tap the hydraulic system to operate external rams, using an external control valve connected to a take-off point under the seat. Standard Motor Co. manufactured the tractor for Harry Ferguson; production started at Banner Lane, Coventry, in the last few weeks of 1946 and was an immediate success. At first, the Continental engine was fitted, switching later to the Standard engine (also fitted to the Standard Vanguard car). The differences between it and the Ferguson Dearborn were minor, an overhead valve engine and a one-piece bonnet or engine cowl, hinged just above the front axle, opening forward to reveal the engine and fuel tank. The highly successful Ferguson TE20 remained with little change except for TVO and diesel engine options until Harry Ferguson merged his business with Massey Harris of Canada in 1953.

An elderly Ferguson TE20 orchard tractor built to a narrow specification.
Both front and rear axles are shorter than standard; the rest of the tractor is standard. The serial number plate is missing but this model was manufactured between 1949 and 1953. The tractor belonged to Mr. Vint of Stonewall, who moved his apple-growing business from Worcestershire to Jersey in the early 1950s.

Ferguson tractor fitted with a Perkins P3 diesel engine, as indicated by the Perkins logo on the radiator grill (Steam Museum collection).
The Perkins P3 diesel engine is a three-cylinder 27-hp engine; it is taller than the Ferguson petrol/TVO engine. To convert the TE20 to fit the taller engine necessitated some modification, involving raising the fuel tank and the bonnet, which was the usual procedure. However, this one was converted locally, by Don Pallot, at the Central Motor Works. He modified the fuel tank to accommodate the taller engine, which enabled the bonnet to remain at the normal height. It was a much neater arrangement.

Mr. Pallot imported a number of second-hand Ferguson TE20 tractors, probably bought at the Cambridge second-hand tractor auctions. The sales always attracted many farmers looking for a bargain. The above tractor was originally manufactured early in 1948 and was one of ten to be imported second hand and modified, at the Central Motor Works. This tractor was further modified, having a Ferguson reduction gearbox attached to the original gearbox. This modification slightly lengthened the tractor by 4.75 in. (12 cm) but enabled it to make use of the extra power of the P3, to operate a Howard Rotavator. The tractor was supplied to the late Mr. James Purvis. It is at present displayed at the Steam Museum. Howard also offered a similar modification for fitting within the gearbox without altering the length. An additional control lever was fitted to a side cover on the right-hand side of the seat.

The P3 conversions were quite popular among farmers, both here and in the UK, giving their TE20 tractor a new lease of life. The Perkins P3 was a popular diesel engine. It was installed in many London taxis and was eventually adapted by Ford Motor Company, for the Ford Dexta, and by Massey Ferguson, for the Ferguson 35. Perkins Engines at Peterborough were eventually taken over by Massey Ferguson Ltd.

Ferguson TEF diesel tractor, serial no. TEF 461729, manufactured during the period of amalgamation of Massey Harris and Harry Ferguson Ltd., 1953-4.

The Ferguson TEF has a four-cylinder 18-hp compression ignition diesel engine with CAV pneumatic governor. Extra battery capacity is necessary for a more powerful starter motor, needed to push the engine over against the high compression. The batteries are carried above the back axle and this tractor is fitted with lights. The rest of the equipment remains the same as the earlier TE20 tractor. The supplier was St. Helier Garages at First Tower. The tractor is displayed here at Samarès Manor on the Ploughing and Cider-Making Day, along with many Ferguson tractors, celebrating fifty years since Banner Lane started producing the 'little grey Fergie', as it is fondly known.

The 50th anniversary parade of little grey Fergies, at Samarès Manor, 1996, to celebrate fifty years of Ferguson tractor manufacture at Banner Lane, Coventry; at the far end, next to the loader, is a solitary original Ferguson-Brown from 1937—it is on steel wheels, just to remind us of how things were!

These M-F tractors were produced after the merger of Ferguson with Massey Harris to form Massey Ferguson: they have Massey's red bonnets and fenders, with Ferguson grey engines, transmission casings, and wheels. They are mostly M-F35 models, but with one M-F135 at the end, beside one of today's monsters.

This promotional advertising plate is mounted on the wall of a farm shed at Eversley, in St. Martin, Jersey.

(*right*) Massey Ferguson model MF35 was manufactured in 1954/5: it has a four-cylinder petrol engine with coil ignition, and is operating here with a Ritmic potato planter.
The Ferguson tractor underwent a model change after the merger to become the MF35. It was heavier and more powerful, designed to handle that other new and exciting post-war machine, the 'one-man' pick-up baler. The pick-up baler was the cause of much excitement when it first appeared in 1949.
The MF35 has the usual PTO and three-point hydraulic lift linkage, with a hydraulic tapping-off point. St. Helier Garage supplied the tractor to Mr. Percy Le Masurier, of La Pointe, St. Ouen.

It is interesting that in the mid-1950s a successful Jersey farmer chose to purchase a petrol engine tractor when diesel engines were rapidly increasing in popularity, but at that time very few farmers in Jersey had experience of diesel and TVO engines. The early MF35 tractors were painted Ferguson grey with gold-painted engines, which lasted for just about one year before the change to red. Before the amalgamation, Massey Harris tractors were always painted red.

This rear view of the MF35 illustrates the three-point linkage fitted with a drawbar and a trailer hitched to it with a jaw-type hitch; the top link is replaced by adjustable stabiliser struts, pinned in the top link position, above the back axle.
In the mid-1950s, tractors were fitted with a 'pick-up' hook, under the back axle of the tractor. The trailer has to be fitted with an appropriate pick-up ring to accommodate the hook. In the above picture the hook can just be seen. The trailer is an older one, having only a jaw and not yet modified with a ring for the pick-up hook. Later trailers were made with the drawbar having both a jaw and a ring, to deal with both systems. Under the trailer drawbar is a stand on which the trailer will rest, to hold the jaw clear of the ground to enable the tractor to be coupled. With the pick-up ring, the stand will hold the ring up for the pick-up hook: the tractor driver simply lowers the tractor hook and will back the tractor until the hook is under the ring, then pick up the hook, with the hydraulic system, and drive away with the trailer. The same arrangement is made on a number of trailed field machines, most notably in Jersey, on the potato harvester.

David Brown

Production of David Brown tractors began at a disused mill in Meltham in 1939, commencing with the VAK1, after the last Ferguson Brown tractor was dispatched. This followed Harry Ferguson's visit to Henry Ford, in America, to persuade Ford to build Ferguson tractors for the American market, and the famous handshake deal between Henry Ford and Harry Ferguson. Mr. David Brown had been pressing Harry Ferguson to make a larger and more powerful tractor. The David Brown company had been manufacturing agricultural implements for several years, producing a trailed plough for the Bristol tractor, among other things, before building the Ferguson tractor. Limited production of David Brown tractors continued during the war making a heavy version for the RAF to tow aircraft on the ground. Production resumed after the war in 1945, with the VAK 1A very similar to the VAK 1. The tractors were exported in large numbers to the USA. The best-known importer was the White Tractor Co. who produced their own range of very big tractors, painted white for the American market. They eventually acquired the David Brown tractor business in England.

The VAK 1 (Vehicle Agricultural Kerosene) had a four-cylinder petrol/kerosene engine, producing 30 hp, a four-speed gearbox, and a 540-rpm PTO. It has a three-point link hydraulic lift; the top link is fitted between two lugs at the top of the back axle casting. There is no draught control, or depth control; therefore a plough or cultivator needed depth control wheels with this tractor, with a loss of some weight transfer.

The VAK 1A was followed in 1947 by the Cropmaster. It was identified by a protective shield above the dash panel which extended down each side to the foot rest. Unlike other tractors it had a bench seat and backrest and it was wide enough for two people. The top link is fitted to the same shaft to which the lower link arms were fitted. To lift the three-point linkage, the shaft is rotated, taking the top link fixture with it. The engine was not quite central, being offset just a little to one side. In 1949 the Cropmaster was offered with a diesel engine and six-speed gearbox. Production ran to 1953, when there followed the models 25 and 30 and the larger Cropmaster 50 with a diesel engine. In 1958 the 850 and 950 were introduced. In 1965 the colour changed to chocolate brown and white, probably to satisfy importers in the USA.

The post-war years were, as said before in this story, an exciting time, with new ideas and machines, and some successes and some failures. Harry Ferguson's three-point hitching system was adopted by many British tractor manufacturers and the 'power take-off' or PTO, as it became known, was agreed internationally as a world standard at 540 rpm. Implement manufacturers had to

redesign their machines to make use of these systems. Another innovation, adopted by the tyre manufactures, was the open centre design of lugs or treads on tractor tyres. They obtained a better grip, because they were self-cleaning. A look at the tyres in the above pictures illustrates the point: the lugs overlap at the centre and do not quite meet the lug in front, leaving a small but effective gap.

A well-maintained David Brown model P25, serial no. AK 21197, manufactured in 1956; it has a four-cylinder, TVO engine with petrol-starting, developing 31 hp at 1,800 rpm, pneumatic tyres on all four wheels, and is painted David Brown red.
The David Brown P25 has a drawbar pull of 19 hp, a PTO, and a three-point lift system, unique to David Brown, with a traction control unit (TCU) similar to the Ferguson draught-control system. The TCU was introduced on David Brown tractors from 1952.

A quaint story has it that David Brown's father was not very keen on his son producing tractors; he was content with the business as it was. The David Brown Company had started in 1860, in Huddersfield, as a family business, cutting gears and producing gearboxes for industry. Tractor production was set up in a redundant mill in the town. When the first tractor was built, the workforce were so delighted they drove it to David Brown's house to show it to him!

Early customers to have a David Brown tractor in Jersey were Mr. C. Le Gallais, at Roselands, St. Saviour, and Mr. Anthoine, of Longueville, St. Saviour, who also had a David Brown one-way plough. It was like two ploughs, one casting furrows to the right, when lowered into the soil, and the second casting to the left. A simple locking device held the bodies in the raised position. They were supplied by the Jersey Farmers (Trading) Union Ltd., better known as the JF(T)U Ltd., who in those days were found on the Esplanade, at Olympia, near the Grand Hotel. They were general merchants to Island farmers, handling fertilisers, cattle feed, etc., and packing and exporting potatoes. The business was run by Mr. Frank Perrée until the late 1960s, when it changed hands and was relocated to Commercial Buildings, beside the harbour in St. Helier.

Massey Ferguson

In the ever-changing world of tractor design, Massey Ferguson introduced the MF FE35 X in the mid-1960s.

The MF FE35 X has a Perkins three-cylinder diesel engine, with a CAV rotary fuel pump supplying the injectors. The gearbox has a second gear lever to select the high range of gears or the low range known as a 'hi-lo', which, in effect, doubles the range of gears. Other innovations include a 540-rpm PTO with ground speed selection, in order to operate machinery at a particular speed, relative to the speed over the ground. The PTO is 'live' when the engine is running; a pulley attachment is an option. A lever at the side of the gearbox enables the driver to select the service he requires. The tractor has take-off points for external rams. The X denotes that the tractor has a differential lock. The hydraulic system also operates a pick-up hitch, for the pick-up ring on a trailer or towed harvester.

At about this time, Massey Ferguson introduced a Multi-Power system, with a switch on the control panel to enable the driver to select a higher or lower gear on the move, to suit the changing load on the tractor as it moves across a field with changing soil conditions. A field may have heavy clay at one end and a light soil at the other.

Ransomes MG

After the Second World War, Ransomes of Ipswich reviewed their equipment and revised their designs, including the MG tractor.

Ransomes MG5 tracklayer manufactured from 1948; it has a single-cylinder, air-cooled petrol engine and a hand lift.
The MG5 was a big improvement on the earlier MG2. It has a single-cylinder, 600-cc four-stroke petrol engine, developing 7 hp. The ignition is by magneto and the drawbar pull is 800 lb. It is steered with two levers, one per track. It has one forward gear and one reverse, a centrifugal clutch, and a speed of 2.25 mph. The track design by Roadless Traction Ltd. remains unchanged. The tracks are 6 in. wide, and the ground pressure is 5 lb/sq in. The track is adjustable to widths of 2 ft 4.5 in., 2 ft 7.5 in., and 2 ft 10.5 in. (72.5, 80, and 87.5 cm). The PTO is non-standard, running at 700 rpm. Various sizes of pulley are available, to operate on the PTO shaft. The hand-operated lift illustrated here was eventually replaced with a category '0' three-point linkage hydraulic lift, but the drawbar remains unchanged. All the MG tractors are painted Ransomes blue except the last model MG6, which was painted green. The local suppliers were La Motte Garage. Some of the options on the MG5 became standard on the MG6, such as the PTO shaft and clutch and the hydraulic three-point lift.

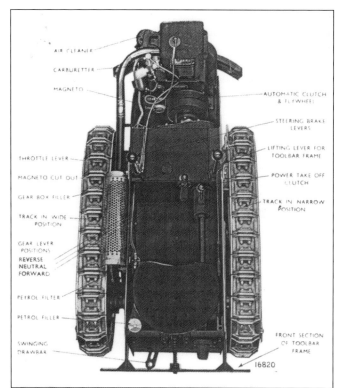

A plan view of the MG5 (courtesy of Ransomes Archives, University of Reading Rural History Centre). The MG 5 came into production in 1948. In 1953 the price was £305. The tractor was gradually improved: power increased to 7 hp, and a new gearbox with three forward gears and a reverse was fitted. A hydraulic lift was offered; an external hydraulic ram raised the lift arms with a PTO. A single-cylinder two-stroke diesel engine was also available. The MG6 incorporated most of the MG5 options as standard equipment. Drawbar pull increased to 800 lb. A diesel engine was offered as an option. A one-way plough was available, with lever-operated locks: while one body was in work, the other was locked up clear of the ground (a similar arrangement to the David Brown, referred to earlier). The MG6 was replaced by the MG40 before production ceased in 1966.

At their peak, Ransomes MG tractors were being manufactured at the rate of six tractors a week, on average. Five out of six were sold to vineyards in France and Germany, the remainder going to the home market and a few to other overseas markets.

Bristol

A small pre-war tractor that came back on the market after the war was the Bristol (see Chapter 9). The manufacturers abandoned the tiller steering in favour of the more common practice, on tracklayers, of two levers, one for each track. Roadless Traction continued to make the tracks, similar to the Ransomes MG.

Mr. Edwin Godel, who farmed at La Chasse in St. Mary, bought one second-hand for ploughing. Eventually Mr. Godel found it tiresome having to load the Bristol on a vehicle every time he wished to move it from one field to another, so he bought a Fordson Dexta in 1957. Meanwhile, before buying the Dexta, he purchased an OTA tractor, for road work and breezing (shallow ploughing). In the 1940s Don Pallot of the Central Motor Works became the Bristol tractor agent and imported several Bristol 20 tractors with the Austin engine.

The OTA

The OTA tractor is a small three-wheel tractor with a Ford 10-hp engine developing 17 bhp at 2,000 rpm; the OTA was manufactured by Oak Tree Appliances in Coventry in the late 1940s.
The OTA tractor had a Ford gearbox and the company made their own auxiliary gearbox to provide six forward gears. Transmission is by worm and wheel, to the back axle, and a belt-driven hydraulic pump to operate the three-point linkage, but without depth or draught control. At a later date, in a design change, the tractor was fitted with two front wheels. In 1955 Rootes Group took over the last producer, Singer Motors, and production ceased. St. Mary's Garage were the local suppliers.

Allis Chalmers

Allis-Chalmers model B rowcrop tractor manufactured in 1954. The illustrations above show a view of the lift linkage and PTO.

The model B tractor has a four-cylinder TVO engine with coil ignition developing 19 hp. Wheels are all adjustable for track width. The exposed PTO shaft is standard, running at 540 rpm, with an optional pulley. The three-point link hydraulic lift is also an option and was not available on the original pre-war tractor. All Allis-Chalmers tractors are painted orange. The tractor allows the driver to have an excellent view of the crop for cultivation between the rows. The first owner was Mr. Fiott, of La Moye and it was supplied by Le Cappelain, St. Peter's Iron Works. The present owner, Mr. Peter Hamon, of Highlands, at La Haule, is maintaining it in beautiful condition. He purchased it for cutting broccoli because of its high clearance.

(left) Allis-Chalmers model D 272 general-purpose tractor manufactured in 1955 in Milwaukee, USA; serial no. 25861.

The D272 has a Perkins P3 three-cylinder diesel engine developing 18-20 hp. All the wheels are adjustable for track width. It has a three-point hydraulic lift linkage bolted onto the back. The original owner was Mr. Le Moine, of St. Saviour, and the supplier was Le Cappelain, St. Peter's Iron Works. It is displayed at the Steam Museum.

Fordson

In the post-war years in Jersey there was very little competition for the Ferguson, which suited the Island's farming needs so adequately. The only exception was the David Brown. The other popular tractors in the UK were too big for Jersey, such as the 'New' Fordson Major and, a little later, the Nuffield. Following the court case over the Ferguson patents, Ford developed a design of tractor to compete directly with the Ferguson, with draught control and depth control. The author was with Ransomes of Ipswich during the late stages of the development, working in the R&D department. One of the development tractors was sent to Ransomes, to design a new range of Ford-Ransomes implements. Most of the implements had been developed many years before, for use with the Ferguson tractor, and needed very little attention if any, except for two reversible ploughs, a single-furrow digger plough and a two-furrow semi-digger plough. The new design required the ploughs to be reversed and locked hydraulically, which proved to be quite a challenge at the time. Eventually the problems were solved and the two-furrow and single-furrow reversibles were successful. The author bought a single-furrow version in 1959 for use on the family farm in Jersey.

The Fordson Dexta model 95-7-E was the Ford response to the Ferguson TE20; it went into production in 1957. This one is serial no. 448449, manufactured in 1959.

The Dexta 95-7-E has a three-cylinder, indirect injection diesel engine producing 32 hp at 2,200 rpm. A Perkins P3 engine was fitted at first, and then Ford's own three-cylinder engine. The wheels are adjustable for width. The standard width is at 52 in. (132 cm) centres and the narrowest setting at 48 in. (122 cm), all similar to the TE20. The PTO is at the standard 540 rpm and a pulley to fit over the PTO is an option. The hydraulic system operates the category 2 three-point hitch, with draught control and depth control. It has a take-off point for external rams. Because the draught and depth control system operated on the pressure side of the pump, as opposed to the Ferguson TE20 system, it gave the Ford certain advantages. It had a faster response, and one could actually see it and sometimes feel it operating through the top link, when ploughing deep in dry conditions. This feature helped the plough to maintain the set depth.

Both the Fordson Dexta and the Major were painted Empire-blue. This tractor was originally supplied to the first owner by La Motte Street Garage where Mr. Gouédard once worked and serviced Dexta tractors. He eventually acquired the tractor and restored it, at Samarès Garage, where he went into business as the proprietor. He runs the business with the help of his son. Both of them are enthusiastic restorers of tractors and stationary engines, etc., exhibiting their work at summer shows at the Steam Museum and Samarès Manor.

This rear view of the Dexta illustrates how things had moved on by 1959 since the early TE20 in the late 1940s; here it is fitted with a fork lift.

The lift linkage is basically identical to the Ferguson; an exception is the adjustable top link and the 'pick-up hitch' linkage for raising the trailer hook that is fitted under the back axle. There are 'outside' stabiliser bars, for attaching certain rear-mounted tools such as this fork lift, and a strong guard over the PTO shaft.

Ford Super Dexta, serial no. 11116, manufactured in 1962. The three-cylinder diesel engine develops 44.4 bhp at 2450 rpm; otherwise the tractor is the same as the Dexta.

It is operating here with a Le Cappelain potato planter, with the wheels set at the maximum track width at 72 in. (183 cm) centres. The owner of the Super Dexta is Mr. Brian Ahier, of Surguy Farm, St. Brelade, who purchased the tractor on 20 October 1962 at a price of £610. The supplier was La Motte Street Garage at Grouville.

International

A well-used International B275 tractor manufactured in 1963; it has a four-cylinder, direct-injection, diesel engine and a two-speed PTO running at 540 rpm and 1,000 rpm.

The B275 has a pulley option and the wheels have track-width adjustment, and like all these light tractors, it has independent rear wheel brakes. The letter B indicates it was made in Britain. It is painted International Harvester (IH) red. The first of these small IH tractors produced in 1958 had a simple hydraulic lift system, to operate the three-point linkage to raise and lower only, with a mechanical adjustable stop to hold the implement at a particular height, to control depth for ploughing. It provides some weight transfer. The tractor is owned by Mr. Le Cornu, at Six Roads, and the supplier was L. C. Pallot, Central Motor Works. It is pictured here on the Steam Museum Threshing Day.

When this tractor first appeared in 1958/9 it was to compete with the Ford Dexta and Massey-Ferguson 35. It was very close to its competitors but, without a depth- and draught-control system, it was never quite equal. The author first ploughed with one with a Ransomes TS54 two-furrow mounted plough with a depth wheel on the Cotswolds in the autumn of 1958, where it performed well in stony soil. The PTO complies with the then new standard of two speeds, one at 540 rpm and the second at a new speed of 1,000 rpm. Later models were given a more sophisticated hydraulic control system, with a pick-up hook for trailers and a hydraulic take-off point for external rams.

View of the back reveals the pick-up hitch; note the blue stand under the trailer's drawbar to hold the hitch ring off the ground, when lowered

David Brown

David Brown model 780 manufac
tured after 1965; engine no.
355011/1022.

The 780 is a mix of the 770 and the 880,
having the 880 four-cylinder diesel
engine and the 770 gearbox. Three
gears have the 'selectamatic' hi-lo gear
selector and an extra gear shift for three
creep gears, giving a total of twelve
gears. It has a live-drive PTO8 at 540
rpm and 1,000 rpm. (Live drive simply
indicates that the PTO ran independently of the gearbox, having its own
clutch in effect.) There is a pulley option
to fit over the PTO shaft. The hydraulic
pump is live, driving a high-capacity 22-
gallon-per-minute (gpm) pump. It has a
position control on the three-point link
lift, to control depth of work. The tractor
has three mounting pads each side, for
centre-mounted implements.

Most manufacturers arranged that the first movement of the clutch pedal disengages the gears in the
gearbox, and depressing the clutch pedal further disengages the PTO. Live hydraulics was another system
that was even simpler; whenever the engine is running, the hydraulic pump is also running, having no clutch,
and cannot be disengaged. Transmissions and gearboxes were getting more sophisticated, becoming semi-
automatic, and went under a variety of different names according to the manufacturer's particular system. Tyre
sizes were getting bigger and wider, such as 12.4-28 rear tyres to cope with the increasing power and torque.
David Brown colours changed, from all-red to chocolate on the engine and gearbox and a white bonnet and
wings to suit the big and busy American market. Mr. George Le Gros, of Le Recompense, St. Lawrence, was
the owner of the tractor illustrated and the JF(T)U Ltd. was the supplier. At present owned by Mr. David Seale,
an enthusiast in Trinity. Here it is driving an International pick-up baler, baling straw from a threshing machine,
at Samarès Manor on the Threshing Day Show.

Here the David Brown
780 is hitched up to a
pick-up baler and the
PTO is coupled up to
drive it; the lower link
arms and outside
stabilisers can be seen.

Ford

In 1968 Ford dropped the names Dexta and Major, moving to four-numeral model numbers beginning with the Ford Model 2000.

Ford model 2000 tractor, serial no. B857840, engine no. SB 31848B; it has a three-cylinder diesel engine developing 40 bhp and a PTO running at 540 rpm, and 12.4-28 tyres. Manufactured in 1968.

The hydraulic lift system has position and draught control, a pick-up hitch and hydraulic coupling points for connection to external rams. Painted Ford Empire blue with grey wheels and fenders, the owner is Mr. Brian Ahier and the supplier was La Motte Street Garage. The trailer on the pick-up hitch is a Ford-Ransome (F-R) trailer. It has a hydraulic tipping ram connected to the tractor's hydraulic system and a connection to the tractor's electrical system, for road work. It is seen here at the Steam Museum Threshing Day in 1999.

This view of the back of the Ford 2000 illustrates the hook of the pick-up hitch in the ring of the trailer drawbar and the adjustable stand, complete with screwing handle on the F-R trailer.

Zetor

In the 1960s the East European countries in the Communist bloc were entering into agreements with manufacturers in the West, resulting in those countries purchasing partly assembled tractors. Others purchased the tooling of tractors that were no longer being manufactured. This practice gave those countries some experience in manufacturing tractors. In due course, instead of variations of some International tractors, for example, they were beginning to make their own designs and exporting them to the West. An example is the Zetor tractor, which was manufactured in Communist Czechoslovakia and was heavily subsidised, consequently being cheaper than tractors produced in the West. They tended to be a bit rough-and-ready and not thoroughly reliable at first, but gradually they improved. In price-conscious areas of England, such as the farmers in the south-west of England and Wales, they began to find a market.

In Jersey, early in the 1970s, Don Pallot of L. C. Pallot and Sons became agent for Zetor and found them to be dependable. The subsidised price made them popular and a fair number of them were sold.

Zetor model Zetormatic four-wheel drive 5544, serial no. 27255, manufactured in 1972.
The Zetormatic has a four-cylinder diesel engine developing 55 bhp. The serial number is 5501/28298 and it was supplied by Halse of Honiton. They had the usual equipment, including a 540-rpm PTO, the three-point hitch system, with a pick-up hook for a trailer and a hydraulic coupling point for an external ram. The fuel injection pumps are enormous compared to the Simms or CAV. Other equipment includes power steering, differential lock, foot throttle for road use and a sprung seat. They were painted Zetor orange/red. Smaller models competed with Ferguson and Dexta tractors. The first owner was Mr. Gordon Le Marquand, of St. Martin, and it is at present owned by Mr. Peter Hamon, who uses it at Highlands, La Haule Hill.

BMC and Leyland

The Leyland tractors were originally Nuffield tractors and became BMC; later still they were Leyland, and lastly Marshall, before they disappeared. The BMC mini was a smaller version of the original Nuffield tractor. It was manufactured after the amalgamation of the British motor industry in the 1960s by Donald Stokes, of Leyland. He went around the country mopping up many of the old British motor vehicle manufacturers. The BMC mini had a 15-hp engine and a simple hydraulic lift system, only able to lift and drop, with a movable peg to adjust the depth of work. An early red one was used successfully at Beauvoir, a private house in St. Saviour. It was used for vegetable-growing and gardening. When it became the Leyland 154 it was much more powerful.

Leyland model 154 tractor, serial no. 54D/303504, previously the 15-hp BMC mini.
The model 154, serial no. 54D/303504/11242, was more powerful, with a four-cylinder 25 hp diesel engine. The three-point linkage and hydraulic lift was unchanged, just a simple lift and drop as before. The PTO runs at 540 rpm and the wheels have the usual track adjustment, like the TE20 and Dexta, with the standard setting at 52 in. (132 cm) centres, on 14 x 24 tyres. The first owner was Mr. Gordon Le Marquand, of St. Martin, and later it was owned by Mr. Peter Hamon who uses it at Highlands, La Haule Hill. Some of these were supplied by Le Cappelain, St. Peter's Iron Works, Cleveland Garage, at Havre des Pas, and Halse of Honiton. This Leyland is now part of the collection of Mr. Charles Le Couteur, at Westlands, St. Peter. Mr. Le Couteur's collection includes some of the less well-known tractors to have come to Jersey farms, such as the above and those which follow.

Massey Ferguson Landini

The Massey Ferguson Landini is a conversion produced in Italy using an MF35 skid unit supplied on a pallet without wheels and front axle from the UK.

Full track conversions were made by various manufacturers. All tracklayers have a light ground pressure per square inch as well as good traction. They are expensive to maintain when the tracks and running gear begin to wear. In those parts of England where tracklayers or crawlers are used extensively, such as the east of England and the heavy clay soils in the Midlands, there are engineering businesses which specialise in this work. Expensive equipment is necessary to carry out the repairs. A horizontal press is needed to push out the track pins and bushes; if done in time, the bushes can be pushed out, turned 180 degrees, and pushed back in to extend their life. If beyond that state of wear, then the track has to be completely dismantled. If the rails on each shoe are worn, then by welding a layer of metal onto each rail, using a special hard welding rod, and then grinding to shape, they can be restored. The sprockets can be built up in the same way, to restore them.

This tracklaying tractor is a conversion by Landini of Italy based on the Massey Ferguson model MF 134, serial no. 3193843, manufactured in 1978; it is an MF35 with a Perkins P3 diesel engine no. AD 3.152 (1962-79) The MF/Landini tractor's tracks and running gear have four track rollers and 15 in. (38 cm) wide track plates; clutch and brake steering are all Landini equipment. It has the usual Ferguson category 2 three-point linkage and a swinging drawbar and a 540-rpm PTO. Painted M-F red and grey colours. Massey Ferguson had a 71% shareholding for a time in Landini, disposing of their interest in 1990.
The tracks on the Landini illustrated are in need of adjustment; running them slack promotes wear. The adjustment is quick and simple: the front idler is pushed forward by a built-in screw adjustment. On this tractor it is sensibly protected by a cover. This Landini was previously owned by Mr. Ivor Barret, of Broughton Lodge, St. Mary, who purchased the tractor in 1986 for £3,000 from an estate in Warwickshire, where it had been used in forestry. Mr. Barrett used it with a modified Kuxman potato digger. The machine had to be offset to enable the tracks to remain clear of the crop while lifting potatoes. It was operated only while climbing up a 7-vergée côtil at Grève de Lecq, St. Mary. Apparently it performed well. Two or three of these MF/Landini tracklayers were purchased by Jersey farmers. It is now part of Mr. Le Couteur's collection at Westlands.

A number of manufacturers made kits to convert Ferguson tractors into half-tracks, such as the famous ones which took Sir Edmund Hillary to the South Pole.

Fordson

Fordson Major E 27N, manufactured from 1945 to 1952; this one has a Perkins P6 six-cylinder diesel engine developing 39 bhp and a pulley driven off the gearbox, and is being used here to drive a threshing machine.

The E 27N has 540-rpm PTO. The hydraulic three-point hitch and lift was an option and they were painted navy blue. This tractor was imported by Aviation Jersey for industrial use but the rear tyres have agricultural open treads, indicating an agricultural origin. It is operating here to drive the threshing machine at Samarès Manor on the Threshing Day. The E 27N tractors were fitted with the six-cylinder Perkins engine. A four-cylinder Perkins engine was tried but Ford preferred the performance with the six cylinders. The Perkins engine was included in the original equipment by Ford Motor Co., but Ford tractor dealers used them as replacement engines for the TVO engine. The regular E 27N was built around the pre-war Standard Fordson N, with the same petrol/TVO engine, the same front wheels but a new axle which raised the front; and the gearbox and back axle were totally different (doing away with the worm and wheel drive of the old Fordson). It had bigger rear wheels, making it a bigger tractor. It was unusual as it had a wet clutch running in oil. It was a stop-gap tractor, while the New Fordson Major was designed and developed.

The problem for the farmer in England in the early post-war years was that, to take advantage of the three-point lift or mounted system, he had to purchase a range of new implements to fit the mounted system. Many would have purchased new trailed implements during the war years, when they were forced by their County War Agricultural Executive Committees to switch to arable farming, to increase home food production in the war effort. They would therefore be reluctant to buy more new implements quite so soon. The situation in Jersey was quite different: the Fordson Major was too big for the Island, the smaller Ferguson and David Brown tractors were more suitable, and after years of Occupation and the opening of the UK market to Jersey farm produce, there was a need by Jersey farmers to re-equip, as many were still using the Jersey big plough. The following tractor is of a much later period as we start the new millennium!

Morrish

The Morrish tractor is a very recent introduction to Jersey and is rather outside the scope of this history, but it is an indicator of the trend for the future.

Morrish tracklayer model G 1703, manufactured in 1996 at Tiverton in Devon; the driver is Mr. Vautier

Morrish tractors have a three-cylinder Kubota diesel engine developing 30 hp. The rubber tracks are set at 60 in. (152 cm). Power is transmitted to the tracks by hydraulic pump and motors, one for each track, and steering is by a small lever-controlled valve. Apart from driving the tracks, the hydraulic system operates the rams to raise and lower front- and rear-mounted implements. This lightweight tractor is ideal for potato planting, the long wide tracks reducing the pounds-per-square-inch ground pressure on the soil. The front-mounted implement has four splitting bankers for 'opening up', for planting potatoes. The rear implement with angled discs will ridge the soil covering the potatoes. The tractor is owned by Vautier Bros., of Ville Machon, and was supplied by E. Le Feuvre.

Over the past fifty years a number of small tractors have come on the market, stayed awhile, and disappeared. Today's tractors are vastly different from those of the exciting 1950s and early 1960s, when there was still a feeling of pioneering new ideas. Examples are Harry Ferguson's three-point linkage, draught and depth control systems, the power take-off or PTO, and the first diesel-engined tractors, particularly in the light tractors; then four-wheel drive, etc. John Deere developed a form of depth and draught control for heavy and long multifurrow ploughs, using the bottom links rather than the top link. Today, with all those early technical problems solved, the tractors are simply bigger and heavier; almost all are four-wheel drive. Engines are much more powerful; the cabs are more sophisticated, with adjustable armchair seats, air conditioning, heaters, radio and two-way radios, fingertip control for every conceivable operation, and more luxurious and expensive than many modern cars. Sadly the fun and excitement of those early post-war pioneering years have gone.

The new technology of the Morrish tracklayer is a reminder of those earlier days.

11 Soil-Engaging Tractor Implements

Ploughs

Early in the twentieth century when tractors and tractor ploughs were produced, both Oliver and International Harvester in the USA and Ransomes in the UK manufactured twin-furrow breezing ploughs and single-furrow deep-digger ploughs equipped with self-lifts that were operated from the tractor seat. According to Mr. Charles Perchard, of Rozel, they were quite a revolution at the time because there were no handles, meaning there was no need for a man to walk behind the plough. When tractors first arrived in the Island many farmers were reluctant to use a tractor plough; they continued to use their old horse-drawn ploughs, simply hitching them to the tractor. The Jersey big plough was not altered for use with a tractor; instead a chain from the plough was simply coupled to the tractor draw-hitch.

The tractor driver replaced the man who previously drove the horses, but a ploughman was still necessary at the handles; there was no saving of labour in the field. The tractor was simply more convenient: it was no longer necessary to be up early to feed and water the horses before breakfast. It reduced the dependence on neighbours getting together, to make up a team of four or six horses, in order to plough. On a farm without cows, it was not necessary to set aside several vergées of grassland to provide hay and an area to exercise and graze the horse when it was not in use for a period. However, there were not many such farms; most farmers still favoured mixed farming.

In due course some farmers did buy tractor ploughs, but others were so attached to *la grande tchéthue*, the big plough, that even after the Second World War, over twenty-five years after the first tractors arrived in the Island, and eight years after the first Ferguson, with all the convenience of the hydraulic lift, they continued to order *la grande tchéthue* from their blacksmith.

Ploughing in the years before and after the Second World War, up to the 1960s, Jersey farmers made use of every square inch of their valuable soil. Two men were employed, one at each end of the field, each with a spade, to dig the two furrow ends. They dug the first three or four feet of the furrow, so that the plough body was dropped into the opened furrow, to start work on each furrow at full depth. Otherwise, if the plough were simply dropped on the ground and drawn forward, it would travel three or four feet before reaching full depth. Today, with two-, three-, and four-furrow reversible ploughs, digging the ends would be impossible, so the headland is ploughed at right angles to the furrow ends. The result is a rather untidy mess, which our fathers would have deplored, but the process is followed by a powered cultivator, driven by the tractor power take-off, to create a suitable tilth over the whole field, leaving little trace of the rather untidy furrow ends.

In 1949 the author was working on a farm in England while organising an ex-serviceman's grant to study agriculture and agricultural engineering. Ploughing with a Ransomes RSLD twin-furrow trailed tractor plough gave him tremendous satisfaction; it would turn two perfect furrows and the cord for the lift was easy to use.

An agricultural contractor, Mr. Eddie Buesnel, at the wheel of his International Junior tractor, ploughing with a Jersey horse plough at La Hougue Farm for Mr. Perchard in 1928 (courtesy of Donald Le Boutillier).

Tractor ploughs

The tractor plough self-lift consisted of a trip-lever with a rope attached to it, and the rope's loose end went to the seat of the tractor. The rope was pulled first, to release the lift at the start of the furrow, to drop the plough body into the soil, and then at the other end of the field a sustained pull on the rope pulled the lever forward, which caused the lift to engage. It was usually a quadrant, with gear teeth, which engaged with a gearwheel on the landwheel axle of the plough. As the plough moved forward, the gearing rotated the cranked wheel axle, causing the plough to lift until a catch was engaged. A tractor driver could drive his tractor and operate the plough from the tractor seat, which was labour saving compared to ploughing with a tractor and a horse-drawn plough.

An International single-furrow, digger-type tractor plough manufactured in the 1930s; it has been beautifully restored, complete with a new trip-cord for the lift.

Both International and Ransomes manufactured totally enclosed lifts on their later trailed implements. They were operated the same way, by pulling on a cord tied to the lift lever. This International single-furrow, tractor-trailed digger plough has a bigger-diameter landwheel to improve the traction to operate the lift. It has a 13 in. (33 cm) wide share which will plough a 14 in. (35.5 cm) wide furrow, 12 in. (30.5 cm) deep. Each wheel on the International has its own height adjustment for depth of work, with long levers within reach of the tractor driver, and operating on notched quadrants. Just inside the landwheel on the right is the enclosed lift mechanism, partly hidden by the wheel rim; the operating lever with trip-cord is just above it. The cranked handle, above the drawbar, will adjust the drawbar angle horizontally, to alter the width of furrow. The drawbar also has a spring release device, to release the drawbar in the event of the share striking a tree root or rock. It has a large skimmer and no disc coulter. The lugs or spuds are missing from the rim of the wheel; without them the wheel would simply slide over the ground, rather than lift the plough. The plough belonged to Mr. Donald Becquet, La Maîtrerie, St. Martin. He believes his father may have purchased the plough, second-hand, at a summer show. He used it with a Fordson, probably a model N tractor. It is at present in the collection of Mr. Charles Le Couteur, of Westlands, St. Peter, who restored it.

Ransomes Unitrac single-furrow tractor plough with UN-type deep-digger body; the lever for operating the self-lift can be seen above the landside wheel. At the top on the left is a subsoiling tine which can be fitted to the plough.

A Ransomes UN body will turn a 16 in. (40.6 cm) wide furrow at 14 in. (35.5 cm) deep. The two crank handle screws will set the depth of work and level the plough: one screw handle operates on one wheel and the other operates the other wheel. It is an excellent plough for burying farmyard manure, top growth such as turf, or mustard, grown as a green manure. The drawbar on the Unitrac has a vertical and horizontal adjustment and a spring safety hitch. A deep skimmer can be fitted beside the swivelling disc coulter. The lever, to operate the

enclosed lift mechanism on the landwheel, is above the plough and has a hole to tie the pull-cord.

Many Ransomes trailed ploughs have a triangular frame drawbar, adjustable with a simple peg or a lever, on a quadrant with notches for the handle to snap into. The lever enables the tractor driver to adjust the width of furrow without leaving the tractor seat. This is a desirable feature in difficult conditions, when a field slopes in one direction at one end and slopes the opposite way at the other. However, not all Ransomes trailed ploughs have (*continued from previous page*) that feature; many have an adjustable but otherwise rigid drawbar, like the Unitrac in the picture. The swivelling, rolling disc coulter is so named because it is fitted to an arm with a swivel at the joint with the stalk that is clamped to the plough beam. The swivel enables the disc to act like a caster wheel and line up with the direction of travel, as the plough is drawn through the soil. On some disc coulters, a skimmer body was attached to an arm beside the disc.

Oliver mouldboards were made of what the Americans described as 'soft-centre steel'; Ransomes' mouldboards were also soft-centre steel but known as 'case-hardened steel', made by their own Steel Case Company in South Wales. Basically the mouldboard was a sandwich, or laminate, of hardened steel on the outside, to resist wear to the front of the board, soft but tough in the centre, to hold the shape of the mouldboard, and then hardened on the back. Close examination of the edge of the mouldboard will often reveal the sandwich; the soft centre will appear to have shrunk. The Oliver mouldboards were reputed to polish up better and wear a little longer than Ransomes' mouldboards.

The Ransomes TS42 trailed single-furrow plough was designed for use with the Ransomes MG tractor.
The self-lift is the open type, with pegs on the wheel hub that can be seen on the inside of the landwheel. The landwheel has a wide rim, with lugs, to obtain a grip to operate the lift mechanism. A pull on the lift-cord by the tractor driver would bring a toothed quadrant down to engage in the pegs, then, as the wheel rotated, the plough body would be lifted out of the soil, the lift mechanism working on all three wheels. The depth control hand screw is at the left of centre, adjusting all three wheels. It has a digger body which will plough 9 in. (23 cm) deep and 11 in. (28 cm) wide. The triangular drawbar with a width adjustment is missing and so is the skimmer.
A grower in Trinity did all his ploughing with a Ransomes TS 42 and an MG tractor.

At approximately the turn of the nineteenth and twentieth centuries, the Melotte Company in Belgium developed a horse-drawn one-way plough, with left- and right-hand bodies. Melotte redesigned the plough for use with tractors and, even later, designed mounted ploughs for the three-point linkage. The Melotte plough rotated through 180 degrees to take one body out of work and lower its opposite into work. It has two wheels of equal diameter. When ploughing in one direction, one wheel is in the furrow; when the plough is turned at the furrow end and the bodies are rotated or reversed, the opposite wheel becomes the furrow wheel. Depth of work was adjusted by a screw wheel operating on both wheels. The model was named the Brabant, after the province of Brabant where the factory is located. The Jersey agent for Melotte was Messrs. Le Cappelain of St. Peter's Iron Works; they sold a number of Melotte Brabant ploughs in Jersey. The name appears to have caught on, as Ransomes of Ipswich also named their horse-drawn reversible plough a Brabant. The Société Jersiaise's collection includes a Brabant supplied by a dealer in St. Malo to a Jersey farmer. As a result, Jersey farmers frequently refer to any reversible plough as a Brabant!

When Harry Ferguson produced the Ferguson-Brown tractor with the hydraulic three-point hitching system, implement manufacturers had to design what became known as mounted implements. Mounted implements were designed without wheels, for the Ferguson system, but with a tripod above the frame, with the apex at the top. The tractor's lower link arms are attached with a ball joint and pin, one to each corner of the base of the triangle. The top link arm is fitted to the apex. The tripod is completed with one leg of the tripod extended to the back of a plough, but is split with two legs on some implements. An implement fitted to the three-point hitch can be raised and lowered by the tractor's hydraulic lift, making the tractor and implement one integral unit. The depth of work was set on the hydraulic lift control, with a lever on a quadrant. The depth and draught control system would hold the plough or cultivator at the set depth, doing away with the need for a depth wheel. The system included a safety device, the draught control that prevented the tractor from rearing up at the front, in the event of a share point striking a tree root or a rock. This had been a dangerous feature on the Fordson model F tractor. In such an event the front of the Fordson tractor would rear up and wind itself over the back axle, with fatal results on an unwary tractor driver who was not quick enough to stamp on the clutch pedal.

Harry Ferguson had achieved his dream. He loved to demonstrate his tractor and mounted plough in a small fenced-off area measuring no more than 50 yards by 20. He would drive in through an open space at one corner, back up into a corner, drop the plough, and proceed to plough the little patch, leaving no space unploughed. He would then drive out, take off the plough and hitch on a mounted cultivator, drive in again, back up into a corner, drop the cultivator, and proceed to prepare a seed bed. He would leave no piece untouched and no wheel marks, driving out again to the applause of the onlookers.

The system, with its range of mounted implements, was a major advance in farm mechanisation in Jersey and the world at large. The Jersey farmer was quick to respond to this new technology. In the rest of the British Isles, as explained elsewhere, where tractors were used extensively, farmers were reluctant to change because it was expensive. They also thought the tractor was rather small. However, that would all change in the United Kingdom when farmers with subsidies could afford to re-equip. The Channel Islands are not a part of the UK so farmers in the Island did not receive those subsidies.

The Ferguson system was so highly regarded worldwide that the three-point hitch was rapidly copied by most tractor manufacturers in the post-war years, but without the draught and depth control system, which was protected by patent. Two examples were the David Brown and Fordson Major, but all the implements had to have depth wheels, and did not benefit from weight transfer. Today, every make of tractor has the famous three-point hitch lifting system, some of them with their own draught control system such as John Deere. The John Deere system does not operate through the top link, as on the Ferguson, but through the lower links. There was one disadvantage with the Ferguson draught control system: when ploughing in very hard, dry soil conditions in the summer, it would not always maintain the selected depth of work. The very nature of the draught control and safety system would cause the lift to raise the plough when the plough entered a very hard patch of ground, such as might be experienced in the middle of a hot dry summer, in a heavy clay soil. Setting the control deeper, increasing the pitch, and ensuring the share was either new or sharpened, would improve performance but not always overcome it. Fortunately, it is not often that a farmer will want to plough in the summer!

A mounted, twin-furrow breezing plough, converted from a horse-drawn plough. Mr. Thérin, the blacksmith in Trinity, made the plough originally; the conversion was made by his former apprentice Mr. Le Lay (note the tripod on the top).

After the war, Mr. Le Lay set up in business as a blacksmith at East Grove, St. John, where this plough was converted. He removed the wheels and axles and fabricated a tripod for the three-point linkage, the top link, and the cranked crossbar for the lower links. The plough is a twin 13 in. (33 cm) furrow breezing plough, with an under-beam clearance of 22 in. (56 cm) to the share point. There are no skimmers or coulters, although there are brackets for them; that is not unusual on a breezing plough. The plough belonged to Mr. Pinel, of Les Ruettes, St. John, who used the plough with his Ferguson TE20 tractor.

A Ferguson single-furrow mounted plough, with a digger body, ploughing at Mr. Percy Le Masurier's farm, La Pointe, at St. Ouen. The Ferguson single-furrow digger plough has a 14 in. (35.5 cm) wide share and ploughs 12 in. (30.5 cm) deep. It was manufactured by Harry Ferguson Ltd. for the TE20 tractor and was priced at £105. The price was expensive compared to local manufacture.

One-way mounted ploughs

The late Mr. Clem Le Breuilly, a Jerseyman and blacksmith, formerly at Rue de La Guillaumerie, Victoria Village, was an unsung hero. Like so many of our blacksmiths in the Island, he was a highly skilled craftsman and engineer. Mr. Le Breuilly had served his apprenticeship at the forge in Trinity, where the new Trinity Arms pub is today. In due course he had his own forge near Victoria Village, and is credited with designing and building the first mounted, quarter-turn, one-way plough, before the Second World War. It was the first of its type in the world. He sold it to Mr. Le Cuirot, of Boulivot. When Harry Ferguson heard about it, probably through St. Helier Garages, the local Ferguson dealer, he wrote in glowing terms to Mr. Le Cuirot. Mr Ferguson congratulated him for having purchased the first mounted one-way plough in the world, for use with a Ferguson tractor. This would have been in 1938, when the Ferguson was of course the only tractor in the world with a system for mounted implements. This is a little-known world first, for Clem and Jersey! The author has to thank Mr. Le Cuirot's son Maurice for that story. Unfortunately there are no pictures of the plough, but very soon the idea was copied by Harry Ferguson Ltd. as illustrated below and by other manufacturers including the late Don Pallot. Mr. Le Breuilly eventually moved his business to St. Clement.

Great care had to be taken when cultivating côtils, to ensure that the soil was not drawn down the côtil. One-way ploughs are particularly useful on sloping land or shallow côtils, for turning the soil up the slope when ploughing across. This procedure counters the tendency for soil to erode down the slope. But setting a plough on a slope requires particular skill, to prevent a wide furrow, due to the sheer weight of the plough pulling it down the slope. Countermeasures have to be taken to overcome the problem.

Ferguson quarter-turn, one-way, single-furrow digger plough manufactured in the late 1940s and 1950s; it has a 16 in. (40.6 cm) wide share ploughing 14 in. (35.5 cm) deep. Mr. Charles Le Couteur is driving the tractor.
Ferguson quarter-turn, one-way digger ploughs were supplied with either 14 in. (35.5 cm) or 16 in. (40.6 cm) wide shares. They had a short solid landside and a spring-loaded landside wheel behind; the purpose of this was to allow the plough to penetrate quickly to the necessary depth, without interference from the tractor's draught control system. For the same reason it was close-coupled, with a short beam. This left little room for an effective skimmer in front; however, Charles Le Couteur fitted extra short bars on each side, to fit large skimmers. It worked very well; this was important when there was green manure, seaweed, or stable manure to bury.

One-way ploughs are convenient to use: there is no need to measure the field and set the 'lands', as described in Chapter 3. The modern farmer would know nothing about that with his one-way plough; all that is unnecessary. He will start ploughing by simply opening a furrow against the hedge. He will turn the furrow toward the hedge; then rotating or reversing the plough at the far headland, while turning the tractor round, he simply ploughs straight back down the open furrow. At the opposite end he will rotate the plough again, while turning on the headland before setting off yet again, back down the field, and so forth. All the soil is turned the same way, hence the name 'one- way'. The procedure is the same with a fully reversible multifurrow plough, where the plough rotates or reverses through 180 degrees on the headland, at each end of the field, before heading back down the field again. Few fields have parallel sides, so short turns are inevitable, but these can usually be left to last and, if they are very short, one simply reverses the tractor down the open furrow, to the point where the short turns start. Drop the plough in the furrow and plough out the short turns, one after the other. An Ebra reversible plough is illustrated below.

David Brown manufactured another type of one-way plough, in the late 1940s. It is best described as being two ploughs, on one mounted frame. On the beam on the right was a body casting to the right and on the beam on the left was a body casting to the left. Both bodies could be lifted but only one could be lowered into the ground. The system was operated by levers which locked each body in place, either up or down. The plough was fitted with digger bodies and was best used on a David Brown tractor. Depth of work was set with a depth wheel on the plough. One of these ploughs was used at Roselands, in St. Saviour, and the former Constable, Major Anthoine, at Longueville, St. Saviour, had another. The author's father borrowed it from time to time to plough a côtil in Swiss Valley, at Beau Désert.

L. C. Pallot's quarter-turn, one-way, mounted single-furrow plough; it has a last-furrow attachment, the rectangular frame at the front with a hand screw handle at one end.
The plough is fitted with Ransomes UD digger bodies; it will plough a 14 in. (35.5 cm) wide furrow, 12 in. (30.5 cm) deep. It was designed by Mr. Don Pallot and manufactured at the Central Motor Works, in Trinity, in the 1950s and 1960s. The plough was designed for the Ferguson TE20, but could be used with one of the International and Ford Dexta tractors, and is displayed at the Steam Museum.

A single-furrow plough, without a last-furrow attachment, cannot plough right up to a hedge or fence; it will leave an area between one and two furrows wide that has to be dug very laboriously with the spade. Having a last-furrow attachment, the hand screw adjustment will move the plough body right over to one side or the other, in order to plough right up to the edge of a field to plough the 'last' furrow. It is also useful on côtils for setting the correct width of furrow. Multifurrow ploughs do not have that problem; they can plough up to the edge. The picture on page 160 also illustrates the three-point linkage A frame on the one-way plough. The A frame and its mounting have to be particularly strong, because the back brace, as on a tripod, cannot be accommodated in the design. The reversing mechanism is operated with a balance chain, which is fitted at one end to the reversing mechanism and at the other end to a low point on the tractor; it is tightened as the plough is lifted by the tractor's hydraulic lift, the chain pulling on the reversing mechanism to turn the plough. This was common practice with many quarter-turn and reversing ploughs. Very often a spring was loaded during lifting, to assist in achieving a smart reversal, to latch firmly each time. In the early days before reversing systems were perfected, some refused to latch; this was often a problem on a slope if the tractor was standing across it, and very often turning the tractor to face down the slope overcame the problem. Otherwise it was necessary to dismount from the tractor and swing the plough manually, until it latched.

Pallot's one-way, last-furrow plough illustrating the reversing mechanism.

An Ebra two-furrow reversible plough, mounted on a M-F 240 tractor, with Mr. Louis Binet on the tractor, ploughing at Maufant.

The Ebra reversible has 12 in. (30.5 cm) wide digger bodies, ploughing 12 in. (30.5 cm) deep, and was manufactured in the 1980s. The rotating or reversing mechanism on the Ebra has a lever, handy to the driver. The plough has 37 in. (94 cm) clearance between the bodies and a 23 in. (58.4 cm) under beam; that is excellent clearance, with plenty of room for the large skimmers to handle top growth without blockages.

A Lemken three-furrow plough, model DL 090 DLC 140, serial no. 900006, with a hydraulic-powered reversing mechanism, manufactured in the 1960s and 1970s.

Like all digger ploughs, the Lemken plough will plough 12 in. (30.5 cm) deep and 12 in. (30.5 cm) or 14 in. (35.5 cm) wide furrows. Hidden from view on the other side is a depth control wheel, As these ploughs get bigger and heavier, the depth control system in the tractor finds it more difficult. That does depend on the make of tractor and the type of hydraulic lift system. The power absorbed will require a 60 plus hp tractor. The plough is standing in the yard of Mr. Le Maistre, of Les Prés Manor in Grouville. The supplier was Messrs Halse of Honiton; they are well-known farm machinery dealers in the south-west of England.

Lemken reversible ploughs became very popular in the UK throughout the 1960s and 1970s, especially in the eastern counties. Colchester Tillage, located in Colchester, were the importers. They did not have all the features of Ransomes ploughs, such as rolling disc coulters, but they were cheaper, were adequate, and gave satisfaction. Today the one-way mounted plough is universal in the Island and they are all multifurrow reversibles. That is, they may have as many as five left- and right-hand bodies.

What of the future? The 100-plus-hp tractors used in the Island today have draught control hydraulic lift systems capable of mounting a five-furrow reversible plough. Our fathers, and indeed many of us, would never have thought that possible in Jersey thirty years ago!

A Lemken five-furrow reversible plough at work at Rozel in 1998, ploughing land for early potatoes for Vautier Bros. at Ville Machon. The five-furrow plough was manufactured in 1997; it will plough 12 in. (30.5 cm) deep furrows and has 16 in. (40.6 cm) wide shares. Toward the back on the landward side is a depth control wheel. The 23 in. (58.4 cm) underbeam clearance allows plenty of room for the large skimmers, to clear top growth, etc. The plough is reversed with a hydraulic ram. The power absorbed will require a tractor with a minimum of 100 hp, such as the John Deere pictured here.

Today, to maintain soil moisture when planting potatoes, ploughing is delayed until only an hour ahead of planting, just allowing sufficient time for spreading fertiliser and soil preparation before planting. This can only be done with modern equipment. The system does require careful planning and a vast investment in expensive tractors and machinery. As farming is changing fast, so is financing the farm and its operations. Very often the tractors are no longer owned but supplied on a three-year full-servicing lease; at the end of the lease the tractor is replaced with a new one! Sadly, Vautier Bros. are no longer farming due to the difficulties of marketing their crop. Those difficulties, mainly due to the local marketing and supermarkets, are ruining the industry.

The whole process of development from the very beginning of the ard, into a plough, lasted over several millennia. Animal draught implements had been in use in the Middle East for a thousand years before the technology reached Western Europe. Farmers in the past had a tendency to be conservative: the ancient farmer seemed content with the ard as the main tillage implement. The developments in the last millennium have been rapid, by comparison, and extremely so in the twentieth century.

Cultivators

As with ploughs, there are different types of cultivator for different purposes. They are usually used after ploughing to prepare a seed bed, before planting, and often to prepare the land for a second crop after the potato season, without the need to plough first. The cultivator is used to break up ground, such as turf or stubble or an area of ground that has lain idle for some time, before deep ploughing. There are cultivators for weeding between the rows of some crops, such as brassicas and root crops.

The solid-tine cultivators are just what the name implies: a number of solid tines are bolted to the frame in a particular pattern, to ensure the soil will be thoroughly stirred up across the width of the cultivator frame. The spring-loaded solid-tine cultivators have tines that are themselves solid but mounted on a pivot pin and held in place by two sturdy springs. The springs also allow the tines to flex back and forth in hard conditions; as the springs tighten up and draw the tine back in place, it will impact on the soil, bursting and breaking up the soil to create a tilth. The arrangement to swing backward in the soil serves a second purpose: it provides protection for the tine in the event of the tip striking an obstruction, such as a rock or stone in the soil.

A trailed solid-tine cultivator manufactured by Le Cappelain, St. Peter's Iron Works.

This cultivator's wheels are 33 in. (84 cm) in diameter and have a 2.5 in. (6.4 cm) wide tyre. The open rack and pinion lift can be clearly seen on the inside of the wheel on the left. There is one to act on the hub of both wheels. It is operated by giving a sustained pull on the blue rope by the tractor driver, as on a self-lift trailed plough. Depth of work is adjusted by the crank-handle screw. There are nine solid tines, each 17 in. (43.1 cm) long, with replaceable points. The tines behind the wheels are to remove wheel marks. The width overall is 5 ft 7 in. (172 cm). It would have been pulled by any of the pre-war tractors. It was modified post-war with a tripod for a three-point hitch and hydraulic lift and further modified, to make it quickly convertible from a mounted implement back to a trailed implement. When operated by a tractor hydraulic lift system, the self-lift is redundant. The owner is Mr. Charles Le Couteur of Westlands, Route de Francfief, St. Peter.

David Brown mounted cultivator with eleven spring tines, with reversible points on the back row.

The overall width of the cultivator is 6 ft (183 cm). The cultivator has three S-type spring tines with 7 in. (17.8 cm) wide 'ducks' feet' points on the front tool bar and six C tines with reversible points 7 in. (17.8 cm) long by 2 in. (5 cm) wide on the second bar. On the third bar are three crumblers. This arrangement is ideal for rowcrop cultivations, weed cleaning between rows of broccoli, etc. The three crumblers are identical to the crumblers used on the horse-drawn potato scarifiers and most suitable in this application. The frame is 74 in. (188 cm) wide and 38 in. (96.5 cm) front to back. The cross-members or toolbars are at 18 in. (45.7 cm) centres and the under-beam clearance is 18 in. (45.7 cm). The tractor tyres are narrow rowcrop tyres, especially for rowcrop work. Here it is operating for Mr. Le Gallais, at Maufant.

The local supplier for David Brown equipment for many years was the Jersey Farmers (Trading) Union Ltd., better known as the JF(T)U Ltd., a company run by the late Mr. Frank Perrée and his father before him. Spring-tine cultivators are frequently used for preparing a seed bed after ploughing and for breaking stubble or grassland, etc.

The advantage of the toolbar-type mounted cultivator is its versatility. The tines are easily moved along the bars or removed and replaced, according to the job in hand, as clearly illustrated here. For general cultivation and final soil preparation, preparatory to planting, such a cultivator would have C tines on both the first and second toolbar, with a full-width star crumbler across the back. The star crumbler is composed of cast-iron pointed stars, on a solid full-width shaft, rotating as one as it rolls over the soil. The tractor would have standard tyres.

This mounted cultivator illustrates the value of the cultivating toolbar and its versatility; it has five spring-loaded solid tines across the back and six in front. Mounted on the cultivator is a frame carrying chemical-injection equipment, for the control of potato root eel worm.

The potato root eel worm equipment comprises three hoppers each supplying two spouts, to distribute pellets, through tubes attached behind each of the six tines on the front bar. The rate of sowing is regulated by the blue land-driven, multi-spoked starwheel on the right via a V-belt to a common shaft to each hopper. The equipment can be removed for normal cultivations. The equipment belongs to Mr. Colin Binet, of Maison du Buisson, St. Saviour.

Subsoilers

The 'pan' is formed by continually ploughing at the same depth year after year; the subsoil in the furrow bottom becomes hard and impervious. Just as heavy draught horses' hooves pounded the furrow bottom years ago, today's big tractor wheels have an even worse effect, particularly the large, heavy tractors. The effect on the subsoil is virtually to seal it off from the top soil, reducing drainage in wet weather and reducing rising water beneath the soil in hot, dry weather. Previously, Ransomes were one of very few manufacturers of trailed or wheeled single-tine subsoilers for deep work. They also

Mounted three-tine subsoiler, for breaking up the plough pan at Les Prés Manor

supplied them with an expander for mole-draining; the operation needed a tracklaying tractor to haul a single-tine implement, a slow and expensive operation, rarely carried out in Jersey, if ever. Ferguson produced a mounted subsoiler, but it was not designed for deep work, although it will successfully break up the soil in grassland to aid drainage and for getting fertilisers into the soil beneath the grass.

Some ploughs fitted a single, subsoil tine behind the plough bodywork beneath the share. It broke the exposed furrow bottom during ploughing. With the advent of four-wheel-drive, high horsepower tractors, which have a higher drawbar-pull, the job is made much simpler and quicker. This enables any modern farmer to purchase a two- or three-tine subsoiler, to subsoil his land and do a job his father could never do.

Although these big tractors are fitted with wide, large-diameter tyres to reduce the pounds per square inch pressure on the soil, they nevertheless compress the soil, which eventually reduces the crop yield, if the subsoil is neglected.

A farmer at Rozel recently told the author of a field with an easterly slope which was not difficult for a tractor; but they never ran a tractor over it. They always used côtil cultivating equipment, with a mounted winch, etc. The soil never became hard but remained fluffy and it always produced a very early, bumper crop of Jersey Royal potatoes.

Rotary cultivators

Mr. Howard, an English emigrant, developed rotary cultivators in Australia before the Second World War. The object was to break up the hard dry soil in Australia. He eventually perfected the design and returned to the UK. After the Second World War he formed a company in Essex to manufacture rotary cultivators (Howard Rotary Hoes Ltd.). At first they were large and heavy, demanding an enormous amount of power for those days. He worked with John Fowler and Co. of Leeds to build a tracklaying tractor, with a rotavator on the back. It was an integral part of the tractor and not easy to detach and re-attach. It was basically a Fowler diesel-powered tracklayer and rotavator and marketed as the FD3 (Fowler Diesel 3 Cylinder), in the early post-war years. There was a concern at the time that the rotavator might have the effect of pushing a wheeled tractor along, reducing the effect of the rotavator to create a tilth. Eventually experience proved this concern to be unfounded. The hydraulic three-point linkage was becoming universal and eventually during the 1950s Howards developed a 4 ft (122 cm) wide rotavator, which was designed for the three-point linkage tractor. Howards were also making small two-wheel rotavators, the little 7 in. (17.8 cm) wide Bantam, the larger 350, and the Gem. Eventually other manufacturers such as Landmaster made a similar range of garden machines.

Howard P60 rotavator, Selector Tilth model.
The Selector Tilth has a gearbox on top of the machine, behind the input power shaft from the tractor PTO. Loosening a couple of wing nuts, the gearbox cover is removed to expose the gears that can be moved about to adjust the speed of the rotor and select a fine or coarse tilth. The rotavator here was manufactured in 1965. The L-shaped rotor blades are 4 in. (10 cm) long. The overall width of the machine is 60 in (1.52 cm) and is set to overlap the left side of the tractor. There are two steel depth wheels. The power take-off runs at the standard speed of 540 rpm. The machine is attached to the tractor's hydraulic three-point lift system and is coupled to the tractor's power take-off (PTO). The local supplier was the JF(T)U Ltd. and the equipment belongs to Mr. Louis Binet, of La Maison du Buisson, at Maufant.

The next two pictures are of present-day cultivators making use of the extra powerful tractors on the market. These four-wheel drive, hundred-plus-horsepower tractors have more powerful three-point linkage systems and more powerful hydraulic pumps, enabling them to lift much heavier loads than hitherto. It is a look into the future and the way things are pointing for the twenty-first century.

Mounted rotavator and roller manu-factured by Breviglieri in Italy in 1995, model 205, type B72V, no. 199309754; it weighs 300 lb (675 kg) and is 7 ft (213 cm) wide. It is similar to, but wider than, the Howard and has a roller.

The Breviglieri rotavator is operated by a tractor PTO at 540 rpm. The fineness of the tilth is adjustable, as it is on the Howard, by removing a quick-release gearbox cover, lifting out a gearwheel and changing it with another. The rotavator blades are clearly visible underneath the machine, and across the back it has a large, full-width roller; one end of it can be seen on the left. The roller is mounted on an arm at each end, with bottle-screw adjustment, which will set the depth of work of the rotor blades. The combination of a wide rotary cultivator and a large roller reduces the number of separate opera-tions. It could not have been considered in the days of the 'little grey' Ferguson or the Dexta tractors. It is only the advent of large 80-100-plus-hp tractors with powerful lift systems that this sort of implement could be considered. It is the property of Mr. Le Gallais, at Cowleywood, and was supplied by L. C. Pallot, Central Motor Works.

Harry Ferguson's idea of lightweight tractors, and implements to reduce the ground pressure on the land, was admired very much but was not really understood by many. His idea has been abandoned in favour of bigger, quicker, and heavier machines. The bigger, more powerful tractors of today and bigger implements, like the one above and the one which follows, will do more than one operation in one pass over the land. They are an indication of the trend with imple-ments and tractors.

Lely Roterra 2O powered cultivator, with vertically rotating pairs of tines, which can just be seen beneath the red framework.

The tines are mounted on short arms, on a vertical shaft. The arms are set at 90 degrees to their neighbour and inter-rotate, as can be seen in the drawing below. The width of work is 8 ft 10 in. (270 cm). At the back is a 12 in. (30.5 cm) diameter crumbler roller, composed of six horizontal 1.5 in. (3.8 cm) diameter crumbler rods, each with a slight helix and so mounted to form a roller and keep it on the surface, in spite of the wide gaps between each rod. The height adjustment is provided by a massive number of holes which provide a wide range of height adjustment. Power is provided by the tractor PTO at the usual 540 rpm, and there is a gearbox with removable cover to gain access to change gears to alter rotor speed. It was manufactured in the 1990s. and supplied by L. C. Pallot Ltd. to Mr. A. Le Gallais, Cowleywood, Maufant.

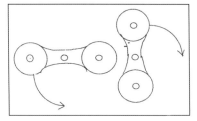

This drawing illustrates the arrangement of the rotor arms, with the tines fitted at the centre of each end.

Roller

A divided flat roller is filled with water to add weight; it is in two 4 ft (122 cm) wide sections with a total width of 8 ft (2.44 cm) and a diameter of 2 ft 6 in. (76 cm). The size and weight of this roll filled with water would require a 60-70 hp tractor to pull it to finish making a seed bed. A problem with heavy flat rollers on very light sandy soils is that they will sometimes create a wave of soil in front of the roller. (Courtesy of Mr. Le Gallais, Cowleywood, Maufant.)

The Cambridge roll is not used in Jersey but is very popular in other parts of the British Isles. This may be due to the high cost of shipping such a heavy item. It is composed of sections of individual cast iron wheels, each with a raised fluted rim around the circumference. They are assembled side by side, on a common axle shaft. The Cambridge roll is frequently used immediately after ploughing, to maintain the moisture content in the soil, and they are excellent for breaking clods when making a seed bed.

Planting machines

General views of the Rit-Mik mounted, dual-purpose potato- and broccoli-planting machine first manufactured in the 1960s.

This picture illustrates the details of the cups fitted to the chain; each cup carries one potato down to the soil and drops it in the open furrow

The Rit-Mik machines were supplied with three chain and sprocket units, with cups attached around the chain; one potato is placed in each cup. A landwheel, to the right of the picture at the bottom, drives a common shaft, on which are the three sprockets and chains, with the cups. As the wheel rotates the shaft, the chains and the cups carry the potatoes down into the soil. This type of drive ensured the potatoes were planted at the correct spacing, irrespective of the speed over the ground. In front of each unit is a furrow-splitter opening the soil just wide enough for the potato; behind are covering bodies which form a ridge, closing the soil over the potatoes. Planting three rows, 18 in. (45.6 cm) inches apart, the potatoes are placed 12 in. (30.5 cm) apart in the row.

It would be quite heavy, with twelve full potato boxes and three operators sitting on the machine; to support this weight, the machine has four wheels. It is operated here on a Massey-Ferguson M-F135 tractor. The above machine belongs to Mr. Colin Binet, of Maison du Buisson, Maufant. Among other users are Mr. Le Masurier of La Pointe, St. Ouen.

At a later time, Mr. Percy Le Masurier altered his machine to dispense with the chain and cups, fitting instead short lengths of plastic pipe, set at an angle, down which the potatoes slid into the soil, with the shoots uppermost. The landwheel was retained to drive a clicker, timed so that at each click a potato was dropped, to fall 12 in. (30.5 cm) apart in each row. Mr. Le Masurier believed that this gave the potatoes a better start, more akin to traditional hand planting.

To plant broccoli plants, the machine is fitted with three pairs of discs: one of the pairs is metal and the other one rubber, and both are of equal diameter. They are mounted side by side, with some pressure holding them together. In work, the landwheel drives the common shaft, rotating the discs as for the potatoes, but the rubber disc is so arranged to be opened, with a space between it and the metal disc. Into this space the plant is placed, root outwards, and as the discs rotate the rubber disc grips the plant between it and the metal disc. On reaching the ground, the rubber disc is opened, releasing the plant. As before, in front of the disc, the soil is split into a narrow furrow to accept the plant and the bodies behind close the soil around the plant. The local supplier was Mr. Ozouf of Augrès Garage.

The Le Cappelain mounted, four-row potato planter on a Ford Super Dexta.

It has four tubes set at 18 in. centres and two operators each feeding two tubes in time with a landwheel-driven clicker. Manufactured and supplied by Le Cappelain of St. Peter's Iron Works in 1974 and costing £140. The equipment is the property of Mr. Brian Ahier, of Surguy Farm.

The paddle-wheel with four bolts and the spring clicker.

The paddle wheel and the disc with four bolts strike a spring-loaded clicker. The seed potatoes are dropped down the tube with the shoot upwards as the landwheel-driven clicker wheel rotates and clicks. The clicker wheel is adjustable, to alter the period between each click, which in turn adjusts the distance between the planted seed potatoes. Traditionally, potatoes in Jersey are planted 12 in. (30.5 cm) apart in the row. The four Osmar-type plastic drainpipe tubes have an internal diameter of 4 in. (10 cm) and are 22 in. (56 cm) long; they are mounted vertically. The planter has two 16 in. (40.6 cm) rubber-tyred wheels, adjustable for height, to support the weight of the machine, the potato boxes, and operators, etc.

In front of the operators are the four tubes and four coulters, with points and wings to create a shallow open furrow, into which the seed potatoes fall. Behind the tubes are five traditional Jersey bankers, or ridgers, to close the soil over the seed potatoes and form the ridges. Above the bankers is a bench seat, for up to four operators; in front of each operator is a rack, upon which the box of potatoes to be planted is placed. In front of the rack is another frame, upon which the boxes of seed potatoes are stacked, sufficient to plant two lengths of the field. Behind the operators is the frame to carry the empty boxes. As each operator empties his box, the tractor is stopped and each operator removes his empty box and replaces it with a full one, and then the tractor moves on.

The wheels are placed to run in the bottom between the ridges. Behind each wheel is a coulter with a share to break up the soil compressed by the wheel, and at the front of the machine are two more coulters, with duck's foot shares, lined up behind the tractor rear wheels, for the same purpose.

The depth of work at which the potatoes are planted is adjusted by the position control on the tractor hydraulic lift and by adjusting the rear wheels on the machine.

The arrangement of tubes, ducks' feet, coulters, and tines with covering/ridging bodies or bankers on the Le Cappelain planting machine.

On the right of the picture, just beyond the duck's foot, can be seen the front-row ridgers for opening a small furrow for the potatoes; in the middle are the potato tubes, and at the back on the left are the ridging bodies, or bankers, for closing the soil over the seed potatoes.

A criticism of these machines is that the seed potatoes were not placed exactly as they should be: as they fall down the tube, they may tumble, and on hitting the soil they may bounce and knock off the delicate shoots. The potatoes should land with the shoots upwards; it is critical for obtaining an early crop. If the tube was mounted at a slight angle, the potato would slide down the tube more slowly, with a better chance of protecting the delicate shoots. This type of planter was also manufactured by the late Mr. Clem Le Breuilly. There were many types of tractor-mounted potato planters, some with cups on chains and others with cups on wheels, to carry the tuber down to the soil. Others were automatic, requiring no operators, but were unsuitable for early potatoes with delicate shoots.

For many years, the potatoes were planted with Le Boutillier's design of potato-planting plough. At first it was pulled by a horse, but after the 1930s some farmers without a horse continued to use the potato-planting plough pulled by a Ransomes MG tractor. However, as time went on, there was a further change, when farmers turned to the two-wheel tractor, such as the Standard, the Coleby, and the Staub, fitted with a potato-planting plough.

The Standard two-wheel tractor fitted with three banking bodies. To plant potatoes the bankers would be removed and a potato-planting plough fitted.

The Morrish tractor and implements

Looking at the present day and the future of planting the Jersey Royal potato crop, we can see that, in the late 1990s and into the new millennium, there was another change. Some farmers turned to a lightweight tracklaying tractor, fitted with hydraulic lifts front and back, manufactured by Morrish of Tiverton. This lightweight tracklayer was found to be ideal for potato planting. It has long, wide tracks, reducing the pounds pressure per square inch on the soil. Ridging and banking bodies are used with large gangs of farm workers, rather than the traditional gang of five planters with the planting plough.

The lightweight tracklayer manufactured by Morrish for planting potatoes.
At the front are four ridging bodies, or bankers for 'opening up' for planting. The ridges are at 30 in. (76.2 cm) centres, which is remarkably wide for Jersey Royals, but the potatoes are planted much closer in the row to compensate. (Vautier Bros., at Ville Machon, Rozel.)

The planting gang busy planting the potatoes in the open ridges.

After planting, driving over the same tracks, the rear implement is lowered with angled discs for ridging the soil over the potatoes. Scrapers provide a flat top to the ridge. The flat top is to control the depth of soil above the potato, so that it is not too deep, to encourage quick emergence.

The covering discs banking the soil over the potatoes; the two vertical bars are lowered when opening to make a line on the soil to guide the driver to maintain the correct distance between ridges

A tractor on narrow tyres, with a toolbar with two slitting bodies 10 in. (25.4 cm) deep, one following close behind the first.

After the potatoes have been planted, they are sprayed with a pre-emergence weedkiller, then covered over with plastic sheeting. But before that, a slitting tool has to open slits, every so many rows apart, to insert the plastic sheet into the soil, to hold it down when the wind gets up.

The first slitter is to create a deep slit in the soil, between two potato ridges. The second slitter is to firm the sides, to prevent the soil crumbling and falling back into the slit before the plastic sheet is laid. The wheel on the nearside is as much a steadying wheel as a depth wheel keeping the implement level. Tractor weights on the toolbar ensure the slitter is at the desired depth. The operators have to be systematic, to ensure the slit is made precisely every so many rows apart.

A second tractor and toolbar for carrying and laying a roll of plastic sheeting on the sprayed ridges of planted potatoes at Ville Machon, Rozel.

The tool bar for carrying and laying a roll of plastic sheeting is fitted with a 4-5 in. (10-12 cm) diameter cylinder, approximately 52 in. (132 cm) wide, on which is carried a roll of plastic sheeting, 4,000 ft (1,203 m) long. In operation, the end of the plastic roll is firmly anchored on the headland; then, as the tractor moves forward across the field, so the plastic sheet is drawn off. At the opposite headland the sheet is cut, and the tractor moves off to lay the next strip of sheet. The sheet of plastic is drawn out concertina-fashion by the planting team, first to one side and then to the other. Each sheet covers fourteen ridges, seven to one side, as it lies unrolled, and seven to the other. They are laid alternately, the slitting tool having been operated on the same basis, as it reduces the amount of tramping on the sheeting during laying. The operators have to take great care to count the rows before making the slits and laying the sheets of plastic.

Drilling machines

Maize and root crops in Jersey were once sown with a man pushing a Planet seed drill, one row at a time. Maize seed was also sown broadcast, by hand, and harrowed in. In England the Planet type of seed drills were mounted, four at a time, on a toolbar, to be carried on a tractor three-point linkage. Continued development led to more precision machines. Agricultural machinery manufacturers, like Stanhay, in England, were making tractor-mounted, mechanical, precision seed drills very successfully in the 1950s and 1960s for sugar beet, which was grown extensively in England for sugar. The following drill was manufactured about 1989/90. This is 'high tech', indicating the sort of machine that will be used in Island farm mechanisation in the new millennium.

A tractor-mounted precision seed drill manufactured by Gaspardo in Italy.

This model SP 520 four-row drill is driven by the tractor PTO at 540 rpm. It is drilling maize at Maufant, operated by Mr. Andrew Le Gallais. It uses a central vacuum pump, driven by the PTO to supply a vacuum to

a part of each individual drill's metering system. Each of the four drills consists of a vertically mounted stainless steel disc, on a horizontal shaft, driven by a landwheel. Each disc is perforated with circular holes; the holes are in a circle, around the inside of the periphery. A vacuum is maintained on one side of the disc, while on the other side, the seeds are held in a chamber, supplied from a hopper above. The vacuum draws the seed from the chamber to the holes in the disc, each hole being of a size to hold the seed without it passing through it. As the disc rotates towards bottom dead-centre, it passes out of the vacuum chamber to a space open to atmosphere, allowing the seed to drop into the feed spout and so down to the coulter. The coulter makes a small furrow into which the seed falls before being covered over. A photoelectric cell monitors the metering system; in the event of failure, an alarm is sounded to alert the operator. In addition the machine has four fertiliser

hoppers, supplying each coulter with a measured amount of fertiliser, through a metering device driven by a second landwheel. The purpose is to give each seed a good start and see it through to harvest. There is a counter on the fertiliser feed landwheel to calculate the area sown.

The drill is at present set to sow maize seed, in four rows at 27.5 in. (70 cm) centres. A number of discs are supplied, each with a different set of holes of different sizes, to suit the many different types and size of seed. The machine has a wide range of adjustments, to alter row widths and the space between each seed in the row, to suit different crops: root crops, brassicas, etc. A central gearbox allows a further range of adjustments, which can be performed by simply opening the box, removing a gearwheel, and turning or changing it, to mesh with a different gearwheel.

The open transmission box at the centre (shown above) reveals the adjustable sprocket-and-chain system. The two larger landwheels have reverse treads to gain the maximum traction to drive the various components, and each drill has a landwheel right at the back to take the weight. At the centre, above the transmission box, the vacuum pump can be seen.

Harvesting machines

The Jersey Royal is grown in banked rows, or ridges, at 18-20 in. (46 cm) centres. This width is unique to Jersey. It is rather close compared to elsewhere, where potatoes are ridged in larger banked rows 24–26 in. (61-66 cm) apart. So for the Jersey potato grower, the horse-drawn diggers were made with a narrower share than standard to suit the Jersey row, and so are all powered diggers and harvesters. When the tractor came along, farmers simply had their machines altered by taking off the shafts for the horse and fitting a drawbar. As time went on, manufacturers made them to fit the three-point linkage on tractors; many were similar to the horse machine, but the forks on spinners were driven by the tractor PTO. Many agricultural engineering companies manufactured potato diggers. A popular machine in the 1940s was produced by Tamken and supplied locally by the CGA, on the Esplanade. It was a mounted machine, driven by the PTO. The digger and share arrangement was almost identical to Ransomes horse-drawn Jersey Belle potato digger. The Ransomes mounted PTO digger has forks on a reel, with a parallel motion so that they remain vertical. Jersey's narrow row widths were a problem for importers of potato harvesters with a wide share, especially on the complete harvesters. They had to arrange to have them modified, although some manufacturers supplied modified machines for the Jersey crop. Elevator diggers had a similar problem with the chain-type elevators, but Johnson built a machine especially for the Island. The early elevator diggers had another problem: as the potatoes were dug, they were dropped onto the soil straight behind the machine. The person shaking the stalks had to follow the machine, throwing the tops aside, and move the potatoes to one side, to enable the tractor to dig the next row without running over the freshly dug potatoes. As time went on, more sophisticated machines with side discharge bar shakers, or riddles, became available to overcome the problem. One enterprising local company, L. C. Pallot, Central Motor Works, designed and built potato diggers suitable for local growers.

The tractor-mounted elevator potato digger, manufactured by L. C. Pallot at the Central Motor Works in the 1960s.
The Pallot digger is driven by the tractor PTO at 540 rpm. It would have been operated with the Ferguson TE20, David Brown, and Ford Dexta types of tractors. The share and side discs followed by the elevator chain can be seen quite clearly. The power is transmitted through a gearbox at the top of the machine (behind the horizontal bar) and three matched V-belts to a rod/bar-type elevator chain. The chain passes over the rollers at the front, behind the share, then over two elliptical sprockets, which shook rather than vibrated the chain, to shake the soil from the tubers, before they were dropped over the back. L. C. Pallot produced 400 elevator potato diggers. This one is displayed at the Steam Museum.

(*right*) Johnson mounted chain elevator, potato digger manufactured in the 1950s and 1960s.
The Johnson digger has an 18 in. (45.6 cm) wide pointed share, in front of the elevator. On each side are two discs, which can be adjusted for depth; they help to loosen the soil, to aid penetration of the share beneath the crop. The rod-type elevator chain is 4 ft 2 in. (127 cm) long, and the bars are spaced at 1.25 in. (3.2 cm) and 1.5 in. (3.8 cm) apart and driven by the tractor PTO at 540 rpm. Transmission is by a Reynolds chain and sprockets at the rear, driving the elevator chain over an idler, behind the share. At the centre, on either side, are two oval-shaped sprockets, which shake the chain to remove the soil from the potatoes. The loose soil will fall through. The local supplier was the JF(T)U Ltd. and the owner the late Mr. Le Boutillier of Le Val Bachelier, St. Ouen, who retired in 1967.

Further developments were the multi-row elevator diggers, lifting two rows at a time.

Samon mounted multi-row chain elevator potato digger and pickers at Rozel.
The Samon multi-row elevator diggers were manufactured from the late 1960s. The elevator is driven by the tractor PTO at 540 rpm with a single V-belt to the elevator. It has two pneumatic-tyred wheels for depth control. The woman behind the machine is shaking and throwing the green tops aside, to leave the potatoes clear for the pickers.

The next stage of development was the oscillating share and riddles, with side delivery, to leave the land clear for the tractor and digger to lift the next row.

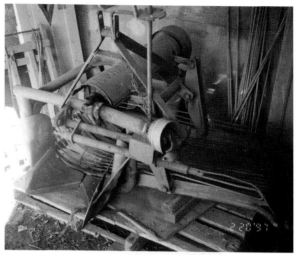

Kuxmann mounted potato digger with oscillating share and riddles that delivers the potatoes to the side rather than behind, leaving room for the tractor and machine to dig the next row before the potatoes have been picked.

Kuxmann diggers were manufactured in the 1960s. The machine is resting on a pallet board and the two-piece 24 in. (61 cm) wide share is divided at the centre; it can be clearly seen with the riddles behind it. The crop was lifted as the machine advanced, by vibrating the divided share, over which tubers passed to a bar-type shaker, which moved the crop sideways, to a second vibrating shaker, before the potatoes were dropped to the ground. The tractor PTO running at 540 rpm drives a crankshaft above the machine, operating two rockers, to cause the riddles and share to oscillate. There is one adjustable all-steel wheel at the centre at the back, for setting the depth. The three-point linkage lower link pins are on a crossbar, which has a lateral adjustment, lining up the share to the potato ridge to be dug; it is just inside the offside rear wheel. The local supplier is thought to have been the JF(T)U Ltd. The owner was the late Mr. Le Boutillier, of Le Val Bachelier, St. Ouen.

Complete potato harvesters

Complete harvesters were being developed in the post-war years. At first they were wasteful and not very efficient, leaving too many potatoes on the ground and damaging too many of those that were lifted. It was critical for Jersey Royals to be handled gently and avoid bruising during lifting. While there were a number of British manufacturers, it was the continental manufacturers who found favour locally.

A general view of a Grimme potato harvester. The Grimme Company designed the Jersey Gem potato harvester for Jersey's 18 in. (45.7 cm) rows with an 18 in. (45.2 cm) wide share. This model, with only slight changes, was manufactured from the 1960s and through the 1980s. It is driven by the tractor PTO at 540 rpm and, like a tractor trailer, it has two wheels, with some weight transfer to the tractor. A Massey Ferguson 135 tractor is operating it here. The tractor's hydraulic system is connected to the harvester to raise the share out of work and lower it into work. The potatoes are lifted over the share and delivered by a bar-chain elevator, similar to a chain elevator, to a large-diameter, wheel-type elevator at the back of the machine. A separate chain elevator discharges the green tops over the back and down a chute to be cast to the side. The tubers are then carried on a conveyor, to pass the sorting team, who pick out any stones, clods of earth, etc. The potatoes then pass on to the bagging point, at the front of the machine.

The drawbar of the Grimme harvester hitched to the tractor and the PTO shaft connected above it; the hydraulic hose is connected to a hydraulic ram for positioning the share relative to the potato row.

(*right*) This view shows the PTO coupled to the harvester and the yellow arrow to help the driver to position correctly on the potato ridge.

The yellow arrow pointing upward is to help the tractor driver position the inverted V-section roller exactly over the ridge of potatoes to be dug. Under the hydraulic hose, beyond the drawbar, can be seen the hydraulic ram that helps the driver to achieve that position by swinging the machine to the left or right. Behind the roller is one of the two discs, on either side of the share, and behind that can be seen a little view of the elevator. The machine is digging Mr. Colin Binet's potatoes at Maufant. The local supplier was Richard Pierson Ltd.

A general view of the Samro Farmer RBK potato harvester at work in St. Lawrence.

The potatoes are delivered to the large box at the front, for bulk-handling of the crop. The box has hydraulic rams to raise and tilt the box to empty it. The harvester has two wheels, towards the back, providing some weight transfer to the tractor to improve the traction and stabilise the harvester. The machine is hauled by the tractor's pick-up hitch. The Massey Ferguson 390 is a four-wheel-drive tractor. The PTO drives the machine at the usual 540 rpm and drives a hydraulic pump on the machine, which operates all the hydraulic services, rams and motors, etc. A valve chest, operated by the tractor driver, controls the hydraulic system. The share lifts one row of potatoes, and is adjusted by rams and discs, either side of the share. The crop is delivered on the first elevator to the wheel-type elevator, at the back, where the tops are removed and discharged by a separate elevator at the back. The final sorting is by hand, to remove any tops, stones, clods, green potatoes, etc. before discharging the crop into the large galvanised hopper. The machine, which is digging potatoes for Mr. Carter, was manufactured in the 1990s.

In this close-up can be seen the many hydraulic pipes to supply hydraulic services on the harvester and the V roller, and one of the two discs above the lifting share; also, the pipework, rams, and arms for raising and tipping the bulk tank.

View of the elevator at the back for discharging the green tops, and the wheel-type elevator; note the hydraulic pipework and services at the centre above the green tops elevator.

The picture below is a view looking into the future of potato harvesting and the equipment that will be used in the twenty-first century.

The Grimme type GZ1700 DL1 potato harvester designed with special attention to the gentle handling of the crop that is so important to the Jersey Royal.

Close-up of the front of the harvester lifting two rows at a time; as can be seen, this is a highly sophisticated harvester.

The machine has two separate lifting shares; it is driven by the tractor PTO operating a hydraulic pump to provide power and rapid adjustment to different components. The harvester is so long the two large wheels towards the rear can be steered, for turning on the headland, etc. A John Deere 6300 four-wheel-drive tractor provides the power. It is seen here being demonstrated at Rozel, by L. C. Pallot, Central Motor Works, in 1998. There are a number of these enormous potato-harvesting machines on the market, some of them in the Island.

Root harvesters

Armer Salmon Cheetah root or beet harvester lifting fodder beet at Maufant.

The Cheetah harvester serial no. 11A 3088 was manufactured in Ireland in the 1960s and was previously used to lift sugar beet in Shropshire. It will lift sugar beet, fodder beet, mangels, swedes, turnips, etc. The machine is driven by the tractor PTO at the usual 540 rpm. It has two big-diameter, reversed, open-cleat tyres. The machine eases the beet complete with tops out of the ground and it is lifted only a little to be snatched by a twin-belt elevator; the beet are then dropped onto a second elevator and in due course dropped into a bulk tank. When full, a trailer draws alongside and the tank is lifted and pivots over to empty its load in the trailer. The machine has several hydraulic controls, to line up the lifter with the row to be lifted, to set the depth, and operate the emptying of the bulk tank. Like all root harvesters, it is not perfect, as it drops the odd beet, but if accompanied by a labourer, it overcomes the problem, and it is very much quicker than hand lifting. Like all harvesters, it has a mass of moving parts, chain and belt drives, etc., making the grease gun a particularly important accessory to carry on the tractor. The original supplier was one of the many branches of F. H. Burgess in the West Midlands, and it is at present operated by Mr. Le Gallais, of Cowleywood Ltd.

This machine is not new technology but is typical of 1960s developments, when agricultural machinery manufacturers were developing complete root harvesters, following the lead by the combined harvesters for the cereal crop and more recently the potato harvesters. They were aiming to produce machines that went further than simply dig the crop out of the ground and leave it on the ground to be gathered manually.

A close-up of the lifting arrangement and the conveyor belts on the Cheetah harvester.

Tipping a load of fodder beet into the trailer for feeding to the cattle.

Machinery for working côtils

Cultivating côtils or steep hillsides has always proved difficult. So much so that during the war years, when every inch of land was needed in the UK for food production, tractor drivers in Wales and Scotland were awarded the George Medal for ploughing steep mountainsides. The author worked on ploughs on those mountainsides, in mid-Wales, when they were still being cultivated in the 1950s, and is not surprised over the awards. Another way had to be found.

The Island has steeply sloping arable land around many parts, mostly overlooking the coast such as Gorey, St. Catherine, Rozel, Grève de Lecq, and L'Étacq, in fact any east-, south-east-, and south-facing valley sides open to the sun. They all have one thing in common: they are difficult to cultivate but warm up quickly. When labour was relatively cheap, they were dug by hand, using a Jersey spade, often at piecework rates; but as the cost of such labour-intensive practices increased, this had to be abandoned. Our côtils were too small and too steep to consider putting in a tractor or tracklayer, as on the Welsh mountain. As a result, many côtils were neglected and became overgrown and derelict, until a way to cultivate them could be found.

The use of winches for ploughing and other cultivation was first developed for agriculture in the 1850s and 1860s. Most notable was John Fowler of Leeds, who manufactured ploughing engines at the Steam Plough Works for hauling balance ploughs in open country. They were exported all over the world. John Fowler had a depot at Magdeburg, in Germany which eventually became every bit as big as the factory in Leeds, and Ransomes of Ipswich built a depot in the Crimea. Unfortunately the First World War and the Russian Revolution brought that to an end.

In Jersey, the late Mr. Phil Cotillard, of La Commune, at Victoria Village, was enterprising when he fabricated a frame around a John Deere model B tractor, to which he assembled a winch for ploughing côtils. This was mounted on the offside of the tractor, beside the engine. Stability must have been a problem, but he apparently used it successfully as a contractor, before Mr. Ken Godel, of Bel Air Cottage, St. Mary, bought the tractor and winch from him and continued to use it.

The Ransomes MG5 tracklayer was also used with a winch. It was mounted on the back of at least two of these popular little tractors. This caused a bit of excitement for one contractor, Mr. Bertie Roulllé when he attempted to start the engine while the winch was engaged in preparing to plough a côtil. Fortunately, he was standing in front of the tractor to crank the starting handle, rather than sitting on it. It suddenly rolled over and continued to roll down to the bottom of the côtil. Undeterred, he clambered down the côtil after it; finding it had sustained only some slight damage to a steering lever, he started it up and drove it back up the côtil and continued ploughing. One or two people had nasty experiences.

A safer way was adopted by Ken Godel using an International IH 275 tractor with a winch on the three-point linkage. The tractor remained at the bottom of the côtil, but using a cable passing around a pulley at the top of the côtil hooked to a chain attached between two trees. The pulley was simply moved along the chain as the ploughing proceeded across the côtil.

Some readers may ask why not haul the plough downhill; would it not be easier? The fact is that this would have the detrimental effect of pulling the soil downhill, eventually leaving the top of the côtil bare of soil with soil accumulating at the bottom. There are problems enough with soil erosion at times, due to heavy rain, without adding to it. It is also much easier for the ploughman, holding and controlling the plough in work, when hauling up the hill.

An early post-war winch was designed by Mr. Don Pallot for Mr. Ken Richardson to plough his côtils at Les Pièces, St. Martin. It was bolted under the back axle of the Ferguson tractor, using the fender bolts. It was driven by chain and sprockets from the PTO. The winch was improved by fitting two open-ended box fabrications to the fender bolts, and left in place. The winch fittings were slid into the boxes, so doing away with the tedious business of having to bolt on the winch each time. The winch was popular and Don Pallot made approximately 200 of them. It did not have a safety clutch and stability could be a problem. Mr. Michael Vautier, at Rozel, used a weight resting on the ground and attached by a chain to the clutch. If the plough caught a root and the tractor attempted to tilt over, the chain tightened, pulling on the clutch pedal to disengage it.

In the 1950s the Institution of Agricultural Engineers saw to the setting up of the National Institute of Agricultural Engineering at Silsoe, in England, and a branch in Scotland, at the West of Scotland College of Agriculture. The latter set about designing and developing a suitable winch for working the braes of crofters in the West of Scotland; Jersey expressed interest. As a result the design details were made available in Jersey. These winches were made in Jersey and have proved to be stable and effective, provided the tractor can stand on comparatively firm and level ground while in operation.

The frame in which the winch drum is mounted is lowered squarely onto the ground, to stand on two widely spaced feet. The 0.3 in. (8 mm) cable is paid out down the côtil, hooked to the plough, and, operating the winch slowly and steadily, the plough is drawn safely at walking speed up the côtil. It still requires careful operation and close attention by both the driver on the tractor and the ploughman. To take the plough down again, the operator will walk down the côtil, hauling the plough after him and making use of gravity!

A mounted côtil winch, made in Jersey, to the design developed in the 1960s by the Institution of Agricultural Engineers at the West of Scotland College of Agriculture.
The transmission from the tractor PTO to the winch has a 4:1 reduction chain and sprocket driving through a safety clutch. The tractor PTO speed is variable and adjusted to suit the terrain and the job in hand. The cable is hauling from the right-hand side of the tractor, on the côtils above Rozel.

Two winches working on two neighbouring côtils one below the other; the red winch closest to the camera is hauling the plough nearing the top of the côtil.

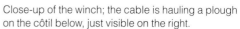

Close-up of the winch; the cable is hauling a plough on the côtil below, just visible on the right.

The plough in the lower côtil is winched up the field, doing perfect work.

A left-hand plough ready to work up the côtil. It is a lightweight single-furrow plough with a 12 in. deep and 12 in. wide (30.5 x 30.5 cm) digger body and has the big Jersey skimmer and disc coulter. These ploughs have no self-lift, to lift the plough out of work; the emphasis is on light weight and ease of handling on a steep slope. A single beam supports the skimmer body and disc, and at the back, a single small stubby handle. The stalks for the two wheels are both lightweight and adjustable for height and width. Adjusting the furrow wheel horizontally will adjust furrow width; adjusting the height of both wheels will adjust the pitch. Adjusting the height of the furrow wheel will adjust the wing. The wheel stalks have been extended, to provide handles to give the ploughman something to hold onto, especially if he has to add his weight to the plough to maintain the depth. They are made locally by adapting lightweight ploughs, such as a planting plough or Ransomes TS 42, changing the bodies to digger bodies and fitting skimmers and disc coulters.

Cultivating these côtils is very much a case of 'going back to basics', using traditional methods, with trailing ploughs, harrows, and planting ploughs. Apart from the winches, mounted implements and machines have no place on steep côtils. The grower may have two of these ploughs, one with a right-hand body and the second with a left-hand body. One year the plough casting to the right will be used, and the next the plough casting to the left. If the grower were to plough casting the soil in the same direction each time year after year, the soil would end up deep on one side of the côtil and shallow on the other. These côtil ploughs are good examples of thoughtful adaptation by local growers and blacksmiths.

They enable growers to take advantage of easterly facing slopes, which drain and warm up early to produce extra early potatoes, which command a high price on the markets. They are helped by the natural light loam soil, which is maintained light and friable, and in good condition, having never been subjected to heavy traffic, which compresses the soil and spoils its structure.

The late Mr. Douglas Bomford, a founder member of the Institution of Agricultural Engineers, was a director of Bomford Bros. Ltd., the agricultural engineers, and the author's employer for several years. He would have awarded 100 marks out of 100 to the designers of these lightweight ploughs, implements, and winches. They are the result of the experience of the growers working those côtils with the help of their local blacksmith.

The plough is taken back down the côtil to plough the next furrow. These côtils are steep and not easy to walk on; one has to be fit with good balance!

The foregoing pictures illustrate the versatility of tractor-mounted winches. After ploughing fertiliser is spread and has to be harrowed in.

To prepare the soil for planting two sections of a zigzag harrow are bolted firmly together to two steel beams.
The harrow has wheels set sufficiently high so they will be clear of the ground in work but will support the harrow when lifted; the handle bar at the back, as on the plough, is necessary to wheel the implement down the côtil to the foot for the start of each bout.
The zigzag harrow will be a standard British drag harrow that has been made without alteration for the last hundred years.

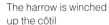

The harrow is winched up the côtil

The harrow is taken back down the côtil for the next bout.

These potatoes are being planted on 9 January with an ultra-light côtil-planting plough. The tractor winch is hauling the planting plough.

In late February the plastic sheeting is removed to reveal the advanced state of the crop.

A côtil potato-lifting plough is a modified light plough: the mouldboard has been cut short and three bars appropriately shaped are bolted to it.

The object of the rods is to crumble and filter the soil, after the share has lifted it, to separate the potatoes from the soil and leave them on the top. The top bar is 19.5 in. (49.5 cm) long, the middle bar 17.5 in. (44.5 cm), and the bottom one 14.5 in. (37 cm). Depth of work is 11 in. (28 cm), the share width 10 in. (25.5 cm). The original

plough, probably a horse-drawn breezing plough, goes back to the early 20th century; the modifications are more recent. The two wheels may be original, although they may have worn and been replaced; the furrow wheel has the bigger diameter as usual, adjusted to level up the plough. The curved handle at the front is one of the old curved pump handles found over a well or cistern; it has been turned upside down (The knob on the end gives it away!). The second, but smaller, curved handle is an old door handle, bent round and strengthened with a rod and welded to a third vertical handle at the back, above the body. The low handle right at the back is used to line the plough up with the row to be dug and used to haul the plough back down the côtil, to dig another ridge. The crop is dug in the first week of April, after only three months in the ground! (Vautier Bros., on the côtils above Rozel.)

It would be quite impossible to use a potato digger on the steep-sided côtils and this implement hauled up the côtil with a winch is certainly quicker and less laborious than digging côtils with a fork. This type of potato-lifting plough, but with conventional ploughing handles and bars in place of mouldboards, for digging potatoes on the flat was fairly commonplace in the days of horse-drawn implements, particularly before mechanical diggers.

12 Tractor-Drawn Machines

The binder

Harvesting scene: Mr Charles Le Couteur's Albion PTO-driven binder and Ferguson tractor at work at Samarès Manor, reaping and binding a crop of oats for Mr. Vincent Obbard.

The Albion binder is a well-preserved example of a very popular make of British binder. It is being used here preparing for the Samarès Manor public Threshing Day. The scene could be pre-war or early post-war with the stookers at work. The knife, knotter, sails, etc. were driven then by a large-diameter landwheel. When tractors replaced horses, the draw pole was shortened and fitted with a jaw for the tractor drawbar. Stooking was a job the author did many times in his school holidays. Bare arms were not a good idea; they would be scratched by the straw, especially barley. The sheaves must stand in the stook and hear the church bells three times before they can be carried! That is how long it takes for the grains to dry out and harden off before they can be loaded on vans and trailers and carried off to the rickyard or threshing machine.

Many hundreds of binders of this type contributed to bringing home the harvest during the two world wars. In those days very few were PTO-driven; many were still hauled by horses or by Standard Fordson model N tractors driven by land girls in the second war. The binder remained virtually unchanged apart from the landwheel drive being replaced with the PTO and minor changes over many years since it first appeared in the 19th century: a complicated piece of machinery that lasted successfully for eighty or ninety years.

The power take-off, or PTO, is a splined shaft at the back of the tractor driven by the engine for power-driven machines towed behind the tractor. The first time a tractor with a PTO was used to both haul and operate a binder was in 1919 with an International Junior tractor. The International Junior was the first tractor to have a PTO operating at 540 rpm, the world standard today, together with a more recent introduction at 1,000 rpm. The PTO drive was not possible until tractor PTOs became universal.

The original landwheel on the binder was a steel fabrication with a wide rim to prevent it sinking in the soil with the heavy load. Around the broad-rim iron tyre were a series of shallow chevron-shaped lugs to provide the necessary grip. As the machine advances through the crop, it is cut by the reciprocating cutter bar, as on a hay mower, and the crop falls onto a canvas slatted conveyor which delivers it to a second canvas conveyor, which has above it a third; the crop sandwiched between these last two is delivered to the knotter table.

A model 5A Albion binder with a 5 ft (152.4 cm) wide cutter bar and serial no. 62148; it was manufactured by Harrison McGregor and Co. Ltd. at Leigh in England, just after the Second World War.
It has one large wheel under the knotter table and a second smaller wheel behind the outside crop divider. The binder is painted Albion-yellow. Previously it was used in Guernsey.

The man on the seat has his hand on the lever that adjusts the height of the sails, which in turn push the crop back onto the canvas conveyor.

The knotter is at the centre of the picture; the curved needle is in the raised position, where it delivers the twine between the open beaks of the knotter. Towards the top right are the discharge arms to push the tied sheaf off the knotter table.
After the knot is tied, the discharge arms will rotate anticlockwise and push the sheaf off the table and in so doing will tighten the knot and pull the knot out of the knotter. The knotter consists of a beak which first opens to receive the twine fed by a large curved needle which rises through the table, separating the flow of straw stalks of cereal on the table in order to form the next sheaf about to be knotted. Having received the twine, the beaks then close, gripping the twine, followed by a complete rotation to make the knot before the sheaf is pulled away, so tightening the knot. The action is tripped by cams, etc. and is so fast that the eye can barely follow it.

Nerves were often frayed when the knotter failed to make a satisfactory tie and the team of stookers arrived at a spot where the previous line of sheaves lay along the field untied! Another problem arose when a canvas started slipping, and it was the 'last straw' when a stone got between the fingers of the cutter bar and damaged a knife section. When the binder goes well and the stookers are busy collecting the sheaves and making stooks on a sunny afternoon, the mood is usually one of contentment, but within moments of a breakdown with the binder, the happy mood alters rapidly, especially when changeable weather is in the offing.

The reaper

A tractor-trailed reaper/hay mower manufactured by A. C. Bamlett, model 1 HR, with a 3 ft (91.5 cm) wide cutter bar, made pre-Second World War or just after. Originally designed to be a horse-drawn reaper but converted by Bamlett for tractor draught, it was a factory modification to meet the then new demand for a small tractor-drawn mower. The lift control lever has been brought forward to be within reach of the tractor driver, with a connecting rod to the old lever, now a stub. The small 3 ft cutter bar suggests it was for one horse originally. A pair of shafts for a horse would have been fitted to the wooden beam. It has two cast-iron wheels with shallow cleats and a live axle to drive a large-diameter gearwheel beside the wheel on the right, with an inside ratchet drive through a gearbox crankshaft and connecting rod. The machine has no seat for a horse driver but the socket is still there in the main casting to accommodate a seat leaf spring. Painted Bamlett-orange. (La Société Jersiaise collection, stored in the Museum store at Augrès, Trinity.)

Hay tedding and turning

A tractor-mounted Vicon Lely Acrobat hay-turner and windrowing machine.
The Acrobat's four 'tined reels' are mounted in pairs on U-shaped frames that are carried on a pivot at the centre; each U frame can be rotated to swing over one way to work in a line of four for windrowing the hay, but for turning hay or swath-turning, the U frame is rotated for the reels to work in pairs. In both operations the tined reels are at an angle to the line of draught, causing them to rotate when drawn over the ground. The Acrobat was manufactured in the 1950s and 1960s. (Courtesy of Mr. J. Le Gallais, of Roselands, St. Saviour.) Hay turning or swath turning is carried out after mowing to dry out the hay. It may be turned two or three times before it is windrowed preparatory to baling.

The Lely Superzip 388 swath-turner and windrower driven by the PTO. This is a much later design than the Acrobat and was manufactured in 1996.

The Super Zip has a working width of 7 ft (213 cm), turning two swaths. When lowered to the ground it is supported on two caster wheels, one at the centre of each reel. It is carried on the three-point linkage of an IH 784 tractor. It is painted Lely-red. The two PTO-driven reels of eight double tines can be rotated as seen here to create a windrow at the centre, or they can both be rotated to turn each swath separately to assist drying. When sufficiently dry, the machine will operate as it is here to combine two turned swaths into a single windrow ready for the pick-up baler. Working on Mr. Jack Le Sueur's farm at Clairval, St. Saviour; his son-in-law Jonathan Rennard is driving.

Model 1000 mounted swath-turner, hay-tedder, and wilter; the tines rotate on a horizontal shaft made by Abt Products Ltd. in Herefordshire.

The tines are mounted on a slight helix to the shaft in sets of four on stout canvas sheeting to allow the tines to swing back if they should strike a hard object.

The helix has the effect of turning the hay, so bringing the bottom of the hay to the top to dry. The machine is PTO driven at 540 rpm and the working width is 5 ft 2 in. (150 cm). It has two pneumatic-tyred wheels adjustable for height, and two sheet-metal doors at the back are adjustable to alter the direction the hay is thrown to form a windrow or simply turn or ted the swath. The machine was supplied by KJP Machinery Services Ltd., St. Lawrence, to Mr. A. Le Gallais of, Cowleywood, St. Saviour.

Several machines similar to this one were being manufactured in the 1960s and after. An early one was made by E. V. Twose, of Tiverton and sold in Jersey by the Jersey Farmers (Trading) Union Ltd. Over the years they have become larger and wider to cope with the wider swaths, cut with longer cutter bars on modern mowers, and to make use of the extra power of bigger and more powerful tractors.

Balers

Before the days of the one-man pick-up baler, as it was originally described, hay was gathered with a hay sweep, first pulled by a pair of horses, one on either side of the sweep. Later sweeps were made to hitch on the front of a tractor. The tines on the sweep were finely constructed, each one only some 5 ins. (13 cm) from its neighbour and approximately 5 ft (150 cm) long with the pointed tip turned upwards to prevent it digging in. The tractor was driven along the windrows, gathering the hay on the sweep and driving it to a stationary baler. Simply reversing the tractor unloaded the sweep, where a second man with a pitchfork would load the hay into the baler. Alternatively, the hay was deposited for a skilled man, with labourers helping, to build a hayrick.

Gathering hay was also performed with the buckrake, similar to a hay sweep but with much thicker tines. It is made to fit on a front-end loader on a tractor and had the advantage that the load could be lifted and tipped in place if need be. Details will be found towards the end of this chapter.

Stationary balers are usually driven with a stationary engine mounted underneath, or free-standing. Flat belts were the normal form of transmission before the V-belt. A detailed description of baling machines is given in Chapter 7. The author as a young man recalls the excitement in the summer of 1949 when the first one-man pick-up baler was advertised in the *Farmers Weekly*.

International B440 pick-up baler manufactured in the 1970s.
The B440 pick-up baler is driven by a 35-hp tractor's PTO at 540 rpm operating the ram at 80 strokes a minute. A 35-hp tractor is the minimum power required. In this instance the baler is at the Samarès Manor Threshing Day and is being used as a stationary baler. The straw is being piled up in front of the pick-up reel that will gather it up to pass it to the auger, which together with the reciprocating fork delivers it to the baling chamber on the right. It is painted International-red and is on two rubber-tyred wheels. The baler belongs to Mr. Len Moon and was probably supplied by Messrs. Pallot, Central Motor Works. The straw is from the threshing machine.

A view of the back of the baler. A bale emerges from the chamber and the spiked wheel above the next bale measures the length of each one before the guillotine cuts through and the bale is tied. The baling twine is fed through to the two knotters for completing the knots. This baling machine followed the very popular International B45 baler of the 1950s (the 'B' stood for British) which was priced below the competition, such as New Holland. They had been manufacturing balers for some considerable time and were probably the first to revolutionise baling with a one-man pick-up baler. The New Holland pick-up baler was considered by many to be supreme. The knotters were always a source of trouble, as they were on the binders, often causing delays and frustration at busy times. While the B45 was popular because of its price, New Holland's knotters were reliable; they also made a wire-tying pick-up baler but, while it was successful, the wire would wear the knotters.

The great attraction of the one-man pick-up baler was simple to understand: one man with a tractor and baler could go to a field of hay or straw and bale it. He would require no assistance provided the hay had been raked into windrows, ready for the pick-up baler to pick it up. Timing was important: the hay had to be thoroughly dry before baling, otherwise it would heat up and become mouldy in the bale. Before pick-up balers came to Jersey hay was bundled by hand straight from the haycock. The author can recall seeing his father demonstrating to the Breton labour how to draw the hay from the haycock, bundle it, then kneel on it to hold it together and compress it while twisting stems of hay to form a rope and wrapping it around the bundle and then bending and tucking in the end in a particular way to ensure it remained firmly tied.

A pick-up baler frequently seen in Jersey was the British-built Jones baler, usually used by contractors and at one time imported and used by the Blandin family. Basically, all pick-up balers look very similar to the IH machine shown here. It is in the unusual role of baling straw fed by hand, falling from the straw walkers of a threshing machine. A real mix of old and new technology! The tractor PTO drives a universally jointed shaft to a flywheel at the front of the baler, then through a gearbox, where power was transmitted to the pick-up tines, and then to the auger behind, which pushes the crop into the bale chamber, assisted by powered fork. Then in turn a ram moves back and forth along the bale chamber to compress the hay. Bale density is adjustable, usually through one or two hand screws, forcing one or two flexible metal plates onto the top of the bale above the chamber, so compressing the bale to the desired density. A pair of knotters similar to, but more robust than, the knotter on a binder tie the bale with baler twine. They were timed usually by a finger wheel, which was rotated by the bale as it was pushed along the chamber. At a given moment, when the finger wheel has run its course as the bale reaches the desired length, a guillotine will slice across the chamber and two long needles will move across the chamber to the knotters to complete the tie. Baler twine, a natural fibre, is similar to the binder twine of an earlier period but has more strands of fibre, making it thicker and stronger. Inevitably, in due course a plastic twine was also introduced.

New Holland Sperry pick-up baler, model 370 Hayliner, serial no. B370 V 1942, hauled by an International 784 tractor driven by Mr. Jonathan Rennard, of Clairval.
The baler is PTO-driven at 540 rpm at 80 ram strokes a minute. The pick-up width is 4 ft 9 in. (145 cm). The pick-up reel will have lines of tines like a comb that will pick up the hay and deliver it to the forks that move the hay into the bale chamber on the right. This machine has forks to deliver the hay to the bale chamber, but the International baler has an auger and a fork to move the hay to the bale chamber. It was manufactured in 1974/5 and supplied by Messrs. W. H. Staite.

The knotters above the bale chamber are similar to the knotter on the binder.

A completed bale leaves the chamber and falls to the ground to be collected later. The open baler twine box reveals the four rolls of baler twine.
All high-density balers worked on a similar principle: a rotating reel of combs pick up the hay from the windrow, an auger, or sets of tines, move the hay sideways towards the bale chamber, where a reciprocating ram pushes it into the bale chamber, cutting it like a guillotine on the inlet side, and compresses it. After a measured amount of hay has been compressed a pair of needles rises up to pass the baler twine to the knotters, where it is grabbed by the beaks of the two knotters, which then rotate through 360 degrees to make the knot. The twine is cut and the ram pushes the finished bale towards the back of the machine, where it remains for the next lot of hay to be compressed against it. Eventually, being pushed further and further back with each stroke of the ram, it falls to the ground.

The examples we have discussed so far are all high-density balers; there were also low-density balers or trussers, which worked on much the same principle but produced a much looser and lighter bale, considered by many to be superior because the hay would continue to dry in the bale. Details of trussers and low-density balers are illustrated in Chapter 7. Trussed hay had to be collected and stacked only when it was thoroughly dry; if it was stacked too soon it would heat up in the stack and self-ignite, leading to a rick fire, or barn fire if stacked in a barn. Two manufacturers of low-density balers used in the UK were Ransome-Lorant of Watford, a subsidiary of Ransomes of Ipswich, and Welgar of Germany. Another low-density baler was manufactured by Allis Chalmers, which made rolled bales. The snag was that the rolled bales were difficult to stack; but they made good-quality hay and the rain ran off them if they were caught in a shower. These rolled bales are not to be confused with the large-diameter rolled bales of today that are contained in netting or large plastic bags.

Disc mowers

A rotary disc-type mower and conditioner cutting grass for silage.
The disc-type machines have four or six discs but the gear train is expensive and, like all gearboxes, absorbs a lot of power: four discs require a minimum of 30 hp from the PTO, and six-disc machines, 50 hp; even more horsepower is needed with a conditioner. They are far less vulnerable than the reciprocating mower to being damaged by sticks, stones, molehills, etc. and as a consequence can be driven much faster over the ground without hindrance.

Taarup mounted hay or silage rotary disc-type mower, model no. 226; the cutter bar and discs have been lifted into the vertical position for transport and storage. This enables the cutter discs to be seen more easily.
The width of cut is 7 ft 6 in. (226 cm) with six rotary discs, each with two free-swinging cutter blades mounted on a bar driven by a gear train in oil. Between each gear-driven disc is an idler gear to provide the correct direction of rotation on each cutting disc. It is PTO-driven at 540 rpm but requires more power than the earlier Bamlett reciprocating mower. It is painted Taarup red. The cutting blades are free swinging, held out in work by centrifugal force and so arranged to swing back under the discs in the event of striking a stone or clod, thus protecting the cutter blade from damage. The first and last discs on the bar are fitted with a flat-topped cone, which directs the crop into a narrow swath. The cutter bar is fitted with a soft cover over a light frame to prevent stones flying when kicked up by the high-speed rotors. It was manufactured in 1975/6 and the owner is Mr. A. Le Gallais, of Cowleywood Ltd., at Maufant.

Tractors with more powerful engines enabled designers to consider these PTO-driven machines. The rotary drum and disc machines began replacing the 120-year-old reciprocating blade mower in the 1960s. The drum type were subject to design limitations, having only two drums each with a diameter twice that of the disc type: the crop had to pass between the drums, and to enable this to happen they had to be contra-rotating, which made a narrow swath. On the disc type, the discs are mounted above the support bar and transmission; on the drum-type mowers the drums hang under the support bar, which also carries the transmission. The smaller drums have two knives per drum, bigger-diameter drums, three, and the biggest 3 ft 3.5 in. (100 cm) have four.

Both types have their place and may be fitted with an integral grass conditioner, which squeezes/ bruises the grass to hasten drying for haylage or haymaking. Both types continue to be manufactured at the time of writing.

The flail forage-harvester

The Taarup flail forage-harvester at work. Normally a high-sided trailer would be used, but in this case the crop is cut and loaded for immediate consumption, which also enables the reader to see the cut grass being discharged into the trailer. The Handy's width of cut is 3 ft 6 in. (170 cm). The flails have a forward curve towards the tip and are 2.75 in. (7 cm) wide and 5.5 in. (14 cm) wide. The harvester is PTO-driven at 540 rpm. The power absorbed with this type of machine is 25-30 hp, requiring four V-belts to the rotor shaft. The machine is attached to the tractor drawbar and has two pneumatic-tyred wheels. The flails are mounted on a shaft in several banks in the form of a row along the shaft and serve a dual role: (1) to cut the crop and (2) to act as the blades of a fan to create a powerful draft to blow the cut material up the chute above and into the trailer. Each flail is mounted with a single pivot pin to a joining link, with a second pivot pin which allows the flail to swing backwards and forwards. There are gaps between the flails, which are filled by the next line of flails in the following row. Overall diameter of the rotor, with flails extended by centrifugal force, is 22 in. (56 cm) approximately.

Front view of the Taarup Handy flail-type cutter-blower forage-harvester, model DM1100, serial no. 21523

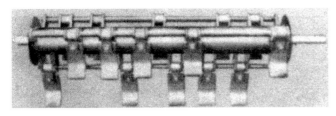

The cutter shaft and curved flails are designed to both cut the grass and blow it up through the chute into the trailer.

The trailer is attached to the tractor with a pick-up hitch, but runs beside the tractor like a reaper. The delivery chute is adjustable in two places: it can be swivelled at the top to direct the cut material to any part of the trailer being towed and the top end can be raised or lowered to direct material to the front or back of the trailer. The adjustments are made by a control handle which extends forward to be reached from the tractor seat. The material being cut will be fed directly to cattle and a low-sided trailer is adequate for the small load; normally, high wire-mesh sides would be used to obtain a full load. These machines are popular for zero-grazing and silage-making. Some farmers like to cut the crop and allow it to fall and wilt to lower the moisture content before picking it up; others allow it to dry even more to make haylage. This type of machine was first produced in the UK in the mid-1950s and they have continued to be developed and produced by several companies. The owner is Mr. A. Le Gallais, Cowleywood Ltd., Maufant. The supplier was Waveney Tractors, of Beccles in Cambridgeshire.

Taarup-Kverneland forage-harvester type TA1100, model DM1100, serial no. 346714.

The specification is much the same as for the older machine above. In work, it is mounted on the three-point linkage and has two 18 in. (45.5 cm) pneumatic-tyred wheels. This machine is mounted on a tractor with a cab, and the controls are installed in the cab to make adjustments to the chute from the driver's seat possible by using electric motors.

The two electric motors for adjusting the direction of the cut material.

Having a cab, the adjustments to the chute have to be made with electric motors, as illustrated above, and controlled from inside the cab. One motor rotates the chute and the other motor at the top will alter the angle of tilt up or down to direct the cut material into different parts of the trailer in order to fill it.

Both machines are painted Taarup-red, the second was manufactured in 1995 and was supplied by L. C. Pallot. They have been in production almost without change for forty years.

In the meantime, Taarup have been taken over by Kverneland, a large engineering conglomerate in Scandinavia who have had interests for many years in farm machinery such as ploughs, and who have acquired several companies, including Ransomes of Ipswich. They are also ship-builders.

Maize and silage-harvester

Maize is grown in Jersey as a valuable food crop for dairy cattle; it was often planted after early potatoes, growing quickly and ready to cut with a sickle in late August, and fed green to the cows when grass was getting short. Today it is grown more widely and harvested later in the year when the cobs are well-formed. It is cut both for immediate feeding to the dairy herd and for silage. Maize of a different variety and known as corn is grown in the corn belt of America and elsewhere. It is grown for human consumption as 'corn on the cob' or cornflakes! The harvesting machine for that crop harvests the cobs, whereas the one illustrated below cuts and chops the maize for silage. The manufacturers are Ford-New-Holland, based in Belgium.

This forage harvester is set up for harvesting maize, cutting and chopping up two rows. It is PTO-driven and has a number of hydraulic controls.

This chopper blower model no. 525/2, serial no. 6704011, will cut and chop up the standing crop in the background then blow it into a following trailer for delivery to a silage tower or pit; but it may be fed directly to the cattle. The harvester is tractor-drawn and PTO-driven at 540 rpm. The power absorbed will be 30-40 hp. It is on two pneumatic-tyred wheels in New Holland colours, red and yellow. It was manufactured in 1989 and supplied by W. M. Staite Ltd.; the owner is Mr. A. Le Gallais, Cowleywood Ltd., Maufant. It has a drawbar ring for a tractor pick-up hitch and a hydraulic ram fitted to a pick-up hitch at the back for hooking up and towing a high-sided trailer. The gearbox has massive gears and heavy-duty chains for transmitting power around the machine to perform particular functions. Power is delivered to the disc-cutters which cut the maize at ground level as it passes between feeder chains which are also power-driven and can be seen under the three dividers. The choppers and blower absorb a tremendous amount of power to chop the leaves, stalks, and cobs and blow the chopped material up the vertical tube and into the trailer being towed behind. The crop has to be drilled in row widths to match the width between the dividers. The pointed dividers complete with feeder chains and cutting discs can be detached from the main body of the machine. In their place, a comb pick-up reel, as on the pick-up baler, is fitted. This attachment will pick up previously cut grass, which has

been allowed to wilt to reduce the moisture content before collection for silage making. The auger then compresses and pushes the cut material through the hatch at the back to the chopper blower behind, where it is chopped up and blown into a high-sided trailer towed behind. Although purchased as recently as 1989, this type of machine has been available for many years since more powerful tractors with PTOs became generally available.

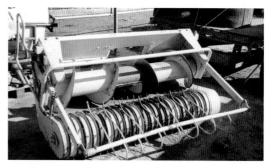

(*right*) The pick-up attachment is fitted in place of the maize dividers

Using the pick-up attachment illustrated above, the partly dried crop is picked up and chopped and blown into the trailer to go into a tower silo to make silage

Round bale carrier

Lawrence Edwards mounted carrier for carrying round bales. The bale carrier's hydraulic hoses on the rams are coupled to the tractor's hydraulic couplings to set the space between the two large-diameter cylindrical arms. They are lowered to the ground one on either side of the plastic-covered roll, and the hydraulic ram will draw the two arms towards each other under the roll of hay or straw to enable it to be lifted and transported to a trailer or about the farmyard. (Mr. A. Le Gallais, Cowleywood Ltd., Maufant.)

Round bales may be bound in a hessian band or black or white plastic.
These round bales are not to be confused with the round bales produced by the Allis Chalmers baler, which are much smaller in diameter and were never wrapped in plastic but were tied with baler twine wound round the bale.

Combined harvesters

The first attempt to make a combined harvester was in Michigan in 1836, where it was not a success. This was at a time when even portable threshing machines were being developed in the USA and the UK and threshing was not particularly well established in America. There were threshing machines in England on the bigger farms and estates; they were installed in a building usually with a horse engine to drive them, but there were several with built-in steam engines which

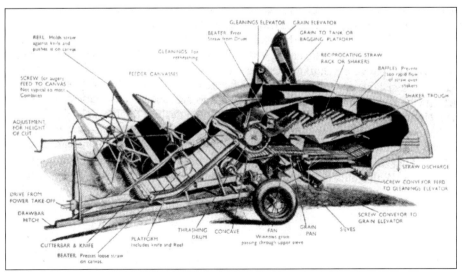

A drawing of the interior design of a PTO-driven tractor-trailed combined harvester (courtesy of International Harvester).

could also be used to drive other barn machinery. When that first combined harvester in Michigan was moved to California in 1854, it worked successfully. It was a horse-drawn machine. The first self-propelled combined harvester was manufactured in 1908. At that time large horse-drawn combined harvesters with a 20-ft (610 cm) cutter bar were gaining in popularity on the great plains of the USA. The machine was driven by a large-diameter landwheel. They required a very large team of horses to haul them. That was in a part of the world where labour was in short supply but horses were plentiful.

McCormick International tractor-trailed combined harvester model B64 .
The B64 combined harvester is PTO-driven at 540 rpm (it was also available with an air-cooled engine). This machine was the straight-through type, virtually the same width from the cutter bar to the shaker at the back. The cutter bar is 6 ft (183 cm) wide, the length of drum and concave slightly less than 6 ft, and it has a single straw shaker rather than straw walkers. The power required is 30 hp in good conditions, i.e. the crop ripe for threshing and the land dry and hard. The harvester has a pick-up hitch and two pneumatic-tyred wheels on a common axle. An agricultural contractor and the farmer operate this machine; Mr. John Billot is on the bagging platform at La Porte, Maufant, in the 1950s.

The small trailed machines with 4 ft (122 cm), 5 ft (152.4 cm), and 6 ft (182 cm) cutter bars were mostly straigh-through machines. The crop was presented to the threshing drum with heads or ears first and evenly spread across the width, so the drum could be of a smaller diameter than usual but equally effective. A beater drum in front of the threshing drum pushes the ears down to go between the threshing drum and the concave. For the same reasons the shaker was as effective as straw walkers. Apart from the cutter bar and canvas elevator, the rest of the machine was the same as any threshing machine. The tailing bed is like an adjustable coarse sieve, to let the grain fall through and to separate the chaff and cavings/tailings (the coarse material). The grain sieves underneath are changeable according to the crop; the grain falls through the sieve onto an auger, which delivers the grain to the grain elevator and finally to the cleaning and grading cylinder, which both cleans the grains and separates the seconds from the best sample, and so to the bagging platform. The tailings elevator lifts the coarse material to a chute to pass with the straw over the straw shaker to get any more loose grains out before the straw and tailings are discharged to the ground. Some manufacturers offered a bulk tank with a discharge auger instead of a bagging platform. With a bulk tank, a tractor and high-sided trailer are necessary to empty the tank.

Front view of the IH tractor and B64 combined harvester; two people are needed, a driver and a man on the bagging platform to change the bags as they fill.
The bags will be placed on a trailer at the headland before they set off on the next round. It is worth noting the comparison in labour between the combined harvester and the binder: both need only a driver and a man on the machine, but the binder requires a gang of stookers to be followed by the people to gather the harvest and carry it to the thresher and a gang at the threshing machine. The combine shows a tremendous saving in labour.

Self-propelled combined harvesters

The self-propelled combined harvester also needs a crew of two, a driver and a bagger, unless it has a bulk tank, when it only needs one man but also has a tractor and high-sided trailer in attendance to empty the tank when it is full.

Fahr model MDL1 self-propelled combined harvester, serial no. 72318.

The Fahr harvester has a 6 ft (183 cm) wide cutter bar and five-batten two-speed pick-up reel for raising a weather-laid crop or one as partially laid in places as in this crop of oats. It has an 18 in. (45.5 cm) diameter, 36 in. (91.5 cm) wide drum with five beater bars and runs at 1,500 rpm for wheat and barley, reducing to 1,400 rpm for oats. It has an eight-bar concave and straw walkers behind; beneath, it has two interchangeable cleaning and sorting sieves and a final cleaning cylinder. It is capable of threshing the whole range of cereals and beans and grasses etc. The power unit is a 35 bhp Perkins four-cylinder diesel engine type C 4/99. The original engine was an air-cooled Porsche Industrial petrol/TVO engine of 37 bhp. All controls are manual. The speed over the ground is controlled by variable speed/diameter pulleys, which are used on many self-propelled combined harvesters. It is on four pneumatic-tyred wheels: tyre sizes are 8 x 32 and 4.50 x 16 on large-diameter wheels for traction and the smaller wheels at the back for steering. It is painted Fahr-red. The Fahr was manufactured in 1957 and the supplier and original owner was Messrs. Le Cappelain of St. Peter's Iron Works, who used two of them for contract work, replacing their threshing machines. The present owner is Mr. Charles Le Couteur and it forms part of his collection of working tractors and farm machines at Westlands, St. Peter.

Rear view of the combine dropping the straw in swaths ready for the pick-up baler

Crop sprayers

The horse-drawn and early tractor spraying machines used large quantities of water to dissolve the chemical to be sprayed. The crop was virtually soaked with a water-based spray in order to ensure that it got a good covering. This required sprayers with large tanks and frequent filling, which entailed having a mixing tank in the field being sprayed, a supply of chemicals in the manufacturer's packs, and a good supply of water. Cut-down or open-ended water casks were used for mixing, and either a cask or water tank was used to transport the water to the field. In the 1950s chemical companies such as ICI, and very often the oil companies began to produce chemical sprays with an oil base and the ability to stick to the plant leaf without loss from run-off. They were applied to the plant in a mist with a fine droplet rather than many large droplets, as with the old sprayers. They became known as low-volume sprays. The advantage was the low volume of liquid to be handled to get the spray onto the crop. The reduction in volume was to little more than one or two gallons to the vergée and a little more to the acre. The manufacturers had to redesign the nozzles of the sprayers and produce low-volume, high-pressure pumps to create the mist to apply the spray to the crop. As time went on, the droplet size continued to be reduced. The tank could be somewhat smaller, such as the Vigzol, a low-volume sprayer carrying a lower volume of liquid on the hydraulic lift of the smaller tractors. The mix could be made up at the farm buildings or in the tank of the sprayer while filling it, the exception being a large field a long way from the farm buildings.

Two Caruelle mounted crop sprayers; the pumps are driven by the PTO.

Caruelle crop sprayers have a 28.5 gallon (400 l) plastic tank. The pump is driven by the tractor PTO at the usual 540 rpm. The power absorbed is 5 hp for the pump and they have to be mounted on a tractor with a minimum of 40 hp. The 20 bar pressure pump is mounted on the sprayer frame with the usual PTO shaft coupled to it. The machine at the back on the right has a 32 ft (9.8 m) folding boom with five sections consisting of a centre of 7 ft 7 in. (230 cm), two sections at 7 ft 7 in., and outer lengths of 4 ft 2 in. (123 cm), all of which fold up. The hinges are angled to hold the boom firmly in place when fully extended, without the need for clips, etc. It also enables the section to swing back in the event of the end catching or snagging on a tree or hedge. The boom is fitted with twenty nozzles, each mounted 20 in. (50 cm) apart. The machine at the front on the left has a wander hose to be held in the hand and double-spray nozzle for weed-killing around the farm, roads, and hedgerows. They were manufactured in France in the 1960s, 1970s, and 1980s. The owner is Mr. A. Le Gallais of Cowleywood Ltd., Maufant. The first supplier was St. Helier Garages who also sold them in England! When St. Helier Garages' tractor business closed, Messrs. Le Cappelain of St. Peter's Iron Works became the local suppliers for a time. L. C. Pallot, Central Motor Works, supplied the British-made Allman sprayers and later they also supplied French-made Caruelle sprayers. The Caruelle sprayer appears to have become very popular with Jersey farmers.

On some tractor-mounted sprayers the pump is mounted on the sprayer frame at the bottom. with the usual PTO shaft coupled to it. On many early British-made tractor-mounted sprayers, such as the Ransomes Cropguard and the Allman, the pump was fitted directly on the tractor PTO shaft, using a short chain attached to the tractor to prevent it rotating with the PTO.

Spraying early potatoes to protect the crop from blight with a Tecnoma sprayer; the operator is Mr. Colin Binet.

The Tecnoma mounted sprayer was manufactured at Épernay in France in 1978. The tank capacity is 80 gallons (360 l). The pump is mounted directly on the PTO splines and runs at the usual 540 rpm, depending on the particular application. The tractor is an MF135 using 5-6 hp approximately to drive the pump, but requiring a substantial tractor simply to carry the weight of the sprayer with a full tank, so power is not the only requirement. Pump capacity is variable, between 5 and 10 gallons (22.75-45.5 l) per hour according to application and pressure up to 20 atmospheres, and rate per vergée between 2 and 8 gallons (9-36.4 l) depending on the application. The spray boom is in four sections 28 ft (8.5 m) long overall with twenty-eight nozzles, and extends over nineteen rows of potatoes at 18 in. (45.5 cm) centres. The two inner sections, each with six nozzles, are clamped in position but can be slid in to close them up for transport, and the two outer sections fold forward alongside the tractor. The pivot, or hinge, is so arranged that gravity holds them in the working position, allowing them to swing back in the event of them snagging a fence or hedge. The pump is used with a valve chest, which may be set to pump water to fill the sprayer tank from a pond or brook. In this case water has been carried to the field in a large tank carried on a trailer. The owner is Mr. Colin Binet, of La Maison du Buisson, and the supplier was Messrs. Le Cappelain, St. Peter's Iron Works.

Filling the sprayer with a spray mix from a tank strapped on a trailer chassis. The back wheels of the tractor have narrow tyres to pass between the potato rows.

(*right*) A water tank strapped on a trailer chassis to transport the sprayer mixture to the field. A boat's oar serves as a paddle to stir the mixture in the tank.

A mounted sprayer with two tanks, one on the front of the Deutz four-wheel drive tractor and one on the three-point linkage to increase tank capacity.
The spray boom is 40 ft (12.2 m) long, covering sixteen rows at 30-in. (76.2 cm) centres. The pump is driven by the PTO at 540 rpm. The tractor is fitted with narrow wheels and tyres. Spraying the early potatoes with a pre-emergence spray, immediately after planting before the plastic sheeting is put on, on Messrs. Vautier Bros'. land at Ville Machon, Rozel.

In the 1960s the Vigzol Oil Company marketed a Vigzol low-volume sprayer manufactured for the company and probably supplied locally by La Motte Street Garage. For many years the Vigzol Company were suppliers of engine oil to Ford dealers all over the UK and Jersey. The sprayers were not expensive and usually involved a deal to supply spray chemicals from Vigzol. The pump driven by the PTO at 540 rpm was small but adequate. They could be carried on the three-point linkage of a TE20 or Dexta-type tractor. Mr. P. H. Bisson, of Oak Lane, La Moye, had one for spraying early potatoes.

Spreaders and broadcasters for fertiliser, seed, and manure

General fertilisers, and many seeds, are sown broadcast with spinner-type and swinging spout broadcasters mounted under a cone-shaped hopper. This type of machine has displaced the long box between two big-diameter wheels, as pulled by horses and modified for tractors. Most manufacturers favour the simple spinning disc.

The Vicon swing-spout broadcaster for spreading fertiliser and sowing seeds; here Mr. Binet is sowing barley for his son Colin.

The Vicon first appeared in the 1950s, becoming very popular. This one was manufactured in 1980. They varied in size; a particularly large one is on wheels and towed like a trailer. The container is plastic, so avoiding problems with rust, the capacity being half a cubic yard or 5-6 cwt, depending on the weight of the material, which varies considerably. The machine is driven by the tractor PTO at 540 rpm and the power absorbed depends on the material being spread, but is unlikely to exceed 5 hp. Painted Vicon red and cream. Here the tractor is driven by Mr. Louis Binet and the machine is broadcasting barley seed, which will be harrowed in or lightly rotavated, serving the purpose of cleaning up the land after potatoes. (That is, the barley will not ripen but will be ploughed in as green manure.)

This is the only make of swing-spout broadcaster but there are a wide range of spinner broadcasters similar in appearance to this machine but using a spinning disc under the hopper. An example is the Melotte Melodrive. Some manufacturers use twin discs side by side but rotating in opposite directions. The material to be spread is delivered via an adjustable hatch to the spinning disc beneath. It is broadcast to fall in a wide band on the soil and is usually harrowed in.

Farmyard manure spreaders

Farmyard manure (FYM or fym; stable manure) spreaders first appeared as horse-drawn machines in the USA. The spreader was a four-wheel vehicle constructed like a narrow wagon with a conveyor covering the floor to push the material to be spread to the rear, where the spreading mechanism is mounted. There were two rotating shafts, each with a number of paddles fitted at different angles to discharge the material in different directions as widely as possible. The whole mechanism was driven by the rear wheels of the wagon as it was drawn along, connected by a robust link chain and sprockets. A mechanical dog clutch disengaged the transmission. Tractor-drawn spreaders, sometimes known as muck spreaders, first appeared in the post-war years; they were similar to a two-wheel trailer but were narrower, and were towed like a trailer behind the tractor. The wheels had rubber tyres with chevron-type cleats, like a tractor rear tyre but fitted with the chevron cleats reversed, to obtain the traction to drive the spreading mechanism. The spreader at the back was the same as the horse machine. In due course this changed and they were driven by the tractor PTO. The draw-hitch was the usual jaw and pin, but was later made with a pick-up hitch ring. However, the introduction of slurry-handling systems on many dairy farms today has changed all that and FYM is no more. The result is unfortunate for country dwellers who will know the foul smell of slurry, which is quite different from the ripe but tolerable smell of FYM.

Howard, who manufactured a range of rotary cultivators, turned to manufacturing the first of the side-discharge muck spreaders in the UK in the 1960s, but they were quickly copied by other manufacturers. The machine consists of a large horizontal cylinder, open on one side along its length towards the top. The manure was loaded into the machine with a front-end loader or a buckrake through the side opening and discharged through it when spreading. A shaft mounted along the length of the cylinder fitted with flail chains driven by the tractor PTO rotates at high speed to fling the material out over one side only. This type of spreader has gained in popularity in recent years and is used in Jersey. They are much larger than the earlier rear-discharge machines and require heavier and powerful tractors to operate them.

Marshall side-discharge manure spreader. It has a pick-up ring on the drawbar and is powered by the tractor PTO.

The Marshall spreader serial no. 47026 has a 6 cu. yd or 4-ton capacity and is PTO-driven. These machines absorb a lot of power, requiring a big four-wheel-drive, 80-100 hp tractor to haul and operate them when fully loaded. The discharge system is usually composed of a sturdy shaft mounted along the length of the cylinder and has chains attached to it at regular intervals, often with a heavy metal square or similar item at the end. In operation the shaft is rotated, dragging the chains through the manure, and they are flung outwards by centrifugal force, taking some manure with them, which is thrown out of the side opening. Manufactured in 1994, this machine is the property of Mr. Alan Le Maistre of Les Prés Manor, Grouville, and the supplier was Messrs. Halse of Honiton in Devon.

The buckrake

The buckrake was derived from the horse-drawn hay sweep and later the tractor-mounted hay sweep that was used in the hayfield for sweeping hay to the rick. The buckrake is a variant of that theme with much thicker tines; it is also shorter and more robust and is used for a different purpose.

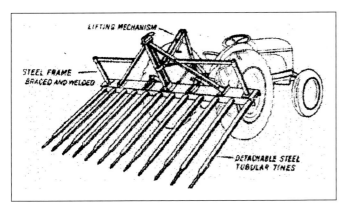

A rear-mounted buckrake being carried on the three-point linkage; here it is raised and tipped to discharge the load.

When this buckrake is lowered the tines are resting flat on the ground; it can be locked in that position in order to raise it bodily on the tractor lift. In work it is lowered to the ground and the tractor is driven backwards into the cut crop to load it. It is then lifted and transported on the tractor to the silage pit. At the pit it is lowered, and the trip is set and lifted again to tip off the load, as in the illustration. It is important to know the tear-load factor for both the machine and tractor to avoid damage to the tractor's hydraulic system or bending the tines on the buckrake, particularly when loading tightly packed silage from a storage pit. They are often used for collecting grass cut for silage and carrying it to the silage pit. Buckrakes today are manufactured to fit onto the tractor front loader, many with a high reach, able to deposit material straight into high-sided trailers.

Four-wheel-drive tractors with large-diameter front wheels make the buckrake even more useful for carrying heavier loads. Buckrakes are available with a choice of tines depending on the material they are most likely to handle. For loading beet and other root crops, larger-diameter tines with a bullnose end are used, but for handling hay or silage, a longer, finer-pointed tine would be more appropriate. The buckrake may be used by the cowman, to carry a few bales of hay to feed cattle sleeping out in the field or moving any heavy load about the farm.

Twose rear-mounted, push-off buckrake, serial no. H 148.

The machine is mounted on the three-point linkage and the push-off ram is coupled to the tractor's live hydraulic system, for pushing the load off the buckrake. Many of these buckrakes, particularly the later ones, are supplied with fittings to enable them to be fitted to a front-end loader. It was manufactured by E. V. Twose of Tiverton and supplied by Halse of Honiton to Mr. Le Maistre of Les Prés Manor.

Quick front-end loader with a grab attachment; Quick serial no. 3301 US 1929.

Unfortunately the loader tines are partly hidden in the green growth, but the grab tines are more easily picked out. All operations are hydraulic, with a valve chest on the tractor within easy reach of the driver and connected to the rams on the loader, via the hydraulic hoses seen here draped over the loader arm. The machine is a mid-mounted type and stands ready for coupling up to the mounting pads, located on each side of the engine or gearbox on the tractor. The driver has only to drive up to the machine and locate the front of the tractor between the brackets. The Quick was manufactured in Sweden and supplied to Mr. Alan Le Maistre, Les Prés Manor, Grouville.

A home-made concrete weight for mounting on the three-point linkage of a tractor to counterbalance a heavy load on a front-end loader to maintain traction on the rear wheels.

Counterbalance weights are supplied by the manufacturers, but an enterprising farmer will often make his own, as we see here. A crossbar that fits between the two lower links and a bracket for the top link are set in the concrete. A 45-gallon oil drum makes a useful mould into which to pour the concrete and let it set. The drum can either be left on or cut away. (Courtesy of Mr. Le Gallais, Cowleywood Ltd.)

Hedge trimmers

The flail hedge trimmer has been given a bad press in the Island by the media, usually after the branchage (roadside hedge-trimming required by the law). Criticism is due largely to ill-informed journalists and others, and one or two unskilled operators of the machines. The ecologists add to the problem by advocating that grass verges and hedges should be cut at a different time, less often, or not at all. The right flail machine with a good operator trimming a well-maintained hedge and grass bank is a pleasure to see.

The origin of these machines was the highly successful hay mower or reaper with a reciprocating cutter bar, which when tried by local authorities to cut roadside verges was not very successful. Mr. Douglas Bomford experimented in the 1950s by fitting a short cutter bar hinged at one end of a steel beam, mounted on the front of a tractor. It was driven by a single-cylinder, air-cooled Petter engine, mounted at the opposite end of the beam to the cutter bar, with a V pulley and V-belt to the connecting rod of the reciprocating knife in the cutter bar. The all-important hinge or pivot allowed the cutter bar to be angled up or down while in work. They became successful with local authorities for cutting roadside grass verges and were known as the 'any angle' mower.

Meanwhile, Mr. Freddie McConnel experimented with a machine to cut hedges. The first problem was the pointed fingers that pierced the twigs and small branches, so the points were ground off to a bullnose and tried again. This time it worked and McConnel went into production. It was while repairing a damaged McConnel hedge cutter in Bomford Brothers' workshops at Pitchill in Worcestershire that Douglas Bomford became sufficiently inspired to manufacture his own design.

The McConnel had been damaged because the cutter bar had been forced against a tree before the tractor driver could stop it, so bending the beam. Douglas Bomford designed a machine mounted on a vertical pivot, with a spring attached between the beam and tractor, to hold the cutter bar in the work. In the event of the cutter bar striking a tree or telegraph pole, it simply swung back against the spring, giving the tractor driver plenty of time to stop before any damage was done. The Bomford also had a horizontal pivot, to allow the cutter bar to float up or down, for cutting the top of a hedge, to keep it straight and level on uneven ground. If the tractor's front wheels went into a shallow hollow with a fixed trimmer, the cutter bar would dip into the hedge. It could be adjusted by the tractor driver with the aid of a large-diameter wheel, but it was too slow, resulting in the hedge top having a dip in it and not maintaining a straight and level top.

The Bomford hedge trimmer required two operators, a driver on the tractor and a man walking and holding a handle on the beam to hold it at the right height and angle. The McConnel needed only one operator but it took a day to fit on the tractor, whereas the Bomford could be fitted to the tractor in an hour or less, by simply bolting a bracket to the centre mounting pads, either side of the tractor, and lowering the beam onto it. Both machines used the same Petter single-cylinder 5 hp air-cooled engine, which also served as a counterbalance to the weight of the cutter bar at the other end of the beam. The cutter bar on both machines could be set at any angle, up or down, from the vertical to the horizontal.

The Bomford machine could also cut grass, particularly the rough growth at the foot of a hedge. The machines became popular with farmers and the Bomford was sold all over the British Isles and the Continent. The author has found no trace of one in Jersey. These machines produced a very good finish to the hedge, and if cut in the shape of an A with a narrow flat top, it made clearing up easier and encouraged bottom growth in the hedge. Regular annual cutting was a reasonable proposition and some enthusiasts would cut their hedges twice a year.

As traffic increased, the cutting of roadside verges became more of a problem, as some careless drivers would throw empty drink cans and bottles onto the verges; these items, together with sticks and stones, damaged the knife blades on the cutter bar, buckling them so that they became jammed in the cutter bar. Time was lost changing the knife and a second man had almost a full-time job sharpening a spare knife and replacing damaged blades, riveting new blades onto a spare knife. The traditional hay mower working near a busy road suffered the same fate. Flail cutting machines were beginning to appear to replace the cutter bar; they were able to cope with the damage and continue working.

The Mott Corporation in the USA had developed a successful flail cutter to get over this problem. The flails, mounted in pairs back to back and sideways on to the work, operated as would a swinging knife, with the cutting edge towards the work. They are fitted along the length of a horizontal shaft and assembled to the mowing machine, with a hood over the flails and a roller behind which was adjustable for height of cut. As the shaft rotated, centrifugal force caused the blades to swing out to cut the grass or hedge.

Mott made their mowers in two sizes of 4 ft (122 cm) and 6 ft (182 cm) wide, with a gearbox mounted in the centre driven by the tractor PTO. Power was transmitted by shaft from the gearbox to a pulley on the end and a V-belt to the rotor shaft. A tripod for the three-point linkage was fabricated on the top. Mr. Bomford ordered one of each while visiting his agent, SMA, in Paris. The 6-ft machine made a very good job of cutting roadside verges, where the verge was flat and the tractor could drive over it. They were popular with the local authorities. However, as we saw earlier with the 'any angle' mower, grass verges are not all flat and level! At Bomford Brothers' works at Pitchill, developments were soon in hand to mount the 4-ft unit onto an articulating arm on the side of a Ferguson TE20 tractor. The arm had three knuckles, one at the mounting point on the side of the tractor, to provide a height adjustment, the second at the apex of an A-shaped arm to extend it sideways and upward and up or down, and the third on top of the 4-ft cutter to adjust the angle of the cutter shaft. Power from the PTO was transmitted by V-belts. The machine was fitted with safety devices, slipping clutches and a release mechanism in the event of striking a tree or telegraph pole. It proved to be ideal for the road authorities. They at last had a machine to satisfy their needs: the flails cut the verges, leaving them neatly trimmed, and no damage was done to the machine by roadside debris.

The day came, at a demonstration, when a customer asked if the Bomford flail machine would cut a hedge. It was tried on a thorn hedge close by and was found to cut one-year growth well and give a finish as good as a cutter bar. However, the tractor required extra stability when hedge-cutting, because the whole weight of the beam and rotor was carried by the tractor, whereas for verge work the cutter unit rested on the ground on the rear roller. The problem was solved with wheel weights, filling the offside tyre with water as ballast and setting the rear wheels further out from the centre line of the tractor, using the adjustments provided.

Inevitably, the demand came for a heavier flail, to cope with heavier growth of more than one or two years. There were many unkempt hedges, which farmers and road authorities had neglected and wished to cut back to a more appropriate size and shape. Export customers, particularly in France, wanted heavier flails. At this time the transmission was changed in favour of hydraulic pumps and motors, and carrying a large tank of oil. A large tank was necessary to keep the oil cool, and by fitting it on the opposite side of the machine to the cutter shaft, it was a good counterbalance.

When some overgrown hedges were cut back to size, they appeared to many to be damaged. Occasionally, unnecessary damage was done, when a heavy flail machine with a careless operator was used on a hedge which only needed a light trim. Understandably, farmers were reluctant to have two machines, one for light trimming and one for heavy cutting. The contractors and some farmers tend to want the heavy flails, but many prefer the lighter flails, which are quite adequate for most farms with well-maintained hedges. The interesting point is that the hedges recover, and after a time the damage disappears, but the media do not publicise that because it spoils their story!

Bomford Brothers continued to make two types of machines, one with heavy flails and one with light flails. Over time the flails were improved, resulting in the Bomford Flailtrim. A cast-steel flail superseded the Mott double flail. The new cast-steel flail has all the attributes of the original Mott flail; it is free-swinging to avoid damaging itself, it gives a good finish to a grass bank or verge side, and gives a good finish for regular hedge trimming.

Some machines were designed to have the extending arm assembled on either side of the tractor, and the oil tank switched over accordingly. This was particularly important for road authorities in export markets, where they might drive on the right and the tractor must work with the flow of traffic, rather than against it.

It is important that the machine is in the hands of a skilled operator, and unfortunately that can still be a problem. Just as a well-ploughed field requires a skilled ploughman, so too does a good job of hedge trimming. In operation, the first cut is a horizontal cut along the bottom, beside the hedge, cleaning up the bottom to enable the tractor to get in closer for later cuts and providing a clear area where the trimmings fall. The second cut is along the side of the hedge, at a slight tilt toward the top, before a third cut is made, again at an angle nearer 45 degrees or so to encourage the debris to fall to the ground; then the fourth cut is along the top. Reaching over to cut the other side of the hedge is not possible, as it was with the old cutter-bar type.

Hedge cutting with a Bomford flail hedge trimmer, transmission by hydraulic pump and motor. The pump is driven by the tractor PTO. The hedge trimmer's cutting head has a shaft driven by a hydraulic motor fitted with free swinging, cast-steel, chisel-type, weighted flails, so designed that, as the shaft rotates, centrifugal force sends the flails swinging out, presenting the cutting edge to the hedge. The width of cut is 3 ft 4 in. (100 cm). The weight of the oil tank on the left goes some way to counterbalance the weight of the cutter head and the arm. The tank is sufficiently large to allow the oil to remain cool. Here the machine, painted Bomford-orange, is mounted on a Massey Ferguson tractor. The machine, manufactured in 1981, was supplied to Mr. Le Gallais by Channel Industries Ltd.

The chisel-type, cast-steel flails are fitted to a swivelling link that is fixed to the lugs on the rotor shaft; the hydraulic motor is at the bottom.
On many of these machines the motor can often be fitted at either end of the shaft, and in some cases fitted on the top of the housing; the power is then transmitted via a V-belt to a pulley on the shaft. The roller at the back acts to hold the cutter steady while cutting the hedge and when cutting a grass verge. It acts as depth control, and the weight can be shared between the roller and the hydraulic ram.

What the public and many in the media do not realise is that, when an old overgrown hedge is cut down to size, it will recover remarkably well from the apparent butchery, and with regular cutting thereafter will begin to look well. If there is any criticism today, it is of those farmers who do not clear up the trimmings after the branchage, leaving them where they fall at the roadside to look unsightly and attract further criticism, especially if they get washed along the roadside in the rain, to block surface-water drains. On grass banks and verges, the trimmings that are left choke the grass and allow weeds to grow in their place. If grass banks and verges were cut more frequently it would reduce the problem, but it is doubtful if that would be acceptable to a busy farmer, who has his eye on his bank balance rather than his roadside hedges and grass banks. The lesson is, do not blame the machine!

After the Second World War many armament factories established during the war, some known as satellite factories, constructed under a canopy of trees in the countryside, found themselves with well-equipped factories but no more orders for products. They cast around trying to find new products; some of them tried farm machinery, with mixed results. For example, those supplying equipment to the aircraft industry were supplying equipment to operate in a relatively clean environment. A ball bearing is fine on an aircraft flying through clean air, but put that bearing in a potato field or a muddy beet field and mud makes an excellent grinding paste, wears through the seal, and the bearing collapses. The disc harrow has wooden bearings and if packed with grease it will keep the mud and soil out. Eventually it will wear, but it is a cheap matter to remove the bearing cap and insert a pair of new wooden bearings, and you are back in business. That is just one example; there were others.

One such manufacturer that did succeed and became very successful was Hayter Ltd., run by Mr. Douglas Hayter and still in business today, although Douglas Hayter retired long ago. They manufactured a range of tractor-operated rotary mowers, taking advantage of the then new PTO. The Hayter machine was a simple design: a vertical shaft, at the bottom end of which is fitted a square plate with a knife section, as on a reaper cutter bar, fitted on each corner. A steel decking covered the cutter, with a bevel gearbox above it, together with drive shaft and universal joints to the PTO. On the top is a tripod for the mounted machines and a wheel on each side adjustable for height. They also made a trailed version. They were sold to orchard growers to keep down the grass, between the rows of trees, that was previously cut with expensive gang mowers. Over time, Hayter built a range of variations, and also manufactured a range of domestic rotary mowers for garden lawns.

Over the years, variations on the same theme have been manufactured, such as a bar mounted on the vertical shaft with a swing blade at each end, acting in the manner of a flail. Locally, some farmers used these machines for cutting the green foliage or green potato tops, before digging. Another variation that was popular in Jersey was the Wolseley Swipe, more of a slasher than a cutter. It has a number of chains attached to the bottom of the rotating shaft. The potato tops were completely shattered, simply leaving short stems, making digging with a digger or harvester a lot easier and leaving less material to clear up after the potatoes have been harvested. In later years some potato harvesters had a 'swipe' fitted at the front of the machine, doing away with that extra operation.

The Wolseley Swipe

The Wolseley Swipe was manufactured by Wolseley Engineering in the 1950s and 1960s. The larger of two models has a working width of 56 in. (142 cm) and the smaller machine with shorter chains has a width of 36 in. (91 cm). Both were driven by the tractor's PTO at 540 rpm. The vertical rotor shaft under the gearbox at the centre is fitted with three chains, each of equal length. The larger model is guarded with a sheet-metal guard over the top and a sheet-metal skirt. The smaller machine is open-topped but has a canvas skirt on a steel frame surrounding it. The bigger machine has one or two caster wheels with a height adjustment that may be fitted at the back. At the time, the local agents for Wolseley Engineering were the Country Gentlemen's Association Limited (CGA Ltd.), running an agricultural merchants business on the Esplanade. The CGA Jersey branch has since closed.

13 Two-Wheel Tractors and Cultivators

Two-wheeled tractors and cultivators were manufactured for horticulture and rowcrop work with a variety of implements. Some implements were toolbars that had various attachments such as cultivating tines, ridging bodies, or bankers; many were made by local blacksmiths in Jersey for potato growers in particular. Many were simply rotary cultivators, with rotors at the back, behind a pair of wheels. Others had rotors in front and removable transport wheels. Horsepower varied between 3.5 and 10 approximately. Two-wheel tractors formed a part of the equipment to be found on many Jersey farms. The prime function of the two-wheel tractor in Jersey was the planting, scarifying, and banking of the Jersey Royal potato.

Fowler

Photograph in the *Chronique de Jersey*, 26 November 1913, of a Fowler A4 motor plough.

In November 1913 a photographer working for the *Chronique de Jersey*, possibly known to readers at the time as 'Samuel', photographed a two-wheel tractor pulling a two-furrow breezing plough. Research so far indicates this is the first and only early recording of a motor plough in Jersey. The text under the photograph reads, 'La charrue automobile dont parle notre colloborateur "Samuel" ' meaning 'the motor plough, so says our colleague "Samuel" under the heading 'L'Actualité en photo', i.e. 'Life in photographs'. The 'motor plough' was the description of many tractors before the word 'tractor' came into general use. John Fowler of Leeds, better known for their steam ploughing engines, manufactured it.

The type A4 motor plough was manufactured in 1913 and was probably driven by Alfred Pepper Senior, in charge of its development at the Fowler works. The engine has two cylinders, water-cooled with a four-blade fan behind the radiator, two forward gears and a reverse. The steel wheels are 3 ft 8 in. (111 cm) in diameter with cone-type lugs. It has two pairs of handles, the lower pair coming into use at the headland when the plough is lifted out. In 1912 the Steam Plough Works of the Fowler Company in Hunslet, Leeds, built a motor plough with a single-cylinder engine and single-furrow plough, the idea of Alfred Wyles. After entering into an agreement with Wyles Motor Ploughs Ltd. of Manchester in 1913, the machine was enlarged with a two-cylinder engine, and a two-furrow plough known as the type 4A. In 1913 Fowler were demonstrating the motor plough in France where they were selling quite well. (The author is grateful to the archivist in *Vintage Tractor* magazine for drawing his attention to the Fowler Company.)

Sources: The details were revealed in the history of John Fowler in M. R. Lane, *The Story of the Steam Plough Works* (1980) and the *Chronique de Jersey* at Jersey Public Library.

British Anzani

The British Anzani Iron Horse two-wheel tractor came on the market just before the Second World War and was manufactured from 1938 to 1958 approximately. It is bigger than most two-wheel tractors, looking more like Fowler's motor plough but not as powerful, having only a 6-hp JAP engine. The four-stroke petrol engine is water-cooled. They are on two steel wheels, adjustable for width. The wheels have spade lugs. Steering is with clutches to each wheel, operated by a lever, on each handle. They have three forward gears and a maximum speed of 4.5 mph, and one reverse. They were used mainly for potatoes and ploughing with a breezing plough. Mr. de Figueiredo, of Vieux Ménage, at Maufant, had one in the late 1940s, and Mr. Bisson, of Oak Lane, at La Moye, must have found his satisfactory because he bought a second one. However, when the smaller, lighter machines like the Coleby came on the market, he switched over to a Coleby.

Standard

The Standard is a pre-1940 two-wheel tractor.
The Standard has a two-cylinder, air-cooled engine developing 6-7 hp. Here it is fitted with three potato bankers for Jersey Royal potatoes. They were popular in St. Ouen, where they were serviced by Edwin Carré of St. Ouen's Motor Works. The local agents were Bel Royal Garage. (Courtesy of the Steam Museum collection.)

Staub

The Staub two-wheel tractor.
The Staub tractor and engine was manufactured in France in the 1960s. The petrol engine is an air-cooled four stroke, developing 7 hp, and is started with a crank handle. The steel wheels have angled spade lugs and were made by Le Cappelain, St. Peter's Iron Works, who were the local suppliers. They were used for potato planting, scarifying and banking, and general cultivations. This one is owned by Mr. Charlie Morris at Noirmont and is fitted with a scarifying toolbar. Mr. Morris started work as an apprentice at St. Peter's Iron Works, continuing to work there for many years until he retired. Details about Mr. Morris will be found in Chapters 21-2. (Courtesy of Mr. Morris.)

Howard

The Howard 350 rotavator has a Kohler single-cylinder, 4-hp air-cooled engine with a rotary cultivator under the hood at the back.

The Howard Rotavator Company manufactured a range of small tractors, mostly rotavators (rotary cultivators) such as the Howard Gem, the smaller 350 shown here, the 250, and the 200 Bantam, which were all popular. The 350 has a 4-hp, Kohler single-cylinder, air-cooled engine. When fitted with a 5.3-hp engine it can be adapted to make ridges, plough, pull trailers, and mow grass. The engine can also be used to pump water and cut hedges. It was the Howard 700 that attracted the attention of the Jersey farmer, primarily intended for use with its easily detached rotavator, which made it a useful general purpose two-wheel tractor. They were manufactured from the 1960s to the 1980s. It has a two-cylinder, two-stroke engine producing 6-7 hp, running on a petrol and oil fuel mixture. When fitted with two locally fabricated steel wheels, with spade lugs, it was used for potato planting, scarifying, and banking. The local agent for Howard Rotavator is the Jersey Farmer's (Trading) Union Ltd.

The ideal power tool for both the Commercial Grower and the Private Gardener, equally capable of heavy digging or fast shallow tillage and weeding.

HOWARD ROTAVATOR 350

Coleby

The Coleby Jersey Senior on steel wheels has a 420 cc BSA single-cylinder, four-stroke, petrol engine. It was popular with potato growers for planting, scarifying, and banking.

(*right*) A view of the front of the Coleby on rubber tyres.

The Coleby was manufactured at Swanley in Kent from the 1950s to the 1970s. The air-cooled petrol engine produced 5 hp at 2,200 rpm and is started with a rope, placed around the small pulley at the front and given a sharp pull. The locally fabricated steel wheels have spade lugs bolted on. The long axles provide plenty of adjustment for track width; the rubber-tyred wheels were standard equipment and are set very close. It has three forward gears and one reverse. Steering is by disconnecting the transmission to one wheel or the other using one of two dog clutches controlled by two push-and-pull rods beside the handles. The Coleby on steel wheels is in the Société Jersiaise/Jersey Heritage Trust collection, in the store at Augrès. The machine on rubber tyres was Mr. John Perrée's and is at present in Mr. Charles Le Couteur's collection at Westlands, St. Peter. The local supplier was St. Mary's Garage.

Mabec

The Mabec model CB 50 two-wheel tractor, serial no. 50442. It has a 10-hp engine made by Bernard of Paris, type W239, serial no. 619092. The steel wheels were fabricated locally for potatoes.

The Bernard petrol engine on the Mabec is a single-cylinder, air-cooled, four-stroke, starting with a rope pull. It has three forward gears and one reverse. It is steered by rod-controlled steering clutches. At the front is a weight, to counterbalance the weight of the implement on the back. It was used for early potatoes and is said to perform better than the Coleby. It was made in 1960, the local agent was St. Mary's Garage, and the owner is Mr. Sydney Poingdestre, of Ville à l'Evêque.

Honda

Honda made a two-wheel tractor. The first model was the S80 followed by the S190 with a twin-cylinder engine. They were also imported from France by the late Mr. Renouf, of St. Mary's Garage. They were fitted with the usual locally made steel wheels, for potatoes.

One-way planting plough

A quarter-turn one-way, planting plough for attaching to a two-wheel tractor.

The plough will have left- and right-hand bodies with mouldboards made locally; they are 30 in. (76.2 cm) long, and the share is 7 in. (17.7 cm) wide. It is mounted on a subframe, with a quarter-turn mechanism, for one-way planting. It would be a heavy attachment, probably necessitating a counter-balance on the front of the two-wheel tractor. They were probably made in the late 1940s or 1950s. This one was Mr. Alfred Le Boutillier's of Le Val Bachelier, St. Ouen.

Landmaster

Landmaster's Gardenmaster rotary cultivator model, for the farm garden rather than the farm.

Landmaster rivalled the Howard Rotavator Company, with several model sizes of rotary cultivators, from 1949 to the 1970s. Like the Howard, the rotary cultivators are normally behind the wheels, but the Gardenmaster is an exception; the 10 in. (25.4 cm) wide rotary culti-vator is in the front. The serial number is 3A-488; it has a 2-hp, single-cylinder, two-stroke engine running on petrol and oil fuel mixture with a recoil starter. It is on two freewheeling 10-in. wheels, with solid tyres. The rotavator is detachable, enabling a rotary mower attachment to be fitted.

Small rowcrop and garden cultivators

The three machines are small cultivators. They are, left to right, a Clifford rotary cultivator, an Allen & Simmond's, and a Colwood on one rubber-tyred wheel. All three have a spark-ignition system generated with a coil incorporated with the flywheel.

The Clifford is a model 28 cultivator, serial no. 5942; it has a 12 in. (30.4 cm) wide rotavator and was manufactured in the 1940s and 1950s. It is very similar to the Howard, but the clearance under the engine is a little restricted. The engine is a 2-3 hp JAP single-cylinder two-stroke, running on a fuel mixture of petrol and oil; it has a rope and pulley starter. It is on two 14 in. (35.5 cm) pneumatic-tyred wheels. Originally owned by Mr. H. Bisson.

In the centre is a cultivator manufactured by Allen & Simmond's Holdings Ltd., of Reading, serial no. 7163J, manufactured in the 1930s and 1940s. The engine is a 2-hp, air-cooled, single-cylinder two stroke, running on a fuel mixture of petrol and oil. It has lost its engine cover, exposing the flywheel and ignition system. It has two heavy, cast-iron wheels, each having two rows of lugs on a solid axle; transmission is through a dog clutch. A choice of cultivating tines is fitted to the toolbar frame: at present, it is fitted with weeding hoe blades. Notable features apart from the cast-iron wheels and lugs are the wooden handles. It is interesting to speculate that this machine may have been the forerunner of the Auto Cult, another well-known two-wheel cultivator.

The last is a Colwood model B, serial no. 12398, manufactured in the 1950s. The Villiers 3-hp petrol engine is model ab/Mk12, serial no. 090A191, single-cylinder air-cooled four-stroke. The machine has two forward and one reverse gear and a dog clutch. It is on one 16 in. (40.6 cm) pneumatic-tyred wheel and is equipped with a toolbar and a choice of tines, at present with hoe blades for weeding. All three are on display in the collection at the Steam Museum.

Wolseley Merry Tiller

Wolseley Merry Tiller 5-hp Titan with a two-speed and reverse gearbox fitted with rotary cultivator blades. An option is 16-in. pneumatic-tyred wheels with lugs fitted to the rotor shaft and a one-way plough at the back.

There were three models of the Merry Tiller: the Major with a Clinton 3-hp engine, followed by the Major with a 3.5-hp Briggs and Stratton engine, and the 5-hp Titan, also having a Briggs and Stratton engine. The early Major was supplied with fixed handles and the Titan with handles which were adjustable up or down to suit the operator and from side to side to avoid walking over the cultivated land. Later, the Major also had adjustable handles. The basic machine was supplied with rotary cultivating rotors, as illustrated. The machine was mounted on a detachable pair of two solid-tyred wheels for moving it to the work area, but these were removed for rotavating. The machines were used mostly for rotavating, breaking up ground, and preparing a seed bed. There is a choice of rotors, rotary cultivator blades, spikes for seed bed preparation, and discs. Other attachments are lawn-care rotors, for slitting, and rotors for extracting plugs to aerate the lawn and help to absorb fertilisers. In addition to pneumatic tyres, there were a pair of 16 in. (40.6 cm) diameter steel wheels with lugs for use with a plough or a toolbar. A front-mounted weight was available to improve traction. A front-mounted rotary mower and a pair of 12-in. (30.4 cm) pneumatic-tyred wheels was also an option. At the top of the range is the Titan, illustrated above, with cultivating rotors. It has an overall cultivating width of 36-in. (91.40 cm). Merry Tillers were mostly used in the farm garden, horticultural applications and glasshouses, rather than agriculture. The manufacturers were Wolseley Engineering, Electric Avenue, Wolverhampton, and the local suppliers were the CGA on the Esplanade, St. Helier, and later, Channel Industries Ltd. at Maufant.

14 Stationary Engines

Steam engines

Three hundred years ago there was a demand for a reliable system to pump water out of mines. Thomas Newcomen, who was born in 1663, was one of several people trying to build an engine and pump. His claim to fame was that he was the first to achieve success in 1712, with the beam engine, the first stationary engine. The engine is driven as much by atmospheric pressure as by steam. The cylinder is vertical and the piston rod is at the top, connected by a short chain link to the beam, which rocks like a seesaw. Beneath the cylinder is the boiler, delivering steam through valves to the bottom of the cylinder, pushing the piston to the top, so rocking the beam. On reaching the top, cold water is sprayed into the cylinder, condensing the steam and creating a vacuum under the piston. The top of the cylinder is open to the atmosphere, so the atmospheric pressure drives the piston down the cylinder on the power stroke, pulling the beam down with it. As the opposite end of the beam rises it pulls up a piston in the water pump, so lifting the water. The piston in the water pump has flap valves that are free to open on the down stroke, allowing water in the pump cylinder to pass through onto the top of the piston, and they flap shut with the weight of water above them when the piston is lifted on the upstroke or pumping stroke. The engines and pumps worked well and continuously, some of them for 200 years, well into the twentieth century. James Watt improved on the technology, resulting in the beam engine being used in factories and water companies until the middle of the twentieth century.

When the crankshaft and connecting rod were invented, the steam engine underwent a change: with a big-diameter, low-rpm flywheel and a horizontal cylinder, it no longer depended on atmospheric pressure to push the piston. In the steam engine, steam continued to push the piston, but this became the power stroke; the connecting rod and flywheel pushed the piston back up the cylinder for the next steam power stroke. The steam engine could be made smaller and became popular in the industrial world. An early stationary steam engine made by Trevithick was installed for Sir Christopher Hawkins to drive a threshing machine in Cornwall in 1811.

Internal combustion engines

The Lenoir gas engines were built in the 1860s, with Reading Iron Works making a few of them. The engine had one cylinder, but ignition and combustion took place at each end of the cylinder, so there was a power stroke with every stroke of the piston, similar to a double-acting steam engine. Other people were trying to design an internal combustion engine using ideas from the steam engine. Lenoir made the first one to work: ignition was provided by a battery, a coil, and a distributor to the two spark plugs. The ignition system was the weakness—it was unreliable.

The technology would be described today as unusual, but one has to remember that these were early days and all sorts of ideas were tried as engineers wrestled with the problem.

Dr. Otto developed the 'Otto Cycle' and built the first four-cycle, internal combustion engine in 1876, running on coal gas as the fuel. Unfortunately he did not go to the next step and design a reliable ignition system. Ignition systems would not be reliable for another thirty years. It was the burgeoning motor industry that brought about improvements to ignition systems and carburettors. Dr. Otto's engine was the first to compress the fuel and air mixture, in the cylinder head, before ignition. The Priestman brothers, William and Samuel, developed an engine to run on a liquid fuel or paraffin, spraying the fuel into a heated combustion chamber, to mix with the air drawn in by the induction stroke. The chamber is heated up with a blow lamp, to start the engine, then it is heated by the exhaust, and the mix is ignited with an electric spark.

Yet another development was the Ackroyd Stuart, heating the mix by compressing it in the cylinder head and igniting it with the heat of a hot bulb, first heated with a blow lamp. These engines were made by R. Hornsby & Sons Ltd., who went on to make the first successful tractor, with the same type of engine. These developments led on to the compression-ignition diesel engine. The hot bulb is about the size of a golf ball, on the outside of the cylinder head. When heated, it provides sufficient heat on the inside surface of the cylinder head to ignite the compressed fuel mixture in the cylinder. Having started the engine with a starting handle, the heat provided by the ignition of the fuel kept the bulb hot, to keep the engine running, and the blow lamp could be turned off. Some engines like the Lanz, had a bracket under the cylinder head to carry a specially designed blow lamp. The lamp had to be removed to refill its can with fuel.

When the technology was understood and the patents were overcome, there was a rush by many manufacturers in Europe and North America to get into production with stationary engines. In America they were given wonderful names, like 'Farmer's Boy' and 'Farm Hand'. Petter, in England, called their oil engine the 'Handy Man'.

Businesses in St. Helier such as Grandin and Norman, at Commercial Buildings, would have installed an engine to drive shafting in their workshops or to generate electricity. This type of engine, with a big-diameter flywheel, ran at very low speeds. Many gas engines were installed in Jersey in the first and second decades of the twentieth century, like the Crossley engine.

Crossley gas engine

Crossley gas engine manufactured in 1912 by Crossley Bros. Ltd. of Manchester. It is a type K gas engine, serial no. 72776. It is a horizontal single-cylinder engine using town gas.

The Crossley engine has a Wico magneto-ignition system, a big-diameter flywheel, and a 9.5 in. (24 cm) diameter flat-belt pulley. Water cooled with a tank reservoir. It was installed at Clifton, St. Aubin, to pump water. Some gas engines were later modified to run on petrol. It was given by Mr. P. Pirouet, to be restored by Lyndon Pallot. (Steam Museum collection.)

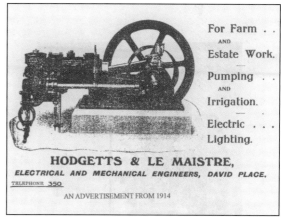

An advertisement from 1914

Petter

The Petter Junior Victory, manufactured in 1919, is a two-stroke, single-cylinder, vertical, safety gas engine, converted to run on petrol.

The Petter Junior is started with a detachable cranking handle and runs at 800 to 1,000 rpm developing 5 hp. It has a 7 in. (17.7 cm) diameter flat-belt pulley and is water cooled, using a 100 gallon galvanised water tank that was mounted on a pedestal beside the engine; the water circulated by thermo-cycle. It was originally an oil engine, but a chisel has been used to remove the word 'oil', and the word 'gas' punched on and the name plate agrees; however it was converted again, to burn petrol. The fuel tank is in the base under the crankcase. The fuel is lifted to the carburettor by a diaphragm pump operated by the crankcase compression. The engine was installed in the 'big shed' at Beau Désert, St. Saviour, on a concrete pedestal on the ground floor to drive cattle food preparation machinery on a machine platform, at first floor level and on the ground floor. The supplier was Le Cappelain, of St. Peter's Iron Works.

The machines on the platform included a chaff cutter and a rolling and grinding mill. On the ground floor was a root pulper/slicer, which was used mostly in the winter months for mangels, turnips, swedes, etc., and occasionally a large circular saw. Power was delivered to the machines by shafting and flat belts. It was easy to start for the farm staff, who used it frequently. It was in regular use from 1929 to 1956. When last seen, it appeared as though it had not been run since the author's father retired from farming in 1956. It was removed for restoration by Mr. Stephen Gouédard, at his workshop in St. Clement.

Another example of a vertical Petter Victory two-stroke engine. It is a type M Junior, serial no. 60819, single-cylinder 8-hp petrol engine, ignition by magneto, and water cooled. Manufactured in 1920.

National

A National stationary gas engine. It is a single-cylinder, vertical, two-stroke engine running at 750 rpm developing 5 hp, a water-cooled engine running on town gas.

This National engine was supplied and installed by the Gas Company at the gasworks in St. Helier, to drive an electric generator. Setting the gas pressure to operate this engine was critical. The engine would run on petrol, with a suitable carburettor. Later the generator was dismantled from the set and the engine used for farm work in Mr. Ken Godel's contracting business. Mr. Godel, of St. John, intends to restore it.

Home assembly

This engine was partly built by the Bedford Engineering Company in 1920 for home completion.
This engine is a model A V 20 1.25 hp, single-cylinder, four-stroke horizontal engine, and is water cooled; it operates at 650 rpm. The serial number is no. 2733. The engine was supplied by Messrs. Frank Hartop & Son and was thought to have been delivered by mail order for home completion by Major Anthoine (Constable of St. Saviour and later Jurat of the Royal Court). Major Anthoine installed it to drive a water pump at Longueville Manor Farm. It has been beautifully restored by Mr. Lyndon Pallot.

Small stationary engines were used to drive a variety of farm machines, including water pumps, for the farm water supply from a well and for irrigation. They were also used to drive shafting to operate machinery such as chaff cutters, root crushers, and rolling mills for rolling oats, etc. for cattle food preparation. In the field, they were driving the vacuum pump on milking bails. Petter air-cooled engines were used to drive tractor-mounted hedge trimmers. In the summer in England they were often seen driving an elevator in the field or stackyard, lifting hay or sheaves of cereals up onto a stack. When the tractor power take-off, the PTO, became commonplace, designs changed, to make use of the PTO rather than stationary engines.

Engines for the farm and country house

The Farmers' engine, manufactured by Ruston & Hornsby in 1925. It is a type PR, class 110, serial no. 126332, four-stroke engine that runs at 700 rpm developing 2.5 hp.

The Ruston & Hornsby Farmers' engine was manufactured from 1923 to 1929. It is a single-cylinder horizontal, petrol/paraffin engine, water-cooled with a cooling hopper on top. It has a 7 in. (17.7 cm) diameter pulley beside one of the flywheels. It was supplied by J. H. Harper, 26-30 Queen Street, to be used on a farm in Jersey, for driving different farm machines. It was restored by Mr. Lyndon Pallot and is in the Steam Museum collection.

The Universal stationary petrol engine was manufactured by Petter in the 1920s, serial no. 63566.

The Universal is water-cooled, with a cooling hopper over the cylinder head. It is a single-cylinder vertical engine running at 700 rpm, developing 3 hp. It is in the Steam Museum collection.

This stationary engine was manufactured by Crossley Bros. in the early 1920s. It has an exposed crankshaft and a horizontal, single-cylinder, petrol/paraffin engine.

The Crossley engine develops 5 hp; the ignition is by magneto. It is water-cooled with a cooling hopper on top. It was installed originally at Les Maltières, St. Martin, to drive a DC generator. It is in the Steam Museum collection.

Ruston & Hornsby single-cylinder, horizontal, stationary engine. It runs on petrol or paraffin at 650 rpm, developing 2.5 hp; the serial no. is 120724 and it was manufactured in 1929.

The Ruston & Hornsby engine has an overhead exhaust valve, driven off the camshaft, and automatic inlet valve with a return spring. The ignition is by Wico induction coil. It has a flat-belt pulley. The engine was purchased in England in 1933/4 for £12 and used by the owner, Mr. John Perrée, at Plaisance and at Home Farm, Le Forêt, to crush apples. Here it is seen running at the Steam Museum Open Threshing Day in 1997.

This Petter Junior no. 11-1A is a vertical, single-cylinder petrol engine, serial no. 51113, manufactured in 1919 or the early 1920s.

The ignition on the Petter engine is by a BTH (British Thompson Houston) magneto, running at 750/800 rpm, developing 2.5 hp; it has a flat-belt pulley. It is water cooled with a water hopper above the cylinder head. The owner is Mr. Emile Ferey, of Vinchelez. It was used to drive a circular saw. It is running here at the Steam Museum Threshing Day 1997.

Another Ruston & Hornsby engine, model PB, a single-cylinder horizontal manufactured in 1933. It runs on petrol or paraffin developing 1.5 hp.

The Ruston & Hornsby engine has a Villiers flywheel magnet; the pulley diameter is 5 in. (12.6 cm). It is water-cooled with a water hopper. It was supplied by J. H. Harper, 26-30 Queen Street, St. Helier. The owner is Mr. Le Brun of La Bicotrie, La Blinerie Lane, where it drives an Evans water pump in the glasshouses.

This single-cylinder horizontal diesel was manufactured by Deutz of Cologne in Germany, in the 1930s, serial no. 703751.

The Deutz engine has an open hopper for the cooling water. The engine was brought to Jersey during the Occupation of Jersey by the German forces, to generate electricity at Elizabeth Castle. It is painted German Army-green. The pulley has been removed. After the war it was used by a local farmer to drive various pieces of farm machinery. It is in the Steam Museum collection.

This stationary engine was manufactured in the 1930s by Bernard of France. It is a single-cylinder, 8-hp, water-cooled petrol engine, model W3, serial no. 368519.

This interesting engine has an enclosed radiator for the cooling water: it is triangular and composed of many copper pipes. The flywheel also has cooling fins. Thought to be fitted originally with a 7 in. (17.7 cm) diameter flat pulley, it now has a four-groove V pulley for V-belts. Presumably designed with a specific application in mind, it was imported by the German occupying forces during the Second World War and subsequently used to drive a saw bench at Rozel. It was restored by Mr. Lyndon Pallot and is displayed in the Steam Museum collection.

During the war years in the UK, while petrol was rationed, farmers had special dispensation for both petrol and paraffin for tractors and stationary engines; many ran on both. In Jersey during the German Occupation, petrol was difficult, if not impossible, to obtain. There were those Islanders who would siphon petrol from parked vehicles.

A group of five stationary engines; they are basically similar but varying in power from 1.5 to 2.5 hp. It was common practice to paint them green, but R. A. Lister's engines were always dark green. Stationary engines were a common sight on farms in the 1920s and up to the 1950s; these are all in the Steam Museum collection.

In the foreground is a Wolseley model WD 1.5-hp, single-cylinder water-cooled engine, serial no. 19978. It ran on petrol at 700 rpm with ignition by magneto. The cast-iron water hopper on the top has fins to help to cool the water.

The second engine is a Crossley model PH 1030, serial no. 120959. It is a single-cylinder, 2.5-hp, petrol engine which runs at 700 rpm. Manufactured in the 1930s; the ignition is by magneto.

The third is a Bernard engine, made in France, model WO, serial no. 361160, single-cylinder petrol engine. It runs at 1,400 to 2,000 rpm, generating 1.9–2.4 hp, and is water cooled with a radiator.

The fourth is a Bamford, model EV2, serial no. 19146, manufactured in the 1940s. It is a single-cylinder petrol engine that runs at 1,000 rpm, developing 2.5 hp. Ignition is by Wyco magneto.

The last was manufactured by R. A. Lister in Gloucestershire, serial no. 120701. It is a single-cylinder petrol engine that runs at 710 rpm, generating 1.5 hp. It is water-cooled with a hopper on top; the ignition is by Wyco magneto.

R. A. Lister made a wide range of engines, some with two and three cylinders, and many were diesel engines. They specialised in making electric generators driven by their engines for country houses and farms, before the days of rural electrification. Some of their systems charge storage batteries, while others generate electricity on demand: for example, when the housewife switches on a light in the house when it gets dark, the generator will start up.

In the last fifty years small stationary engines of the sort described above became redundant as electricity extended into rural areas. Farmers were able to install electric motors at the point of use to drive their farm equipment. They were started at the push of a button, required little maintenance, and were quiet and efficient. It was only in isolated places where they were still a necessity, such as the milking bail, out in a field and away from the farm buildings, or the isolated farms, where to have electricity delivered by overhead poles, across miles of open country, would be very expensive.

A group of three stationary engines all restored by Mr. Robert Allo of Greenwood, Trinity. They include a Lister diesel engine and a Lister petrol engine, and an American engine named the Hired Hand.

The engine at the back, with a 50-gallon water-cooling tank standing on a platform behind, it is a Lister model CS, serial no. 73213. It is a single-cylinder, water-cooled, compression-ignition diesel engine manufactured in 1950. When running at 600 rpm it will generate 3 hp. It was installed at St. Mannelier, St. Saviour, to drive a Lister H4 water pump through a direct flexible coupling, to pump water from a meadow to the glasshouses.

In front is a second Lister, model D, serial no. 106664, manufactured in 1933. It is a single-cylinder, 2-hp, petrol engine which ran at 1,000 rpm. It was installed at La Chasse, St. Saviour, mounted on a trolley to drive a pump and spraying equipment in glasshouses. The company was managed by the late Mr. Ben Wakeham.

The red-painted petrol engine was made by Associated Manufacturers in Iowa, USA, named a Hired Man, serial no. 5927, manufactured between 1920 and 1925. It ran at 750 rpm, generating 2.5 hp. It is a single-cylinder, water-cooled, horizontal engine, with exposed valves, connecting rod, and crankshaft, which has a simple sheet-metal cover. Ignition is by low-tension system. It was installed at Robin Hill, St. Martin, for Mr. Carlyle de la Mare.

Single-cylinder compression-ignition diesel engine manufactured by R. A. Lister in 1934. It is a model CS, serial no. 15287, developing 3 hp.

The Lister engine is water-cooled, having a large radiator and fan. It was imported before 1940 for an unknown user. It was used by the Germans during the Occupation. After the war the late Mr. Bert Dallain, in St. Ouen, used it to drive a circular saw, and it was donated by Mrs Dallain to Mr. Lyndon Pallot for restoration. It is displayed here at a Steam Museum Open Day.

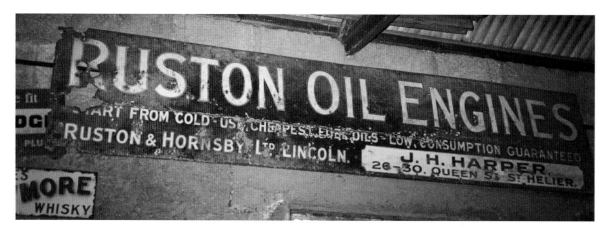

This advertising board was recovered by Mr. Gouédard, Senior, and is displayed in his workshop at his business premises at Samarès

The author is extremely grateful to the many people who have collected and restored to running condition the many engines detailed here and allowing them to be photographed and recorded. They are there for us to enjoy today.

15 Barn or Shed Machinery

Farm machinery operated in a shed or barn is known in the industry as barn machinery. The word 'barn' is quite unknown on the traditional Jersey farm. In Jersey there are cow stables, horse stables, sheds, and lofts, hence the expression 'shed machinery'. The expression 'barn' was introduced into the Island by local branches of English estate agents and probably by English employees in the media.

The winnowing machine

One of the earliest barn or shed machines was the winnowing machine. It first appeared in the seventeenth century, for separating the grain from the husk, etc. after threshing with the flail. The machine is operated by a horse engine or a crank handle, which operated the fan of a blower and a crankshaft. The crankshaft rocked the sieve to move the grain. The fan blew a draught of air through the grain as it fell from a tray on the top. The fan blew away the dust and husk, leaving the grain to fall through a rocking sieve, which sorted out any heavy rubbish, leaving the clean grain to fall down a chute into a sack. The machine was a useful advance for cleaning up the grain sample after threshing with a flail, an essential operation before milling wheat into flour for bread-making.

Before the winnowing machine, farmers had to use a winnowing basket, which was a large shovel-shaped basket described in Chapter 18. It was a slow, tedious process, done in the winter, to give the farm labour some work. Probably a good way to catch a cold standing between two open doors!

The first winnowing machine in the Island was made by Jean Le Grand in 1790. He lived at the mill at La Hague, in St. Peter. It was shown at a big agricultural show in St. John, where it was described as being 'very useful for blow-cleaning grain, wheat and barley etc'. Fourteen people had used it and reported that the work done was economical and would recover the expense of purchase in three seasons.

There was a winnowing machine in a loft at Beau Désert in St. Saviour. The author recalls using it with his father in the late 1940s to clean up several bags of oats that had, unusually, not cleaned up well during threshing. The seed was to be used for sowing the following year's crop on the farm. It did an excellent job, producing a very clean sample. The machine may well have been a hundred years old at the time.

This winnowing machine was made in the late 18th or 19th century. It has a flat-belt pulley for driving with a horse engine.
The fan is 33 in. (83.5 cm) long, has a diameter of 24 in. (61 cm), and has four 9 in. (23 cm) wide paddles operating at 75 rpm approximately. The pulley has a crank pin, operating a connecting rod to shake the sieve/riddle, which removes any remaining rubbish. Winnowing machines have no hopper above the feeding tray; the grain has to be tipped onto the tray at a steady rate through a grill in a hatch on top. The present owner is the National Trust for Jersey and the machine is displayed at the Moulin de Quétivel.

Two winnowers. In the foreground is a L'Âne ('the donkey') made in Rennes, serial no. 62386; the blue machine in the background is slightly bigger with minor differences and was made by Renaut.

Inside the machine in the foreground is the sieve in a shaker which swings on hangers, two of which can be seen. The sieves can slide out and be exchanged for a sieve with different-size holes depending on the grain or seed being cleaned. Very often two sieves of different sizes are used and exchanged according to the crop. On the outside of all these machines is a connecting rod driven off the fan shaft to a linkage that causes the hangers to swing the sieve back and forth. It is a short but rapid stroke to keep the material moving along the gently sloping sieve and allow the wind from the fan to blow out the husk and light rubbish, while the grain falls through the sieve to the bagging-off chute. They are displayed at the Steam Museum.

When the threshing machine came into being, the winnowing machine was incorporated in the design, forming a part of the whole machine.

Chaff cutters

Machinery for preparing cattle food, such as chaff cutters and milling machines for crushing oats etc., and root crushers (also described as slicers and pulpers), is more recent than the winnowing machine. The mills and root crushers first appeared in the mid-nineteenth century and went on being manufactured well into the twentieth century.

Chaff cutter manufactured from approximately 1850 onwards for cutting hay or oat straw in short lengths of 1 in. (2.5 cm) or 2 in. (5 cm) long. This view is of the feed channel and two pegged rollers that will adjust the length of the cut and squeeze the hay etc. on the ledger plate and present it to the knives

The machine is hand-operated and made by Bentall of Maldon, Essex. It is in the Samarès Manor collection. Chaff was mixed with chopped or sliced roots, mangels, etc., and fed to the cows and heifers regularly each day through the winter.

The crank handle on the cutting wheel and the two cutting knives on a chaff cutter. The knife in the centre is just passing the ledger plate, ready to cut the hay

Power-driven Bentall chaff cutter, model CSE, serial no. 7203. It is a later type than the one above

This machine is basically the same as the older manual machine, but this one has a pulley for a flat belt and an automatic-feed mechanism. Probably manufactured in the 20th century. Driven by a horse engine or stationary engine, either directly or via shafting. Among its uses was cutting gorse, probably for horses' bedding, although gorse was also fed to horses. This one is in the Steam Museum collection.

Bentall chaff cutter, model CED, serial no. 2403. The cover for the gearbox, the feed channel, and crank handle have been removed.
(Steam Museum collection)

Cake mill

A cake mill manufactured by W. N. Nicholson & Son of Newark, model no. 3 NW. The mill is for crushing compressed cake for feeding to cattle, such as cotton cake and linseed cake. The material is fed into the hopper at the top and passes between two pegged rollers that crush it into smaller pieces. It is operated by hand.

The machine has a pair of contra-rotating, cast-iron pegged rollers which were driven by hand through a gearbox. The pegs are pyramid shaped, about 1 in. (2.5 cm) deep, set in rows along the surface of the rollers and meshed, one roller with the other. The gap between them is adjustable with a handle, which turns a cam at each end of one roller, drawing it away or taking it towards the fixed one. Adjustment was made according to the coarseness of the material required. The crank handle is attached to a large-diameter wheel, similar to the chaff cutter. It also acts to a limited extent as a flywheel. This machine was manufactured in the late 19th or early 20th century. It is on the farm of Mr. Arthur, La Pompe, St. Mary.

The pyramid-shaped teeth on the rollers can be seen at the bottom of the hopper. Some cattle foods were imported from overseas in cake form or slabs, like a large thick biscuit thought to be 3 ft (91.5 cm) long x 12 in. (30.5 cm) wide and approx 1 in. (2.5 cm) thick, such as cotton cake and linseed cake. Both have good food value and are valued for their oil content. Cotton cake came from India and America, linseed cake also came from America, and linseed is also grown in the UK and has been grown in the Island. Cake in slab form is not seen today, for a number of reasons due to changes in cattle food manufacture and the electric hammer mills introduced in the 1950s. Concentrates for cattle are available in the bag, supplied by cattle food manufacturers as nuts (short-length extrusions). So the machine fell out of use.

Farmers could grow their own cattle food but chose not to, although it is profitable. Cash crops were considered more profitable on relatively expensive Jersey farmland, although with the big changes taking place in local agriculture, that may alter, and we may see a return to dairy farmers growing their own cattle food.

Rolling mills

A roller and plate grain mill manufactured by Wm. Gardner of Gloucester, probably in the late 19th or early 20th century.

The roller is nearer the camera and the adjustable plate opposite. The mill is driven by a flat-belt pulley at one side. The hopper looks like an adaptation.

The roller is 12 in. (30.5 cm) long with a diameter of 5 in. (12.5 cm), having a finely ridged or ribbed surface crushing the grain against a cast-iron plate, all mounted in a cast-iron box. The gap between the roller and plate is adjusted with the handwheel, at the side in the foreground, to move the plate towards or away from the roller. The wooden hopper above it looks like a later addition. The flat-belt pulley has a diameter of 17.5 in. (44 cm) and is 4 in. (10 cm) wide, operating at a low 400-500 rpm. The power would be delivered by shafting. The mill was most likely to have been used to crush oats or barley and was probably last used during the German Occupation. A part of the mill equipment at Moulin de Quétivel. (National Trust for Jersey collection.)

Bentall roller mill model RSH, used to crush or roll oats for cattle and horse feed.

Although it is fitted with a crank handle, it is also fitted with a wooden flat-belt pulley for mechanical power, when the handle would be removed. The hopper is quite small, which suggests it is designed for small quantities, or more likely it is fed by a chute from a floor above. (Steam Museum collection.)

Engine, shafting, and a rolling and grinding mill

Frequent reference is made to shafting to deliver power from an engine to the point of use. In the next picture is a typical installation of a stationary engine and shafting via flat belts to a combined twin roller and grinding mill.

A mill, an engine, and overhead a shaft installation. The mill has an overhead feedpipe to the hopper. The engine is a Lister two-cylinder, 30-hp diesel engine that runs at 1,000 rpm; it has plenty of power available to operate more machinery.

The engine is on a concrete pedestal in the background. It has a flat belt to a pulley on the overhead shaft. The shaft bearings are supported under the rafters. There are two flat-belt pulleys above the combined rolling and grinding mill. In order to stop the mill, the belt is moved from the driving pulley and onto the idler, allowing the engine to continue running. The mill is a combined grinding mill which is totally enclosed and a two-roller mill with one roller exposed. Before the machine is run, the operator will select which operation he wants with a selector in the gearbox. The machine runs at 200 rpm. Both rollers have a smooth surface with up to four helical grooves on each roll to maintain movement of the material. The distance between the rolls is adjustable. The material to be crushed/rolled or ground is delivered to the mill down a pipe from the floor above. The mill is an Albion manufactured by Harrison McGregor and was installed by Mr. Charles Le Couteur, who has restored and installed the equipment at Westlands, St. Peter. The grinding mill is out of view in this picture but can be seen in the next one, which is the manufacturer's parts list.

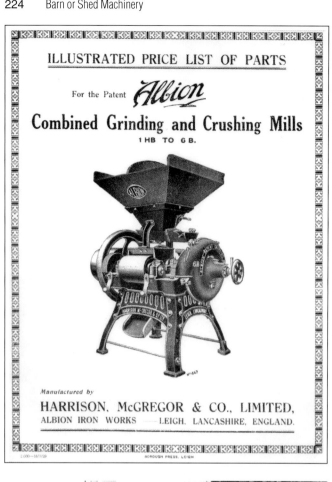

A page from an Albion catalogue and parts list; the grinding mill is on the right with a bagging-off chute. The wheel on the end is to adjust the fineness of the flour by moving the fixed plate towards or away from the rotor. The two crank handles in front of the exposed roll are for adjusting the gap between the rolls.

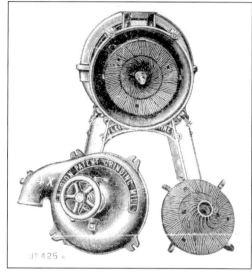

The grinder with the cover removed to expose the rotor inside at the top and fixed plate at the bottom on the right. The cover with adjusting wheel and the bagging-off spout is on the left.

This mill is also a combined grinding mill and twin-roller crushing mill. It is similar to the Albion manufactured after 1900 by Henry Bamford & Sons of Uttoxeter.

On the Bamford, both rollers and the grinder are driven through a gearbox, and when installed, power is delivered by flat belt from a stationary engine directly by shafting. It has a small hopper that suggests it worked with an overhead feed. The machine runs at 200 rpm. (Courtesy of the Royal Hotel, St. Martin.)

This rolling mill for rolling grain is installed with a feed hopper fed from the floor above. It was installed in the 1950s or later, and is driven by a three-phase, 3-hp electric motor. Manufactured by Bentall of New Maldon, Essex. It is a good example of electrical power used on farms since rural electrification. Installations like this Bentall usually crushed or rolled oats on farms, for feeding to horses and cattle. Installed at Samarès Manor for Messrs. Obbard to prepare cattle food for the dairy herd. Now part of Mr. Vincent Obbard's collection.

As more and more farms in rural areas were being connected to receive mains electricity, the stationary engine was being replaced with electric motors, and manually operated machines were being fitted with electric motors at the point of use, saving labour.

In Chapter 7 are details of a small threshing machine manufactured by Garvie of Aberdeen, model no. NS, serial no. 73646. It is also a shed machine, originally installed in a farm shed or loft. (Courtesy of the Steam Museum collection.)

Root chopper, slicer, pulper

Root chopper, slicer, or pulper manufactured by Bentall, described as the unchokable model XWPM, serial no. 8689, operated by a crank handle.

On the top of the Bentall root chopper is a hopper that is filled with mangels, swedes, turnips, or fodder beet. At one side of the hopper is a 2 ft (61 cm) diameter sheet-metal wheel or disc with holes partly punched into it, forming a scoop on the side facing the hopper. As the wheel rotates, the sharp edge of each scoop cuts off slices of the roots, which fall through the scoop into the discharge chute underneath. This one was last used in 1939. (Courtesy of the Steam Museum collection.)

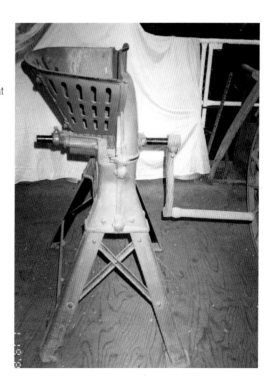

The roots were always scraped clean to remove any soil stuck to them before they were thrown into the hopper. All dairy farmers had a root crusher, slicer, or pulper and several manufacturers in the farm equipment industry made them. They all looked alike and used the same principle; while many had a crank handle for manual operation, there were also those with a flat-belt pulley and power driven by horse engine or stationary engine. An example is a machine manufactured by R. Hunt & Co. Ltd., Earls Colne, Essex, illustrated below.

(*left*) The Eclipse root slicer/pulper type O for manual operation. It has a 2 ft (61 cm) diameter slicing disc made by R. Hunt & Co. of Earls Colne, well known for their Cambridge rolls. it is in the Royal Hotel collection at St. Martin.

(*right*) Another of Bentall's 'unchok-able' root slicers/pulpers. This one is unusual: it has two slicing discs, one on each side. It is designed to be power-driven with a flat-belt pulley that could be fitted on either side but has been removed.
The Bentall machine was made in 1903; it has a serial no. 11109.9103, patent no. 15952, and runs at 100 rpm, absorbing 0.75 hp. All these machines discharged the pulp or slices between the legs, where it was collected in a wooden box, or very often in a cabot basket. (Royal Hotel collection St. Martin.)

An advertisement by John Jones of Mulcaster Street, a local machinery agent in 1904.

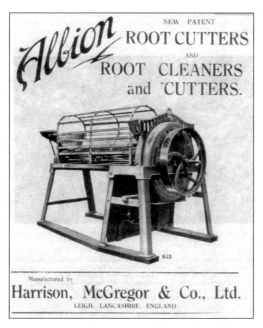

This illustration was taken from a manufacturer's catalogue dated before 1920.

Under the cage were two long rollers, made up with rods, each having a slight spiral to keep the roots moving towards the chopping/slicing disc. The rollers shook the roots to remove any soil that remained on them. They were loaded at the hopper, using a root fork. A root fork was made with steel knobs on the end of each prong to prevent them piercing the roots. It was shaped like an extra-large shovel with the side prongs raised to prevent the roots rolling off the sides. This type of slicer was made by more than one manufacturer and there were several in Jersey, such as at Beau Désert, St. Saviour (that one was driven by a Petter Victory two-stroke, stationary, petrol engine and shafting). The number of these machines and mills fitted with pulleys suggests that quite a number of Jersey farms had a stationary engine and shafting installed. Many of those stationary engines are in the collections in the Island such as the Steam Museum.

Seed grader

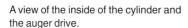

This machine was at the States' Howard Davis Farm at Trinity. It is quite old, and was made by Leon Youf, of St. Lô, in Normandy. It is a honeycomb-type seed grader operated manually with a crank handle.

The grader's cylinder is 6 ft 6 in. (200 cm) in length and 19 in. (48 cm) in diameter, with a 4 in. (10 cm) diameter auger along the bottom to move the seeds along. This machine was used to clean up a seed sample after passing it through a winnowing machine to improve further the purity of the sample and remove every trace of weed seed and any other material, performing a similar operation to the final sieves and rotary screen in a threshing machine. The machine is loaded at the hopper on the top. (Jersey National Trust collection at Quétivel Mill.)

A view of the inside of the cylinder and the auger drive.

Tomato graders

An early tomato grader with five trays, each having a set of holes smaller than the one above.

The top tray of the grader has 2.5 in. (6.2 cm) diameter holes, the second has 2.25 in. (5.7 cm) diameter holes, the third has 1.75 in. (4.5 cm) holes, the fourth has 1.625 in. (4 cm) holes, and the last 1.375 in. (3.5 cm) holes. Tomatoes are tipped gently into the top drawer and they work their way down through, the smallest going to the bottom drawer, the largest remaining at the top. Probably made to order by a local carpenter approximately 1900 or earlier, in the early days of the tomato industry. (La Société Jersiaise collection at Hamptonne.)

A hand-operated mechanical tomato grader with a gently sloping table and five different hole sizes.

Rising and falling rods, moving under each row of holes, lift the fruit forward and along over the progressively larger holes, until they come to a hole large enough to fall through, sorting them by size. Each size of hole has a separate chute, through which the fruit are channelled. The grader has nine rows of holes, progressively larger towards one end, starting at 1.375 in. (3.5 cm); 1.625 in. (4 cm); 1.75 in. (4.5 cm); 2.1875 in. (5.5 cm); 2.625 in. (6.5 cm). The machine is manually operated with a crankshaft at one end and a shaft at the other end, with connecting rods and hangers. Probably made early in the 20th century. It is in the Steam Museum collection. Graders would have been used with a cleaning machine as described below.

Fruit cleaners and polishers

Tomatoes were often packed on the farm. The first operation is to clean the fruit to remove dirt and any traces of spray before they are graded and packed. Some farmers and growers might do it entirely by hand, using a length of stair carpet spread along a long, slightly sloping table, with raised sideboards. The fruit are stroked with a soft-bristle brush and graded by hand before being packed. Almost always a job for the evening, after spending all day in the field, picking the fruit.

Fruit cleaner and polisher; it uses a standard width of stair carpet as a conveyor to move the fruit along to be cleaned and polished by a reciprocating brush above.

The brush is mounted in slides on either side, moving to and fro driven by the crankshaft and connecting rod. A spare brush is on the floor beside the machine. The machine is driven by hand or an electric motor, driving through a reduction gear. The connecting rod is fitted between the brush and the crankshaft, which is assembled to the red frame on the top. The machine was made by Drake and Fletcher of Kent, who specialise in this type of equipment for the fruit growers of Kent. (Shire Horse Farm collection.) This type of machine was used when outdoor tomato growing was a profitable main crop or second crop after potatoes, during the first sixty or seventy years of the twentieth century. In those days there was a demand for outdoor tomatoes, as they were always firmer and have more flavour than the indoor crop. This machine would have been used with a fruit grader, for tomato packing on the farm. There was a boom in tomato-growing after the Second World War and the German Occupation, when a lot of growers packed their own tomatoes on the farm. This type of machine was used by many growers.

Another Drake and Fletcher fruit cleaner using stair carpet for the conveyor and a reciprocating brush.

This machine is a little bigger than the first machine, but is otherwise much the same. It was originally made for manual operation but has been converted to run with an electric motor. (La Société Jersiaise/Jersey Heritage Trust collection, at present at Augrès.)

Tower silo

Coleman concrete tower silo for making and storing silage for feeding to cattle. Behind it is a grain store for storing up to 800 tons of barley.

The Coleman tower silo is filled by blowing the material up a chute on the side of the silo. It is unloaded for feeding to stock by an unloading machine, suspended from the dome at the top and driven by electric motors. An auger travels round in a circle to deliver the silage to one of many windows down one side of the tower, depositing the material into a second chute, where it falls to the ground. As the level of silage falls, the machine is lowered and discharges the silage out of one of the unloading hatches lower down. Down the side of the tower, every two or three courses of the blocks, are hatches for discharging the material into a tube fitted to the outside of the tower. A domed metal top has a removable panel for loading the material. Also fitted to the side is a second, smaller-diameter tube fitted with a powerful blower at the foot, for blowing the silage up into the tower.

The silo is constructed of interlocking concrete blocks and lined with sealing material. The blocks are supported by steel straps, surrounding the outside of each course of blocks. Some towers are constructed in steel. (Courtesy of Mr. Le Gallais, Cowleywood Ltd., Maufant.)

16 Dairy Farm Equipment

History of milking by hand and machine

Taking milk from cows by man goes back a long way. Nin-Khursag, the goddess and protector of herds, is remembered in a frieze from a temple that is displayed in a museum in Baghdad. The 5,100-year-old frieze shows a milker squatting behind a cow milking by hand, between the cow's hind legs! This may be artistic licence, because there can be a no more awkward or difficult way of milking a cow; a newborn calf knows better! The milker would be very vulnerable to the cow's natural functions.

To hand-milk one cow, a milker has to squeeze his or her hands between 500 and 600 times. Hand milking is laborious and labour-intensive, with a large herd of 20-30 cows, in earlier years, occupying a team of four or more milkers for each milking. Someone new to hand-milking will find that their hands and wrists will ache after milking two or three cows, but in due course, after a few days, this difficulty will pass, as the hands get used to the unusual activity. As the population increased, so did the demand for milk and the demand for skilled milkers. They were always in short supply, so the desire to mechanize the operation grew strong, resulting in the milking machine that we know today.

There will be frequent references to the teatcup, the liner, and the pulsator, so some explanation will enable the reader to have a better understanding of these components of the milking machine. The teatcup with a rubber liner inside is the component which is placed on the cow's teats, to draw out the milk. The pulsator is the component that makes the teatcup behave like a sucking calf. Both components are driven by a vacuum created by an air pump that draws air out of the system, known as a vacuum pump. Many modern pulsators are driven electrically.

Experiments with milking machines began early in the nineteenth century; various ideas were tried. The first recorded idea was in 1819, when catheters were inserted into the cow's teats, to overcome the closing muscles in the teat and let the milk flow out by gravity. At first quills were used, but they could injure the milk canal in the teat, causing disease. This was followed by metal catheters patented in Britain in 1836. Their constant use caused the muscles in the teat to weaken, allowing the milk to dribble from the teat. However, it was a simple system and not expensive to install, and went on being offered up to 1919 before eventually being abandoned.

The first attempt to try suction was in England in 1851, with a bag or sheath placed over the udder and teats. A rubber pipe connected the sheath to a bucket and a second pipe connected the bucket to a vacuum reservoir, under a hand-operated piston type. The vacuum pump applied a continuous vacuum to the sheath. The constant vacuum drew blood down the udder and teats, a process that became painful to the cow, which reacted by kicking off the sheath. In 1862 L. O. Colvin, an American, produced an improved version, having four separate teatcups mounted on the side of a milking pail and incorporating a diaphragm vacuum pump. It was operated by pulling two hand levers together like a pair of shears. It attracted a lot of attention when it was exhibited in England. Two effects caused its failure: the first that the extra flow of blood in the teat caused it to swell, partially closing the milk canal in the teat, so reducing the milk flow; and secondly, it was uncomfortable to the cow. Again the cow reacted by kicking it off!

In the late nineteenth century attempts to mechanize milking continued in many countries with dairy herds. Two lines of development emerged. One was the application of suction to imitate the calf, and the second was the application of pressure, to imitate hand-milking.

The first pressure-type machines appeared in 1870. They attempted to massage the teat with either plates or rollers. One idea was to place a tube or liner over the teat; rollers on the periphery

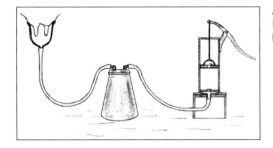

An early attempt at making a milking machine in 1851. It failed because it became painful to the cow, which kicked it off (Courtesy of Alfa Laval).

of a wheel rotated against the liner and side of the teat. The roller travelled down the teat squeezing out the milk. Yet another was much the same, with rollers on endless belts. They were operated by rotating a handwheel, which was awkwardly placed beside the udder. They were heavy, necessitating the use of a strap over the cow's back to support them. To add to the problems, they were difficult to keep clean and all had poor milking results.

It will be noted that all these machines, both suction and pressure types, needed somebody to operate each machine while they were on the cow, so there was no labour-saving. It was quicker to milk by hand! As a result, they soon disappeared from the market.

Meanwhile, work on improving the vacuum-operated machines was continued by many people in different countries. William Murchland is worthy of attention: in 1889 he produced a machine with single-chamber teatcups. These were metal cups each with a rubber collar, which a little later became a rubber liner. The machine was installed with a vacuum pipeline passing over each stall in the stables, and was operated by a hand pump. Murchland also proposed a glass milk line, and his cowshed had dung channels; both ideas were advanced for the time. Several similar machines were produced in Scotland during the last decade of the nineteenth century. One such exhibited at the Royal Show in 1891 won a silver medal. The teatcups were made of cow horns, with rubber collars operated with a hand-operated piston pump. The strokes of the piston provided a certain pulsation in the vacuum, which was criticized when the machine was officially tested, thus indicating some lack of understanding by the examiners of the need for periodic relief from the constant effect of the vacuum on the cows' teats! The Murchland machine did achieve some success and some were sold overseas, including Australia.

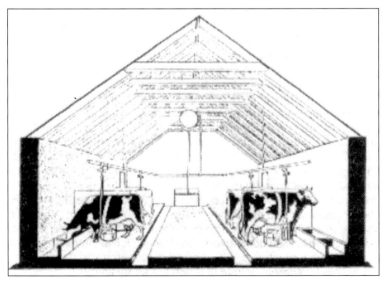

Murchland's overhead vacuum-line, bucket units, and advanced design of cow stables with dung channels, in 1889.

In 1892, when Struthers and Weir in Scotland patented a two-chamber teatcup, they had the foundation of something more successful. One of the first machines to use pulsation was the Thistle machine, patented by Dr. Alexander Shields, also of Scotland, exhibited at the Royal Show in 1895. The pulsation device was located next to the vacuum pump, with a pipe connecting it to the milking machine. The system, unfortunately, drew large quantities of air from the cowshed into the milk line, making it difficult to produce good-quality clean milk. The machine required a large steam engine to drive it, and it was expensive. However, it did find its way onto many dairy farms at home and abroad.

A pressure system experiment used a teatcup with a liner inside and two pistons, one above the other. Operating alternately, they opened and closed the top and the bottom of each teat, repeating the action of the milker's hand, squeezing the teat from top to bottom. It was operated by compressed air, but each unit was heavy, requiring a strap over the cow's back, to support the teatcup assembly to stay on the teat. Yet another machine had three such pistons, but all these ideas came to nothing.

In Sweden, Dr. de Laval experimented with a mechanical machine using plates and rollers. He formed a company AB Laktator to produce it but it was not an efficient milking machine and it failed, the company going into liquidation. AB Laktator is not to be confused with the highly successful AB Separator Company in America, which handled the cream separator and eventually in due course became involved with milking machines.

Among the supporters of the vacuum system, an argument developed between those in favour of the constant vacuum and those in favour of the intermittent, pulsating vacuum, particularly in Australia. A competition was arranged in England between the two systems in the late 1890s. By this time, hygiene was becoming an important issue, so the Murchland machine was judged the better of the two. Following this defeat, the Thistle Company failed.

One of the Thistle directors, Robert Kennedy, joined another Scotsman, William Lawrence, of Glasgow. Between them they designed a milking machine with a pulsating vacuum system, with a small vacuum-operated motor, on the cover of the milking bucket. So in 1897 the first pulsator, as we know it, was mounted on a milking bucket. It was tested again by the Royal Agricultural Society of England against the Murchland. There were no winners and no prize awarded.

It was only when the pulsation principle was properly understood, after further study of the action of the sucking calf, that the milking machine would become a practical proposition.

At the turn of the century, inventors and engineers turned their attention to the teatcup. In 1902 a patent was taken out in New York by two people, Hulbert and Park, for a teatcup with an inflatable rubber liner, with three annular chambers. There was the usual vacuum and, in addition, compressed air acting on the annular chambers, controlled by a spring-loaded valve. The compressed air created a downward pressure on the teat. However, this idea was overtaken by a two-chamber teatcup, invented in Australia by Alexander Gillies, which, when combined with the Kennedy-Lawrence machine imported from Scotland, was a great improvement on anything else so far. It was known as the Lawrence Kennedy Gillies, or LKG, machine and was the basis for the modern milking machine. It incorporated the pulsator on the cover of the bucket unit, communicating with the outer annular chamber of the teatcup to produce the necessary massaging effect on the teat. A couple of years later Gillies improved his two-chamber teatcup by introducing a small air hole, to admit just sufficient air to assist the milk to flow away. This is a feature that still exists on machines to this day, but on some machines it may be in the claw of the cluster rather than the teatcup.

At the time, this innovation caused some controversy, because one Ambrose Ridd of New Zealand had been designing and developing his own milking machine, evidently with some success. He had also introduced an air hole in the teatcup for the same purpose. Although a cash settlement was made, Ridd continued to be difficult. It was an example of the many problems facing those manufacturers who worked in research and development, when a successful idea occurs to different people at much the same time.

An anxiety at the time for the industry was that milk yields appeared to reduce slowly when milking machines were used; as a result, many farmers abandoned the machine and returned to hand-milking. Between 1905 and 1910 it appeared to be generally accepted that to be successful the teatcup must have two chambers and be operated with a pulsator. However, the operation of the teatcup and pulsator was still subject to development and trial and error. J. and R. Wallace, for example, introduced a two-chamber teatcup, with a pulsator at the base of each teatcup. The wall of the rubber liner was thinner at the top than at the bottom, and pressure was applied first at the top of the teat, using compressed air. The machine was awarded a silver medal at the Royal Show in Doncaster and sold successfully both at home and abroad. But it was also subject to modification and the use of compressed air was eventually abandoned.

Nevertheless, the demand for milking machines was unabated and this drove the development onward. J. Bartram founded the Vacca (later Vaccar) Company in England to market and develop the LKG machine. He produced a mobile machine on wheels for milking in the field. In Sweden the development of a successful milking machine was slow to materialize, due to the country's engineers' and inventors' continued interest in developing the mechanical pressure-type machines. They were all of the opinion that the suction machine was not the way forward. Many designs were offered to AB Separator and passed on to the engineers at the de Laval Company to investigate, including the LKG and Wallace machines, which received particularly thorough examination. While the company was interested because demand was so great, they did not wish to have another expensive failure.

A young New Zealander, Robert Daysh, born on his father's farm in 1882, was milking cows during his schooldays. The remarkable thing about this story is that Daysh was born only thirty-one years after the first emigrant ship arrived at Littleton in New Zealand. Young Robert had a mechanical bent; at 18 he had made his first milking machine. After service with New Zealand forces in South Africa during the Boer War, he sold a number of machines to neighbours and eventually further afield, in both New Zealand and Australia. By 1912 he had a machine which was to become the basis of the Alfa Laval milking machine. Realising the wider potential in the rest of the world, he travelled to America. He was familiar with AB Separator's cream separators, which sold widely in both Australia and New Zealand. Arriving in America, he approached the de Laval Company, AB Separator's company in America, to find the company experimenting with milking machines without much success. He was invited to join and started work immediately to develop his machine. Following the past disappointments in both Sweden and America to find a machine to equal the very high standards the company had set for themselves, they were particularly careful not to rush into manufacturing. Many machines went out on test over the next five years and were monitored; test after test was carried out and changes made. Long-term testing followed: the cows' reaction, the milk yield, the practical operation, and so forth. Finally, the machines proved successful and all the machines put out on a sale or return basis with farmers gave satisfaction, and the farmers bought them. Manufacturing commenced in 1918 and brought immediate success.

As the twentieth century progressed, both the teatcup and the pulsator would receive considerable attention and development, resulting in many improvements. It was a long, frustrating story for many of those involved, but all the effort ultimately succeeded. So many people in so many countries—England, Scotland, Australia, New Zealand, America, and Sweden—contributed to the many steps towards a successful milking machine.

The de Laval milking machines installed in 1918 consisted of a stationary petrol engine to drive the vacuum pump. A vacuum reservoir tank to keep the vacuum steady at approximately 50 per cent of atmospheric pressure included a master pulsator at the pump. A simple mechanical slide arrangement, operated by the pump assembly, controlled the pulsations transmitted along its own dedicated pipeline. Therefore there were two pipelines, the pulsation pipe and the vacuum pipe. Along the vacuum pipe were the sanitary trap, the vacuum gauge, the vacuum control valve, and the taps, distributed along the length of the pipe in the stables. The pulsation pipe had a relay control. The milk bucket with its lid clamped on, the cluster complete with the claw and teatcups, with pulsation pipes and liners hooked on the handle, and the pulsation relay, completed the milking bucket as a unit.

It is interesting to note the percentage of dairy farmers using milking machines in different countries at the start of the Second World War. New Zealand, so dependent on dairy products for exports (having the biggest herds of dairy cows, mostly Jerseys at that time) was far and away the biggest user of milking machines, and the biggest installations at that (see Table 1).

Table 1

	%		%
New Zealand	90	The Netherlands	3
Sweden	35	Belgium	2
Great Britain	30	Australia	2
USA	10	Germany	0.2
Denmark	10	France	0.2

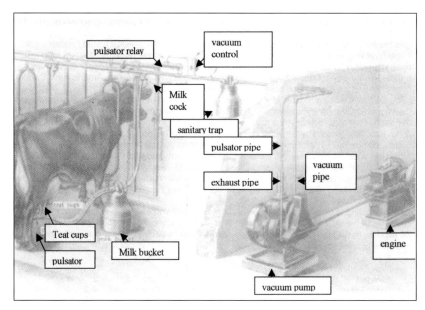

A de Laval milking machine installation in 1918: the petrol engine is on the right, the vacuum pump and pulsator in the foreground, and the vacuum and pulsator pipes, the sanitary vacuum gauge, etc. A milking bucket stands beside the cow with the cluster on the teats (Courtesy of Alfa Laval).

More recent developments

In the 1950s and 1960s, following rural electrification, the power unit would be a fractional horse-power electric motor, with a V-belt-driven vacuum pump. Both pump and motor were much smaller than the original units. The pump assembly would not include a master pulsation unit and there would be only one pipeline, the vacuum line with the sanitary trap, gauge, control valve, and the taps. This became virtually standard practice with all cowshed installations of milking machines, whatever the make.

The bucket unit, with its pulsator on the lid, a cluster of teatcups, and associated rubber tubing, is the basic milking machine.

Each milking bucket had its own pulsator. Two examples were the Alfa Laval type P, a small cubic bakelite box no more than 2.5 in. (6 cm) across with associated nozzles, and the larger Gascoigne Positive. They were clamped under the lid handle of the milking bucket.

The Alfa Laval vacuum pump would be a simple vane type, with a shaft rotating off centre, in a cylinder with spring-loaded vanes, slotted in the shaft. Springs in the slots under the vanes push them against the wall of the cylinder to sweep the wall of the cylinder, drawing air in from the system through an aperture in the cylinder wall and expelling it to atmosphere through a second aperture, as the pressure increased. The rotary pump provided a steady, continuous vacuum, without the fluctuations in the vacuum that the piston pump by its very nature was bound to produce, and needing an airtight tank to provide a vacuum reservoir to smooth out the vacuum in the pipeline.

The bucket unit begins to operate when it is connected to a vacuum pump. All makes of bucket unit are made of stainless steel or aluminium, with a steel handle. (Aluminium buckets were less expensive.) It may look complicated with all the rubber tubes, the cluster of teatcups hanging by its claw to a hook at the side of the bucket, and the lid with all its fittings. But the milk bucket is simply that, a bucket for collecting the milk, having the usual swivelling carrying handle for use when the bucket does not have its lid on. The swivelling handle is used to clamp the lid onto the bucket. The lid also has a handle with a number of notches or dimples along the top, over one of which the swivelling handle is pushed to clamp it in place. A rubber seal fits between the lid and bucket to keep it airtight. Having clipped the lid onto the bucket, the complete bucket unit can be carried by the handle on the lid. The lid also has a hook on the handle for hooking on the claw of the cluster with all the rubber pipes and teatcups, making it convenient to carry the complete bucket unit in one hand.

Like the cluster, the pulsator is carried on the lid, clamped in place under the lid handle by a threaded stud and a knurled wheel nut. The pulsator has nozzles or short metal pipes for connecting the various rubber tubes, which are simply pushed onto the nozzles. The pair of tubes connecting the pulsator to the claw have an internal diameter of 0.25 in. (6 cm) and are usually moulded together. A short tube connects the pulsator to a nozzle on the bucket lid to connect the vacuum to the pulsator. A bigger-diameter pipe will carry the milk from the claw to the bucket, via a nozzle on the bucket lid. The longest single rubber pipe on the milking bucket connects the overhead vacuum line to the bucket, also via a nipple on the lid.

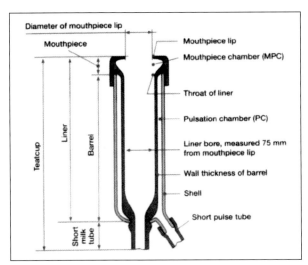

Components of a teat cup.

Mechanical pulsators on bucket units are operated by two diaphragms in sealed units, usually working at a rate of sixty pulsations a minute. The nozzles on pulsators are not sealed, so it is important that water does not enter them. Therefore the pulsator is attached in such a way that it is quickly detached from the lid when the bucket is to be washed. Simplex machines lived up to their name: their pulsators were simple and trouble-free, easily dismantled and reassembled. They could be cleaned and dried if water got in. The diaphragm pulsator comes into action the moment it feels the effect of the vacuum. Its purpose is to interrupt the vacuum in the outer chamber of the two chamber teatcup. When milking, the inner chamber is constantly open to the effect of the vacuum, while the pulsator affects the outer chamber. The pulsator regularly cuts off the vacuum to the outer chamber and opens it to atmosphere. This causes the liner to collapse around the teat to exclude the effect of the vacuum, momentarily, on the teat, and massage the teat, allowing the blood to circulate in the teat and the milk to be let down. The pulsator then switches back to exposing the outer chamber to the vacuum and the liner is drawn back from the teat allowing the milk to flow. So the cycle continues in the teatcup, an action similar to a sucking calf. Some pulsators operate on all four teatcups together; others alternate between front and back teats.

The teatcup is a metal cylinder, approximately 5 in. (12.5 cm) long and of 1.5 in. (4 cm) diameter. The bottom of the cup curves inwards to an opening of 0.75 in. (2 cm) diameter. A rubber liner is moulded to fit inside the metal teatcup. At the top of the liner is a flat top collar of a larger diameter than the metal cup, with a deep skirt to fit around the outside of the cup to prevent it sliding into the metal cup. It is pulled down when assembled to seal the rim at the top and the opening at the bottom. At the centre of the flat top of the liner is a circular 0.75 in. diameter hole to fit onto and grip the cow's teat. The hole for the teat is made in several sizes, as some breeds of dairy cow have much bigger teats than the Jersey. At the bottom, the liner is narrower to become a small-diameter pipe with an internal diameter of 0.3125 in. (0.8 cm). It passes through the 0.75 ins. (2 cm) hole in the base of the metal cup. The end of the pipe is pushed onto a nipple on the claw to carry the milk away.

The cluster unit is composed of a central metal claw with nozzles, to which the various rubber pipes and liners are attached. There are two chambers, one for the milk and one for the pulsator, each with their own nozzles for connecting to the teatcups. The claw will often have a window to permit the cowman to monitor the milk flow in the milk chamber. The four milk pipe nozzles are fitted onto the claw at an angle so that they slope upwards from the claw. The ends are bevelled, cut off at a horizontal angle in the working position. The purpose is to prevent any loss of vacuum by stopping air flowing into the claw when the cluster is being fitted onto the cow, one teatcup at a time. To achieve this the cowman has to hold the claw in the palm of his hand, facing upward so that the teatcups hang down and rubber pipes at the end of the teatcup lie over the aperture, closing it off and so preventing any flow of air into the claw that would result in some loss of vacuum. If a teatcup should fall off a cow during milking, the rubber pipe will close over the end of the bevelled pipe, so preventing any loss of vacuum and any foreign bodies being sucked in.

The technology has moved on over the years; the principle is the same but the teatcups, while looking much the same, have changed, and some pulsators are electronically controlled. In 1956 Gascoigne introduced the electronic pulsator with a more accurately controlled pulse.

In a later development of cowshed installations, some systems have stainless steel, glass, or transparent plastic milk pipes known as a milk line. It is fitted alongside the vacuum line above the cow stalls, delivering the milk direct to the farm dairy. This is labour-saving, having no milking buckets to carry to and from the dairy. There are only two small assemblies in the stables, comprising the cluster of teatcups and a single master pulsator and associated piping. The milk goes straight from the cluster unit to the milk line overhead. A milk jar would receive and hold the milk of one cow at a time, in order to weigh it and record it. Releasing the milk from the jar, it would flow to a water-cooled milk cooler, whence it would drain into the milk can. In later installations, the milk would flow from the jar to a chilled bulk milk tank for storage. The bulk tank, operated by a refrigeration unit, is also known as a milk cooler; it both cools the milk and maintains it at a cool temperature, above freezing, where it remains until it is collected by the bulk milk tanker.

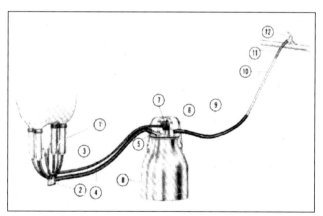

The cluster, the pulsator pipe and vacuum milk pipe, the bucket and pulsator, and the vacuum pipe to the vacuum line:
(1) teatcups; (2) milk and pulse claw; (3) twin pulse tube; (4) milk tube; (5) milk cock; (6) bucket cover; (7) pulsator; (8) milk bucket; (9) vacuum tube; (10) extension; (11) wearing piece; (12) vacuum tap.

Alfa Laval have a long extensive history and valuable experience gained during the development of their successful milking equipment. (All graphics are courtesy of Alfa Laval.)

Melotte

The Melotte Company was founded by Alfred Melotte in 1852 at Remicourt, in Belgium, to supply farm machinery. They were known particularly well for their Brabant horse-drawn, one-way ploughs. Alfred's two sons, Alfred junior and Jules, took over the business when he died in 1878. Jules Melotte developed a cream separator in 1888 that was highly successful, achieving a higher rate of separation and using less power than other machines. They sold exceptionally well in all parts of the world: here in Jersey, in Australia, New Zealand, and in particular the United States through their agent Henry Babson, who owned Surge. Jules Melotte died in 1919 and Alfred continued on his own. In 1926 Melotte entered into an agreement with Henry Babson to supply Surge suspended bucket-type milking machines, later to be known as the Surge-Melotte milking machine. The development work had been successfully achieved by Henry Babson in the USA. When sales of cream separators began falling off, Melotte focused their attention on the Surge machines, selling them successfully at home and in the Netherlands and France. They achieved 50 per cent of the sales in the home market by the 1950s and a high percentage in neighbouring countries.

In the UK before the Second World War they had a branch in Bristol, where they traded as the Melotte Separator Company of Bristol, but after the war they were re-established as Melotte Sales Co. in Grantham, Lincolnshire.

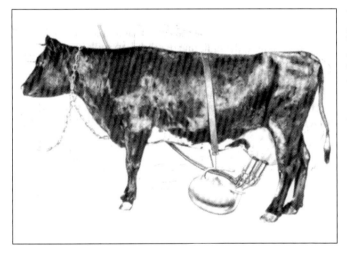

The Surge-Melotte suspended bucket unit sold in Jersey by Messrs. Le Cappelain, St. Peter's Iron Works (courtesy of Alfa Laval).

Suspended machines were popular in America, where they were manufactured by a number of companies. The arguments in favour of the suspended machine were: fewer parts, a shorter route for the milk to the bucket, and no claw, as each teatcup was fitted directly to its own nozzle on the lid of the bucket. As the pail filled, the weight of milk caused the suspended bucket to tilt downward, preventing the teatcups creeping up the teat and assisting in stripping the udder. There were many arguments against, such as there being no room for the milk bucket if the cow has a low-slung udder, a restless animal caused milk to slop about in the pail, to be sucked milk up the vacuum pipe, etc. However, the marketing success of Surge-Melotte convinced many farmers, so much so that de Laval in Sweden and AB Separator in America were compelled to manufacture them in the mid-1950s in Sweden and America.

Gascoigne

George Gascoigne founded Gascoigne Milking Equipment Ltd. in Reading in 1924. He had been interested in the research of vacuum-type milking machines of the nineteenth and early twentieth centuries. After several years of research and development in the 1920s, he launched his own system in 1927. The factory in Reading was producing bucket units in 1930 and the company grew quickly at home and abroad.

After the Second World War, in the late 1940s, branches were opened in Ireland, in France, and at Leeuwarden in the Netherlands; the last became known as Gascoigne Nederland in 1948. The company's success was based on the Positive bucket unit, deriving its name from the Positive pulsation system. The Positive could be used with different systems. In the late 1960s the company opened a branch in Kyodo in Japan, installing the first milk pipeline system in that country.

Many milking machine manufacturers offered not only mobile milking bails, with four or six side- by-side stalls, but also small portable machines, usually on a two-wheel trolley with one or two bucket units. In 1949 Gascoigne were offering portable milking machines on two-wheel trolleys, with either one or two bucket units. An example was the Miracle Single Bucket trolley and the Miracle In Churn trolley for the small herd.

Gascoigne aluminium milking bucket with the pulsator under the lid handle. On the right is the hook for the claw and cluster (Courtesy of the Steam Museum).

Some manufacturers offered equipment and chemicals for washing and sterilising all the components that came into contact with the milk. Gascoigne went even further, offering galvanised tubular cow stalls, yard feeding troughs, etc., probably in co-operation with Gush and Dent, who manufactured this type of equipment. Also manufactured were portable weighing machines with galvanised tubular frames for goats and sheep and a larger one for cows, which also served as a grading crush.

In the 1970s Thomas Tilling Group acquired both Gascoigne and Melotte, and they were amalgamated to form the Gascoigne Melotte Group with headquarters at Basingstoke. The connection with Surge was severed.

As a result, Messrs. Le Cappelain of St. Peter's Iron Works lost interest in selling Surge-Melotte milking machines, and to add to the problem the Jersey branch of the CGA, which had handled Gascoigne machines, eventually closed. Gascoigne Melotte were eventually represented by Jersey Milk (now Jersey Dairy), but their main interest was with Fullwood, a well-known manufacturer of milking machines and bulk storage milk-cooling tanks. Jersey Milk promoted the use of bulk cooling tanks, to ease the collection service, with milk tankers rather than lorries carrying milk cans. This practice was labour-saving for both the dairy and the dairy farmer.

Many manufacturers offer a range of dairy equipment, including milk coolers. Some milk coolers were simple heat exchangers, having an element composed of a double skin of corrugated galvanised sheet metal and a local supply of cold water as the cooling medium. The cold water taken from a cold water tap, or preferably a well where the water will always be cool, is fed into the bottom of the cooler by a hose and flows upwards between two corrugated skins. On reaching the top, the water is drained away by hose. Milk straight from the cow is poured into a metal hopper above the cooler and flows down the outside over the corrugations on both sides of the cooling element. The cooled milk collects in a trough at the bottom and drains through a tap and a hose into the milk can beneath. When the milk can is full, the tap on the trough is closed and the milk hose transferred to another milk can. The milk cooler is quick and easy to dismantle, for washing with the rest of the dairy utensils. More expensive coolers had a refrigerator unit to maintain the coolant at a temperature just above freezing. Another type was the in-churn cooler, some with a water motor to rotate them. Yet another type was a tank filled with cold water in which the churns or cans were immersed.

While at school in England during the war, the author had to work on farms in the school holidays. It was a statutory requirement in the UK for all the dairy farms to have a milk cooler. Surprisingly, their use was not universal in Jersey. There was a strange reluctance to use them in spite of the warm summer temperatures in the Island. Very few farms were connected to the mains water supply; those who had it may have been reluctant to pay for it to cool milk. Those with a well may have been afraid of the well running dry in dry weather conditions.

The author recalls his father's anger in the early post-war years on a hot summer day when the dairy had rejected the milk because it had turned sour. The author tried to persuade his father to have a milk cooler but he argued that it did not get hot enough in Jersey to justify it. Some farmers placed their full milk cans in a bath or tank of cold water while waiting for the milk lorry to collect it. This was satisfactory while the milk lorry continued to come into the farmyard, but when the cans had to be placed by the farm gate or along the lane at the side of a main road to be collected it was a different story. If the place had little or no shade from the hot sun, there could be problems.

Finally, the bulk milk tank-cooler was produced and many were installed on Jersey dairy farms. On some farms, with milk lines installed in the parlour or stables, the milk is delivered straight to the bulk tank-cooler. The milk would have passed through a recording jar and been released back into the milk line. Where bucket units remain in use, the milk is poured straight from the bucket through a filter into the cooling tank. The milk is then collected from the farm by the milk tanker and taken to the dairy for distribution.

The milking operation

The cow is an animal and not a machine. It has a mind of its own and has to be treated as such, as the cowman or herdsman knows only too well. In order to milk a cow successfully, there is a 'ritual' to be followed before milking can commence. For example, it is wise to have the cow in the right mood; this is important to encourage the cow to let down its milk. This is achieved by giving it something it likes to eat, such as a mix of food concentrates either as a meal or as nuts (meal compressed into nuggets known as nuts), the quantity measured according to the amount of milk a cow yields. The advantage of this procedure is that the cow knows it will have this treat at milking time and will be ready and waiting. Just before milking it helps to further encourage the cow to let down its milk by massaging the udder, usually done these days by washing with warm water and drying the udder and teats. The cow is then ready to be milked.

In the old days the milkmaid or cowman would take a stool and milking pail, then, sitting beside the animal, gently squeeze and pull the teats, directing the milk stream into the neck of the pail. The problem during hand-milking is making sure the milk pail does not fall over! This is easily done with a restless animal, especially with an animal being milked for the first time. Some milkers would grip the pail between their legs. Traditionally in Jersey the milking pail or can is the famous Jersey spherical milk can with a flat bottom and open neck or collar, some having a lid on a short chain. In due course they were replaced with an ordinary galvanised bucket, which was probably a lot cheaper. The author's father had his milking buckets specially made. They were cylindrical, having a large diameter, a flat bottom, and vertical sides. They did not fall over!

Milking with a machine, the cowman or milkmaid places a bucket unit beside the cow, unhooks the cluster of teatcups, and holds the claw in a way that will prevent any loss of vacuum; then he or she will push the vacuum hose onto the tap on the vacuum line and open it. The cluster of teatcups is then fitted to the cow's teats and the milk starts flowing into the bucket. Modern milking parlours do not have milking buckets but have a cluster at each stall, so the cluster is simply lifted off its hook and the teatcups fitted to the cow, and the milk will flow along a milk line to the farm dairy.

In the early days, when a milking machine was being used for the first time, some cows took to machine-milking quite calmly but others took time to get used to it, kicking the cluster off not once but again and again. It became a case of try, try, and try again. If the animal continued to resist, the cowman would have to resort to hand-milking and try again at the next milking time. This might go on for two or three days until the animal got used to it and settled down. Occasionally a difficult cow might have to be sold out of the herd. Also in the early days, after removing the cluster, the cowman would strip out any milk remaining in the udder by hand. Eventually this procedure was discontinued as machines became more efficient and different techniques were adopted, such as pulling down gently on the cluster for a few minutes before removing it. It was claimed by Melotte Surge that their suspended milking bucket, carried on a surcingle over the cow's back, had that pull-down effect, which increased as the bucket filled with milk.

Hand milking

This advertisement for a traditional Jersey milk can appeared in 1908.

Traditional old Jersey milk can supplied by J. A. Samson, 14 and 16 Halkett Street, St. Helier. The capacity in the traditional Jersey measure is 3 pot, or 1.5 gallons (6.8 l).

The traditional milk can was made of pressed steel, soldered and tinned. It has a spherical shape with a flat bottom and a deep rim around the base; it also has a lid. This one was the property of the author's grandfather—Mr. Elias Billot, La Porte, at Maufant, St. Saviour. Some cans were made with a fluted neck for hand-milking. Miniature copies of the Jersey milk can are made in silver by jewellers in St. Helier and are a favourite local gift.

Butter making in earlier times

On the farm most of the cows' milk will be for human consumption, as liquid milk, and some will be put aside for feeding to the very young calves. In the old days some milk was set aside for making butter or cream and some for farmhouse cheese. Before the days of the bulk milk-cooling tank the milk would have been put in six-pot (3 gallon) milk cans to await collection by the dairy's lorry. Some milk would have been sold by the pint to neighbours. This was stopped on public health grounds, when all milk had to be pasteurised before it was sold to the public. All the many small local milk rounds had to cease trading because the HTST (high temperature, short time) equipment for pasteurising was too expensive for the smaller roundsmen.

Two gallons of Jersey milk will make 1 lb of Jersey butter. Time past, butter was made on the farm by the farmer's wife and carried off to town to sell in the market. There were small table-top butter churns as well as the popular barrel type and some folk simply used a six-pot milk can, balancing the can on the rim and rocking it to and fro! The author remembers his late father doing it while sitting down at the kitchen table reading the *Evening Post*! Small domestic butter churns for the table top were available post-war, consisting of a four-sided glass jar with a screw-on lid. A vertical shaft passes through the lid; on the shaft are four angled paddles and above the lid is a cranked handle. The author recalls his mother having one in 1947, but it was rather small.

When the butter was made it was patted into shape, using butter pats with a moulding carved into them to leave an impression of the butter maker's name on the surface of the butter. In earlier times the milkmaid or farmer's wife would have used a wooden plunger-type butter churn. The churn was made like a barrel but was conical in shape, with a circular lid with a hole in the centre, through which the handle of the plunger was inserted. Butter was made for home consumption and some for the Saturday market in town.

Hand-plunger-type butter churn, 18th or 19th century, made by a local cooper with metal galvanised hoops (Samarès Manor collection).

Table-top churns

These small butter churns were made during the 18th or 19th centuries. They consist of a small box with a shaft passing through the centre. The shaft has a cranked handle at one end outside the box and four paddles mounted on the shaft inside the box. Turning the handle rotated the shaft and paddles to agitate the cream in the box.

A table-top butter churn with four paddles and a cranking handle. This box churn is made of a hardwood, 16 in. (40.5 m) long and 13 in. (33 cm) wide, and deep with a V-shaped bottom. It has four paddles, each with two slats, mounted on a horizontal shaft that is rotated by a crank handle with a wooden grip. The lid of the churn fits inside the rim with a flange around the edge, to extend over the edge of the box. This churn, in spite of its age, was probably pressed into service during the Occupation, when many old pieces of machinery found a new lease of life! It is in the National Trust for Jersey collection at the Moulin de Quétivel.

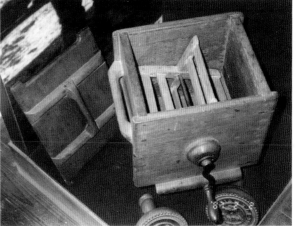

This butter churn is very similar to the one above, but slightly smaller and of the same age. Beside it are two butter pats.
This churn is also made of hardwood; the dimensions are 9.5 in. (24 cm) long, 8.25 in. (21 cm) wide and 10 in. (25 cm) deep, but with a rounded bottom and four slatted paddles measuring 8 in. (20 cm) wide and 4 in. (10 cm) deep. The paddles on a horizontal shaft are rotated with a crank handle and a wooden grip. The lid fits inside the rim with a flange around the edge extending over the edge. Beside it are butter pats, with the producer's moulding carved into them, to leave an impression of the maker's name on the butter. The churn is in the Société Jersiaise/Jersey Heritage Trust collection at Hamptonne.

Waide butter churn

A popular butter churn was the Waide, used on many farms in the Island during the nineteenth and early twentieth centuries. Mr. Elias Billot senior, at La Porte, Maufant, had one of these churns, which was used regularly before the First World War and, like so many of them, was brought into service again during the German Occupation.

A Waide butter churn made by Waide & Son of Leeds in the late 19th and first decades of the 20th century. It is an end-over-end barrel churn (courtesy of the Steam Museum).

The Waide consisted of a wooden barrel with two iron spigots fitted on either side of the barrel; they were mounted in bearings on a varnished wooden frame. The barrel is scrubbed on the inside and varnished on the outside, like the frame. To fill it, the lid on one end of the barrel was unclipped from the barrel and lifted off, the cream was poured in, and the lid replaced and clamped shut with four hinged clamping screws. On one side of the barrel was a crank handle to rotate it, end over end. Instead of a crank handle, they may be fitted with a flat-belt pulley and be power-driven. Commercial dairies might have had five or six of them, all power-driven.

Jersey milk cans

Jersey milk was sold to the dairies by the 'pot' (pronounced 'po'), a Jersey measure. The pot is equal to half a gallon, so a 6-pot milk can holds 3 gallons (13.62 l). The 6-pot can was always known as a milk can and never referred to as a milk churn. It was usual for the farmer to have his name stamped on the rim of the lid of the milk can and sometimes on a brass tab soldered to the lid. The farmers would have sufficient cans to contain all the milk from at least four or more milkings. The dairy would collect the cans full of milk in the morning, after the morning milking, together with the milk from the previous evening's milking. That day's cans were returned the following day, when the next morning's milk would be collected. The dairy was supposed to wash the cans before they were returned but they were always washed again on the farm, and scalded with boiling water or placed in a steam chest. They were then turned upside down and placed on a rack, until they were needed again. Eventually, sterilizing was done with chemicals during washing.

A Jersey 6-pot (3 gallon) milk can and upturned lid with a milk strainer on top.

The can with the lid on.

The Jersey 6-pot (3 gallons or 13.62 l) milk cans have a cylindrical lid which are a 'push fit' into the neck of the can and attached to the can by a chain. They were supplied by Messrs. Samson from their premises in Halkett Place, St. Helier, and Alistair Day, the tinsmith in New Street. Allen's, the tinsmiths in Bath Street, would repair milk cans, and they made the conical milk measures with a collar and spout. The milk measures of the day were the half-pint, pint, quart, and a cylindrical one-pint measure with a long handle for dipping into the can to draw out a pint. The long handle had a hook on the end so that it could be hooked over the lip of the can. All the measures had to be checked by the States' Department for Weights and Measures and stamped accordingly. (Samarès Manor collection.)

Milk strainers

A 6-pot milk can, but made of aluminium with fixed handles on either side; the milk strainer and filter, or le couleur, is of pressed steel and tin-coated.
The strainer was fitted with a renewable filter, placed between two perforated plates and placed on the can, before the milking started at milking time, to strain the milk when pouring it into the can. The milk cans were made of sheet steel, rolled and riveted, then tinned. The 6-pot milk cans were used on all Jersey dairy farms and for collection by the commercial dairies.
The filter is cylindrical at the top, tapering in the middle, to a neck narrower than the neck of the milk can. Inside the neck is an annular rim to support a flat perforated disc. Over it is laid the filter element, which is a disc of material rather like cotton wool in a thin paper sandwich, and above that a steel-domed perforated disc. This sandwich-like filtering assembly is held in place with a circular spring clip. A new filter element was used at the start of each milking. The milk was poured on the side of the strainer body and never in the centre. This was to protect the element. Pouring milk in the centre would have torn a hole in the element, rendering it quite useless. The filter and aluminium can would have been imported in the 1950s and 1960s and the local suppliers were the CGA on the Esplanade and other farm suppliers. (La Société Jersiaise/Jersey Heritage Trust collection at Hamptonne.)

Milk measures

Two restored milk measures: one-pint measure on the left and a one-pot (0.5 gallon) measure.
These would have been made locally by people such as Samson in Halkett Place or Days in New Street, and other tinsmiths. There were also quart measures and half-pint measures, each having their mark stamped on them on a dab of solder to indicate they had been checked by the Weights and Measures Department.

The author can recall the milkman delivering milk to the doors of houses where a jug had been left outside by the back door, often with a cloth or saucer over it. The milk was poured into a measure at the doorstep and poured into the jug. Some houses had a small navy-blue milk can, complete with a lid. The lid could be used as a cup.

Cream separators

To have a cream tea with cream from the Jersey cow is a delight. To obtain a small quantity of cream in a farm dairy, when milk cans were used, was not difficult. It could be skimmed off the milk, with an appropriate skimming ladle or a large saucer, particularly if the milk had been allowed to stand for a few hours, or overnight. To stir the cream into the milk, the ladle had to be rinsed in cold water first to prevent the cream sticking to it! The cream separator was used on a farm where a regular supply of cream was needed.

Two manufacturers stand out as the early suppliers of cream separators to the dairy farmers in Jersey; they were de Laval of Sweden and Melotte of Belgium. Both companies came to the market early with cream separators, Melotte in 1888, by which time de Laval were marketing their Alfa Laval machine. Mr. Perrée, of Oaklands Manor, in St. Saviour, was importing the Alfa Laval cream separator in the 1890s. Mr. Le Cappelain of St. Peter's Iron Works supplied the Melotte separator. The late Theophilus Le Cappelain told the author that Melotte cream separators were very popular in the Island in the earlier years of the twentieth century. They became a leading cream separator throughout the world, especially in the USA, where thousands were sold though their agent, Henry B. Babson, of the Surge milking machine company.

ALPHA-LAVAL CREAM SEPARATORS

OVER 120,000 IN DAILY USE.

Exceed all others put together.

THE "ALPHA-LAVAL" hand-power Separators have NEVER BEEN BEATEN IN THE UNITED KINGDOM, but have taken Highest Honours at every Competition and have competed against and BEATEN all other kinds.

Users say they pay for themselves in less than 12 months

☞ GET ONE ON TRIAL from the Agent at "OAKLANDS," St. Saviour's, and compare with your Setting Pans or with any other Separator.

An 1897 advertisement.

Alpha-Laval cream separator manufactured from 1888 onwards, operated with a crank handle (Samarès Manor collection).

Depending on the model, there are between twenty-five and thirty-five cone discs, 7 in. (18 cm) in diameter.

The operation of the cream separator starts at the top, with a large metal bowl into which the milk is poured. The milk is fed through a float valve into a steel bowl rotating at high speed. The milk passes down a hollow centre, through a distributor, into the spaces between a column of conical discs, ensuring that the rotational speed of the bowl is transmitted to the milk, thus creating centrifugal force in the milk, sending the heavier components to the periphery and the light cream to the centre of the cones. It rises upwards, forced by the incoming milk, to an outlet spout; the remainder at the periphery also rises upwards to a second outlet spout. Cream and skimmed milk are collected from their respective spouts in separate containers. The centrifugal cream separator is driven by a crank handle at one side. To achieve the best results it is better to separate the milk when it is still warm from the cow. It is important that the machine must be brought up to the operating speed, over 6,000 rpm, before the milk is fed into it. The machines are so designed that they are quick and easy to dismantle for washing and reassembly afterwards.

Alfa Laval cream separators were mounted on a free-standing cast-iron stand, or on a smaller stand, to stand on a bench. The local supplier was Mr. Perrée, at Oaklands Manor, St. Saviour.

A set of Alfa Laval cream separator cone discs (Whitianga Museum collection, New Zealand).

An interesting display of 'the butter school': it was an exhibit celebrating the 100-year history of the Royal Jersey Agricultural and Horticultural Society in 1933 circulating in the show ring at Springfield.

It was one of the many exhibits in the afternoon parade, illustrating the activities during the first hundred years of the Society. The butter school circulated around the Island, visiting parish halls before and after 1900. It was organized by the Society, engaging an instructor from London, each year for several years, to promote clean milk production and butter-making. In the foreground is an Alfa Laval cream separator and the two buckets, one for cream and one for the skimmed milk. On the right is the Waide butter churn. Under the table can be seen two '6-pot' milk cans.

In the background on the left, in front of the lorry, is a lady in her Jersey bonnet. (Courtesy of Mr. Don Le Boutillier.)

A Melotte cream separator poster at about the turn of the 19th and 20th centuries (courtesy of Gascoigne Melotte from a publication celebrating the company's history).

Melotte cream separator manufactured by Écrémeuse Melotte of Belgium. It has a column of discs of 6 in. (15 cm) diameter (courtesy of the Livarot cheese factory museum in Normandy). This one is power-driven, having a flat belt pulley. It is very similar to the Alfa Laval separator in appearance. Both came on the market at much the same time in 1888. The Melotte cream separator was popular in the Island.

In the last decades of the nineteenth century there were frequent references to the butterfat in the milk of dairy cows and to butter-making. The Jersey cow has a reputation for producing milk with a high level of butterfat at 5 per cent. This interest led the Royal Jersey Agricultural and Horticultural Society to organize a travelling 'butter school' to visit the Island from London. The demonstrator, described as a 'butter maid', promoted clean milk production methods, first washing the cows' udders and teats and her own hands before milking. Then followed a demonstration of an Alpha-Laval cream separator, followed by a Waide Victoria butter churn and a demonstration of a French butter drier. The time to complete each operation was recorded. The Society was sufficiently pleased that they invited the butter school back each year. Subsequently, butter-making competitions were held at parish cattle shows and the Island agricultural shows in August.

This report was found among the family papers of Mr. Elias Billot of La Porte, Maufant, and is dated 19 December 1913. It is a report following a sample of butter sent for examination, which one might assume marks the success of the butter school.

Clean milk production

Prior to clean milk production methods, the milk was filtered with a clean piece of linen or cotton cloth tied over the neck of the can. Clean milk production methods required the use of a properly designed milk strainer as described earlier. For the rest, it was washing!

Washing and drying the cow's udder and the milker's hands before milking was essential, followed by washing and sterilising the milking pails, cans, and cooling machines after each milking. The procedure for washing the utensils always starts with a cold water rinse to prevent milk drying on. Then, after the utensils had been washed, they had to be scalded with boiling water and preferably placed in a steam-sterilising chest at 210°F for ten minutes.

There were various types of steam-sterilising chest or cabinet, depending on the system of steam generation, solid fuel or oil-fired boiler, gas or electricity. The steam cabinet is insulated with a double skin, usually of galvanised sheet metal, with a large door. They were supplied in different sizes: the cabinet has to be large enough to take all the milking buckets, milk cans, and milking machine components. Steam is fed into the chest at low pressure through jets in the cabinet. In the bottom are drain holes to allow the condensed steam to flow out and prevent a build-up of pressure in the cabinet. Steam must accumulate in the cabinet and heat it up to 210_, and continue to flow into the cabinet for a further ten minutes. Some sterilising chests were more elaborate, having steam jets arranged for various components such as teatcups to be placed on them to ensure the steam passed through. Some items, such as milking buckets, were placed over them. Steam generators also provided hot water for washing as well as a wandering steam jet (a jet on a hose for use around the dairy). These steam generators were designed and sold specially for use on the farm dairy. Mr. Arthur, at Les Ruettes, in St. John, had one for his milking bail. After a time, the steam chest was dispensed with in favour of chemicals, such as detergents and sterilising agents, used in the wash and said to be equally satisfactory. Chemicals were labour-saving, particularly in the milking parlour where they could be pumped around the milking equipment. The equipment had only to be dismantled for washing once a week.

Between the wars a milk-testing scheme was set up to measure the butterfat content in the milk of each cow. It was a condition that clean milk production methods had to be followed in order to take part. The milk testers usually came once or twice a week for the morning or afternoon milking. Each cow's milk was weighed and recorded. It was also checked for mastitis and a sample taken in a little glass tube for testing at the laboratory at the Howard Davis Farm in Trinity, now the headquarters of Jersey Agriculture, a division of the Department of Economic Development. The results were recorded and a copy sent to the farmer concerned. In due course, some of the cattle classes at the agricultural shows took into account the milk production and butterfat content for the competing cows. Cattle breeders used the records to help them select and breed bulls and cows from those cows that were high-milk and high-butterfat producers.

Manufacturers' agents in the Island

Agents for milking machines in the Island were the Jersey Farmers' (Trading) Union (JF(T)U Ltd.), who were the agents for Alfa Laval milking machines. Jersey Dairies were the first agents for Gascoigne, followed by the Jersey branch of the Country Gentlemen's Association (CGA), on the Esplanade. Le Cappelain, St. Peter's Iron Works, had been the agents for Melotte cream separators for many years. Some time later they were appointed agents for Melotte-Surge. Lawrence de Gruchy was the agent for Fullwood milking machines. The Jersey Milk Marketing Board at Five Oaks adopted the trading name Jersey Milk and was appointed agent for Hosier equipment. Hosier were best known for many years for their milking bails.

As time went by these arrangements changed but so did the manufacturers. Retirement in the Le Cappelain family led to changes in the management of St. Peter's Iron Works and a loss of interest in milking machines. No doubt the merger of Melotte with Gascoigne and dropping the connection with Surge and Babson in America influenced them. The merger led to a lot of problems for agents and distributors across Europe for Gascoigne-Melotte. This happens so often when mergers take place between large machinery manufacturers who each have a wide network of distributors in many countries.

In 1982 there were further changes, when Fullwood were represented by Jersey Milk, and they also became representatives for Gascoigne when the Jersey branch of the CGA closed. But Jersey Milk's main interest remained with Fullwood, probably due to their bulk milk tank-coolers, which Jersey Milk were promoting.

The first milking machines In Jersey

The first milking machines were installed in the Island in the 1930s, although the exact dates are a little uncertain. The late Major Riley's father installed a milking machine at Trinity Manor when a new twenty-stall cow stable was built in 1932. The vacuum pump was placed in the old cow stables next door and the vacuum pipe with the taps ran along above the stalls. Mr. Ogier installed a milking machine at about the same time. Miss Jean Arthur informed the author that her father, at Les Ruettes, purchased a Gascoigne milking bail in the summer of 1933.

These machines are also known to have been installed in the 1930s. An Alpha-Laval milking machine was installed in the cow stables of Mr. Eugene Peredés, at Fairview Farm, in St. Saviour, for his big herd. His cow stables were considered very modern at the time. A Gascoigne milking machine was installed at Samarès Manor when Mr Buesnel was the herdsman. It is thought Mr, Ernest Gaudin also had a milking machine in the 1930s.

The milking bail

The Gascoigne milking bail on skids installed at Les Ruettes, St. John, for Mr. John O. Arthur in 1933. It has six stalls; three cows are milked while three are changed over.
Mr. Arthur is on the left, and the cowman on the right was Mr. Fred Cotton from Cornwall (La Société Jersiaise photographic archive)
The milking bail is an independent mobile unit on skids, or wheels and can be towed to the fields on a farm where the cattle are grazing away from the buildings. If it is on skids then it has to be loaded onto a van or wagon to move it any distance. A milking bail consists of a roof over four or six side-by-side milking stalls with storage for food concentrates fed to the cows in feeding bowls while they are being milked. It has no floor, with the exception of a compartment to house a stationary engine, to provide the power to operate the vacuum pump, and an alternator for the lighting. The compartment is also used as a store for various tools and spare pieces of equipment, including cup liners, buckets for washing, and so forth.

The milking bail has to be moved frequently to a clean, fresh area of the field, and when the cows are moved to another grass field. They are often used in the field all the year round, but in Jersey it was habitual to bring the cows into the cow stable during the winter. On some farms a concrete hard was constructed near the cow stables, for use in winter. It has the convenience of being able to wash down the floor after milking. This was done at Les Ruettes, but after two years Mr. Arthur decided to leave the bail on the hard permanently, bringing the cows to the bail twice a day for milking and returning them to either the stables or the field, according to the season and the weather. In 1938 it was changed to electric power.

Hosier

Hosier was a well-known manufacturer of milking bails before the Second World War, but particularly in the years after. They were not particularly attractive to look at but they were adequate and cheap. A Hosier bail was built on a permanent concrete base at Cowleywood Farm at Maufant in 1968 for Mr. John Le Gallais and the late Mr. Bobby Woods. On one side was a collection yard consisting of a semicircular concrete hard-standing, with a galvanised iron railing surrounding it and an electric gate, which slowly pushed the cows towards the entrance doors of the milking stalls. Following a change of management some twenty years later, it was dismantled and a herringbone milking parlour was built on the site.

Portable milking machines

Portable milking machines were manufactured on two- or three-wheeled trolleys for smaller herds of up to half a dozen animals. They were designed to meet the requirements of the UK Milk and Dairy Regulations of 1949. They consisted of a small stationary engine, driving a vacuum pump for outdoor use, or with an electric motor for indoor use. The milking machine manufacturers offered many such units, having one or two buckets. A mast carried the vacuum line and tap to which the rubber vacuum pipe on the milking bucket was attached. An example was the Gascoigne Miracle bucket milker. On other trolleys the mast carried the cluster, along with both a vacuum line and milk line delivering the milk into a milk can on the trolley. An example was the Gascoigne 'Miracle in-churn milker'. Yet another was the Gascoigne 'in-churn recorder', a more elaborate portable machine with two recording jars and a releaser.

The Gascoigne Miracle bucket milking machine in the field, with two cows tethered to a vehicle. The mast carrying the pipes can be seen above the milkmaid's head

Mrs. Anne Perchard, at La Ferme, recalls that in her youth her family had a Gascoigne Miracle milking machine.

This single bucket unit was assembled by Chris Steel. Chris Steel's single bucket unit comprises a Simplex vane-type vacuum pump with a vacuum reservoir, a Suffolk engine, and an Alfa Laval bucket and pulsator. It is an example of a home-assembly bucket unit for two or three cows in the field or in the stables. The power unit is a Suffolk Punch lawnmower engine, model no. 21 A/ZC 1489. (Samarès Manor Open Day.)

Surge Melotte trolley-type, in-churn milking and recording machine, with a single suspension-type cluster unit for a small herd of five or six animals. Under the cluster unit and monitoring jar is a weight which compensates for the weight of milk in a Surge bucket unit and the draw-down effect. After each cow is milked, the churn is lifted off the trolley base to be weighed by the recorder above, then lowered onto the base again.
Manufactured in the 1960s at Melotte Works in Grantham. The local supplier for Melotte Surge was St. Peter's Iron Works. (MRB collection 1962.)

The Simplex milking machine has an aluminium bucket unit, complete with pulsator clamped on the lid under the swivel handle. and a cluster unit with teatcups.

On this Simplex bucket, a rubber tube from a nozzle on the bucket lid would be connected to the tap on overhead vacuum pipe. When the tap is opened, air is immediately withdrawn from the bucket. It is felt by the pulsator, which commences to pulsate. Some manufacturers offered a choice of stainless steel or aluminium buckets. This unit, as the name implies is simple, having the simplest of claws for the cluster, and the pulsator can be opened by the cowman for servicing if need be. Manufactured during the 1940s and 1950s. (La Société Jersiaise/Jersey Heritage Trust collection at Hamptonne.)

Milking parlours

The milking parlour is a term used for a farm building in which dairy cows are milked. It is more popular these days to have a separate purpose-built building. Older installations will have four or six side-by-side milking stalls constructed with galvanized tubular steel railings. At the front of each stall is a gate with a latch and a long handle brought to the back of the stall for the convenience of the cowman to open and close the gate. Also at the front of the stall are the food bowl and a hopper above, with a control device for the cowman to feed a measured amount of the rationed concentrates to the cow in the stall. It is usual for this equipment to be galvanised and made so that it is easily cleaned. Between each pair of stalls is one vacuum tap for attachment of the milk bucket unit. The floor will be of concrete for ease of washing down.

In side-by-side, four-stall parlours, two cows are milked at a time. While two cows are being milked, two more cows are being changed over in the other two stalls. After the cowman has led in the next cows to be milked, he will give them their ration of concentrates and their udders are washed and prepared for milking. Having attended to that pair, the cowman will move to the other pair, by which time they will have finished milking and be ready for the teatcups to be removed. The cow is then released from the stall by the front gate and the next cow is led in. Some farmers in earlier years installed a milking bail on a concrete surface, as a permanent fixture, rather than having it in the field and moving it. It served the same purpose as a milking parlour, and was less expensive but rather more open to the weather.

In Jersey the agricultural scene has changed dramatically over the last twenty or thirty years. Whereas there were several hundred dairy herds, varying in size from five or six cows to thirty or forty animals, including calves and heifers, today there are fewer than fifty dairy herds, and getting even fewer. As the number of herds decreased the size of the herds increased, in some cases to over two hundred. The herringbone parlour, having the facility to milk many more cows at a time than either the abreast type or the six- or eight-stall tandem type, became an attractive proposition to the local dairy farmer.

The herringbone milking parlour, using bucket units, first appeared in Australia during the First World War, but did not find favour elsewhere. New Zealand had milking parlours of different types, but in the 1950s, when dairy herds were getting ever larger, the herringbone milking parlour was found to be much quicker. One man was able to milk between six and eight cows at a time, depending on the size of the installation, instead of just two or three at a time.

The herringbone parlour is so called because when the parlour is filled with cows at each of several milking stalls, along each side of the parlour, the view from above will resemble a herring bone. A sunken floor, or well with steps down to it, extends along the length of the middle of the parlour between the two lines of cow stalls. In operation it is less tiring for the cowman, who does not have to bend over while attending to the cows. The parlour has galvanised tubular railings, shaped like a zigzag, running down the side of a line of stalls. At each end of the series of zigzags are gates, at the one end to let the cows in, and at the other end to let the cows out. The gates are controlled by levers operated by the cowman from the well.

MILKING ROUTINE

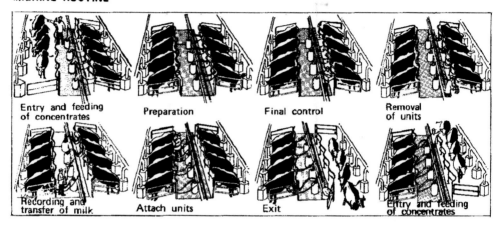

The herringbone parlour and method of operation.

The size of the herringbone parlour may vary according to the size of the herd. It may have six, eight, or more stalls along each side. Six a side was quite common. The number of stalls depends on the number of cows the cowman can comfortably manage, such as when milking up to two hundred cows in a couple of hours. However, they are constructed even bigger today for the big herds. There is a twelve-a-side parlour in the Island! There were arguments for and against the herringbone parlour when they first appeared; such as, the animals will never get used to it, there would be a frightful mess in the parlour if an animal were to pass water or drop its dung in the parlour, all operations would have to stop until the mess had been cleaned up and washed down, etc. Today all these things have been allowed for in the design. In fact, the cows soon become familiar with the system and are usually well behaved. They simply file in, the first one going to the end position, the remaining cows stopping when they can go no further. Each position has the usual equipment: the feeding bowl with controls for the rations, the cluster of teatcups, a milk-recording jar, with its own scale, to record the weight, and the appropriate controls, etc. The modern herringbone milking parlour with computer control systems has key pad controls at each milking station for measuring the rations to each animal and recording the milk produced by each animal.

The cows on one side of the parlour are milked while those on the other side are being changed over. One lot of cows files out after being milked and the next lot files in, they are prepared for milking, and the clusters go on. At this point the cowman moves to the other side, checks that the first cow has stopped giving milk, and the cluster is taken off; then on to the next, and so on down the line. When all the clusters have been taken off, the gate is open in front of the first animal and all the cows file out and the gate is closed. Then the gate at the opposite end is open and the next lot file in. Milk is delivered to recording jars. When the cow has given its milk, the quantity of milk is recorded and the milk is released into the milk line and on to the cooler in the dairy alongside. Adjacent to the parlour on one side will be a covered collection yard, into which the cows are herded or collected preparatory to milking. On the other side is the farm dairy which will receive the milk, which usually goes straight into a cooled bulk holding tank.

There are many manufacturers of milking machines apart from those referred to above, such as Vaccar, one of the early manufacturers, Manus, with very innovative ideas, Simplex, and Westphalia. Fullwood made a late appearance in Jersey: their products include the bulk cooling tank. Their agents until recently were the Jersey Milk Marketing Board at Five Oaks.

Alfa Laval six-a-side herringbone parlour, viewed from the end where the cows exit. Installed at Cowleywood Farm, Maufant (courtesy of Cowleywood Ltd.).
After milking, the machine is washed in situ with water-based washing detergent solutions and finishing with a sterilising agent passed through all the milk pipes, jars, etc. The local supplier was JF(T)U Ltd.

A more recent installation in Jersey. A view of one side of a ten-a-side herringbone parlour installed for Mrs. Anne Perchard at La Ferme

Cooling tanks

A Packo bulk milk cooler at Cowleywood Farm, Maufant. The local supplier was Jersey Milk Farm Engineering Services (courtesy of Cowleywood Ltd.)

Author's schooldays

When the author was a schoolboy, and old enough, he had to hand-milk three cows before going to school in the morning. His father insisted the cows' udders and teats were washed with a cloth and warm water. Both his father and his uncles were slow to adopt machine milking. In 1947 the author's father had a Gascoigne milking machine on trial. It was on a trolley with an electric motor to drive the vacuum pump operating two units. It seemed to work all right, but after milking the author's father spent a couple of hours washing it! His mother's reaction was to exclaim, 'It is taking longer to wash that machine than it takes to milk the cows; if you can't do better than that, it had better go back!' To the author's disgust, it went back.

A titbit about milk. During the war a Royal Navy shore establishment suffered a temporary infestation of rats. They could not understand why the black buttons on sailors' overcoats were missing, leaving only the brass ring by which they were sewn onto the coats. The story has it that the buttons were gnawed by the rats because they were made from compressed milk powder!

17 Farm transport

The Jersey box cart

The wheel had to be invented before we can consider transport! It is thought that the first wheels were derived from the potter's wheel some 4,500 years BC in the Middle East. An early cartwheel was solid, made up of three or more flat boards, one butted to the next side by side and nailed together with an extra board at 90 degrees across the others, and the whole nailed or pegged together. It was then cut into a round disc and bored out at the centre to make a hub for the axle. The earliest spoked wheel with an iron tyre to be found is thought to have been in use in 1500 BC, probably in the Middle East or India, where the Iron Age began some 900 years before it reached the Atlantic coastal regions in 500 BC.

The Jersey box cart, as we know it, followed many centuries of development.

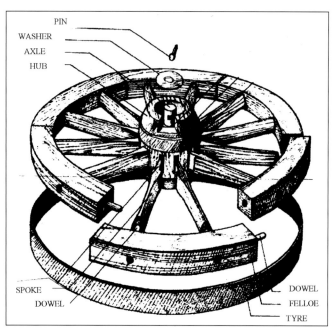

This wheel is similar to a Jersey cartwheel, bouler, or rouelle. It illustrates how the spoked wheel is constructed.

The 4 ft 10 in. (148 cm) diameter wheels have twelve oak spokes, each joined in a socket in a heavy central hub turned out of elm. The outer end was joined in a socket, in a felloe of ash, preferably from a piece that had grown curved, forming a T with the spoke. The outer surface of the felloe was also curved, and each end bored out to fit a round oak dowel to make a perfect snug fit to its neighbour to form the 2.5 in. (6.2 cm) wide wheel rim. The outer surface of the felloe to which the tyre is fitted is shaped to match the concave across the width of the inside of the tyre. When it is assembled, a heated wrought-iron tyre is fitted and the complete wheel plunged into a water butt, to cool the tyre and shrink it to bring all the joints under pressure to make a tight fit. The wheel is slightly dished to add strength, and has plain bearings which are greased liberally. The axle bearings are made at a slight angle to the centre line of the axle. The outer tip is therefore lower than the inner end, so that as the wheel rotates, it tends to slide up the axle, thus keeping it on. At the outer end, a washer and pin holds it in place on the axle. The angle of the axle is set so that, as the dished wheel rotates, its spokes are vertical between the hub and the ground at bottom dead-centre, the point when the spoke takes the load. The iron tyre and wheel rim are wide to reduce the sinkage in soft ground in a wet field in the winter. In hot, dry weather, water has to be thrown over the wheels in order to swell the timbers to maintain a tight fit.

The box cart could be changed according to the load. The solid sides are vertical, fitting into iron sockets along the side of the bed. The sides are quickly removed and replaced with slatted sides to let the water drain out when carrying vraic, although many farmers carried vraic with the solid sides.

If there were hills on the way home, when carting vraic from the beach, a second horse in traces (chains) was hitched to the front of the shafts; the traces were hooked to the horse's collar and the loose ends to a ring bolted to the end of the shafts. Cutting and carting vraic was tightly controlled by law: over the centuries there were several court cases dealing with the culprits who tried to cheat the system. Vraic was cut from the rock, the horse and cart going down the beach into the water with the falling tide, and as the marks on the rocks were uncovered by the falling tide then cutting would commence. When loaded, the horses often knew the way back to the slip better than their driver!

To carry a load of mangels, risers of approximately 12 in. (30.4 cm) deep were fitted all around the top of the cart's sides and were joined at the corners with a hoop and peg. Along the sides, they slope outwards over the wheels. The cart is emptied by first removing the tailboard and then pulling a couple of pins at the front of the bed and pushing up at the front. Hay ladders were fitted to the front and back of the cart to carry a load of hay, the front ladder extending over the horse.

Most farms have an underground liquid manure cistern (tank), near the cow stable. It was usually under the manure pit and often surrounded by a granite wall. On top of the wall is a hand pump, with a granite slab which is a platform for the operator to stand on. When the cistern is full, it has to be pumped out and the liquid carried to the field to be spread, usually in a large cask laid on its side in the box cart. To carry a load of liquid manure or water, a square-shaped cradle is placed in the cart. It is usually made with four stout pieces of timber bolted together with heavy coach bolts and reinforced with wrought-iron fittings. The two cross-members have the central section scooped out with an adze and finished with a spokeshave to the shape of a cask lying on its side. The tailboard is removed and the cradle placed on the bed of the cart, and a cask laid in the frame lying on its side so that a large opening in the side of the cask is on the top. The opening is either round, or more often square, and it is through here that the liquid is pumped. When full, a lid made to fit the hole is fitted and very often a couple of old sacks are thrown over to reduce leakage and splashing. At the back of the cart, in place of the tailboard, a distributor box is fitted. This box is made of wood, to the width of the cart and slightly beyond the sides. It has three lines of 1 in. (2.5 cm) diameter holes, drilled along the bottom at 3-in. centres. This may vary and there may be more holes in the sides and along the back. The box is reinforced with wrought-iron fittings that fit into the tailboard sockets.

The back of the cask, at the bottom, has a 2 in. (5 cm) diameter hole through which the liquid pours out into the distributor box. It is closed with a wooden bung often wrapped in sacking and tied with wire. A length of stiff wire is fitted to the bung and the other end fastened to a convenient place at the back of the cart. The bung is hammered into the hole with a mallet. In the field the bung is loosened from the hole with the mallet and the driver, standing well back at the side of the cart, will give the wire a pull to release the bung. Should the driver muff it he may get splashed, so he has to be careful. Lucky was the driver with a cart having a slide valve with a wire to pull it open from the front of the cart! The liquid then flows through the distributor box and the horse pulls the cart, distributing the liquid to fertilise the land. This job is often done on grass, when rain is in prospect to wash the area before the cattle go on. If cattle were let onto the grass to graze too soon, their mouths and muzzles would burn.

As we see in those wonderful drawings by Edmund Blampied, the farm cart was once the only form of transport for the farmer and his family. It was an unsprung vehicle, and a hard ride sitting on a plank laid across the cart with a blanket placed over it. Farmers and their Breton labour were often to be seen standing in the cart as they drove the horse. In due course, the Jersey van came along; it was a four-wheeled sprung vehicle, and a very much more comfortable form of transport for taking the farmer and his wife and family to town.

The Jersey box carts, or *hérnais* were made by local carpenters and wheelwrights.

The Jersey box cart has been developed over several centuries and has been in its present form all through the 19th and 20th centuries, and probably long before that. It continued to be used on the farm until the 1960s when the pneumatic tyre on the tractor and the tractor trailer came into widespread use. This box cart is in Mr. Vincent Obbard's collection at Samarès Manor.

The 4 ft 10 in. (148 cm) diameter wheels have twelve-spoke wheels with a 2.5 in. (5 cm) iron tyre. The dimensions inside the box are 3 ft 4 in. (110 cm) wide and 4 ft 10 in. (148 cm) long. The sides are each made with two planks 18 in. (46 cm) high. Some farmers had pneumatic-tyred wheels fitted to their cart. The carts were almost always painted blue or grey on the outside but pink on the inside, with red shafts and wheels. Normally, one horse pulled the cart; occasionally, a second horse in traces would be hooked up in front of the horse in the shafts, but only for heavy loads, and in particular when climbing hills. If the second horse was not in use, it was tied to the back of the cart to follow along behind. The cart in the picture is standing with the shafts supported by a prop fitted under one of them, which was quite useful when hitching to the horse. When not in use it was hooked up under the shaft.

Jersey box cart with tail-, headboards, and risers removed.

The Jersey box cart with slatted sides, extension at the back, and a hay ladder; the solid sides, tail-, and headboards have been removed (courtesy of La Société Jersiaise photographic archive).

The slatted sides are normally associated with vraicing to allow seawater to drain away. The cart above has a hay ladder extending well forward over the horse, and an extension on the back. It is fitted in place of the normal tailboard,

with two tall posts fitted in sockets on the extension. This was for carting hay or the cereal harvest. When the Jersey farm van came into being, it was used with hay ladders front and back, replacing the box cart for hay and harvesting. The cart is displayed at the Hamptonne Museum.

The Jersey box cart, with vraicing sides and headboard.

The liquid manure cart for carting the liquid to be spread on the land.

The two hooks on the horse shafts would have to be lifted over to the outside of the shafts before backing the horse in, otherwise the horse could easily be injured!

A liquid manure cart like the one above, built for the purpose with a permanently fitted cask, is a rare vehicle. It is quite sophisticated and probably made to order for an agricultural contractor. The basic frame has two extra-heavy side members to support the cask, to which it is strapped with steel bands. Casks used for liquid manure were probably former cider casks and could have a capacity of up to 800 gallons (3,600 l). The cart, like the box carts, would have been made by a local carpenter, wheelwright, and blacksmith.

The wheels are the same as the box cart, but the axle has two right-angled cranks, one at each end of the axle, to lower the frame and centre of gravity. Underneath the cask, at the back, it has a valve-controlled aperture through which the liquid passes to empty the cask when the place in the field for the next discharge is reached. The lever controlling the valve at the back of the cask is clearly seen, extending over the top to the front of the cask and very convenient for the driver, who sits on the cask. He has only to raise or lower the lever accordingly to open the valve, without leaving his seat. The driver probably sat on a folded sack, his feet resting on the wide-angled footboard. Beneath the frame at the back under the discharge valve is a distribution box; the box, some 8 in. (19 cm) wide front to back, extended across the width of the cart. It has a pattern of holes in the bottom and along the back similar to the distribution box described above. The cask is filled through a hatch at the top.

It was a regular operation on the farm to empty the cistern and cart the liquid manure for distribution on the land.

Some farmers had a cart fitted with a rectangular galvanised and with a square hole on the top to fill it. It is closed with a hinged flap. At the back, a slide valve is fitted with the usual distributor box on the back of the cart.

Low-loading cart

A low-loading cart for transporting 500-gallon cider casks from farms to the harbour in St. Helier for the export trade; this one was made locally in the 1840s. The bed of the low-loader is 3 ft 3 ins. (100 cm) wide and 11 ft (351 cm) long, much longer than the bed of the box cart. The axle has a deep crank which can be seen quite clearly, between the bed and the wheels. The low-loading cart is easier to load and has a low centre of gravity. The wheels are the same as those on the box cart.

The 4 in. (10 cm) diameter drum winch and rope at the front has two loose cranked handles that fit on the square-section iron fittings at each end of the drum, to wind the winch and so roll the cask up the loading skids onto the cart. The low-loader was originally used by Mr. J. H. Perrée of, St. Mary, in the 1850s. He appears to have been a contractor who carried casks of cider to the harbour for export, by the farmers. (La Société Jersiaise/Jersey Heritage Trust collection at Hamptonne.)

The Jersey farm van

The Jersey farmer's van, or *vainne* (in Jersey French), made by Mr. Grant (Mr. Vincent Obbard's collection at Samarès Manor).

They were all made locally and carried the maker's name. It is a four-wheel, wheel-sprung vehicle, having springs on all four wheels; it is both a road and farm vehicle. They were made from the 19th century onwards; this particular one could have been made before or after the First World War. Note that the brake blocks on the rear wheels are linked to a threaded shaft and a hand-cranked screw under the outrigger, or side seat.

Of the four wheels, the two rear wheels are 4 ft (122 cm) in diameter with fourteen spokes and 2 in. (5 cm) wide steel tyre, and there are two smaller 2 ft 9 in. (83.5 cm) diameter front wheels, with twelve spokes and again a 2 in. wide steel tyre. These wheels had to be smaller so that the van could be steered, one front wheel going under the bed of the van if the van had to be turned short. All four wheels are made of wood: the hub is of elm, with spokes of oak to take the weight of the load. There are two spokes to each felloe, which is made of ash with oak dowels to locate and lock it to its neighbour. The hub is bored out with an auger, on a special locating tool to ensure that it is central. The bore is both straight and precise, the sides parallel to receive the cast-iron sleeve, which is driven into the hub and forms the bearing surface between the hub and axle. A notch is cut in the hub to allow a cotter pin to slide into the end of the axle. The cotter pin is to hold the wheel onto the inclined axle end to which it is fitted. The wheel and axle are made so that the spoke taking the load is vertical as it passes through bottom dead-centre, where the tyre is momentarily touching the ground. Finally, a steel tyre is shrunk on, like the wheel.

Semi-elliptical leaf springs are fitted between the rear axle and the bed. At the front the leaf springs are either elliptic or semi-elliptic between the axle and the turntable or forecarriage.

Brake blocks operate on the tyre of each rear wheel and are applied by a crank handle beside the driver. Turning the crank turns a screw to operate a linkage that presses the blocks against the wheels. The brakes will be applied when descending a hill, especially with a load, to hold the van in check. A few vans have an additional foot pedal to operate the brakes.

Beech, oak, and ash were used in the turntable, supported with wrought iron fittings. The bed and sides are probably made of oak and ash. The bed and sides' internal dimensions are 3 ft 8 in. (318 cm) wide by 8 ft 8 in. (265 cm) long. The sides are 16 in. (40.5 cm) deep, made of a single piece of 0.75 in. (2 cm) timber. All the metal fittings were wrought iron, made by local blacksmiths, and have stood the test of time. The wheels are painted with black gloss or very dark red, green, or blue, and the outside of the body likewise, while the inside is pink or cream.

Unlike the heavy English farm bow-wagon or the lighter barge-wagon, the Jersey van developed over the years into a vehicle to meet the Island's particular requirements. It is as much a road vehicle as it is a farm vehicle, for the hayfield or potato field. It is a light, highly manoeuvrable, sprung vehicle, with leaf springs on all four wheels, suitable for the narrow roads and small farmyards. It can be fitted with seats and backrests and was frequently used to take the family to town, and to carry schoolchildren on the annual summer school outing. With seats removed and rails fitted, it carried a load of potatoes in barrels to town, so it is quite a sophisticated, multi-purpose, horse-drawn vehicle and load carrier. Especially high sides are another extra that can be fitted to carry one or two cows to a parish show. Normally drawn by one horse but sometimes with a second horse in traces to haul a heavily loaded van out of the field and onto the road. But when on the hard surface of the road, one horse would manage.

The Jersey van with hay ladders at Samarès Manor Threshing Day.

Hay ladders 4 ft 9 in. (145 cm) high are usual for carrying hay bundles to the loft or sheaves of cereals to the threshing machine. At the foot of each leg of the hay ladder is a hook, which fits into a fixed ring in the bed of the van, several inches from the headboard for the front ladder and the same distance in front of the tailboard for the ladder at the back. The hay ladders simply rest against the headboard and tailboard.

Two vans with different front springs and turntables. The blue one has a footbrake pedal. The horse shafts of the green van have been taken off and are leaning against the footboard.

The van on the right has a foot pedal in front of the footplate. It is for operating the brakes on the rear wheels, as well the crank handle and screw, beside the driving position, under the outrigger or seat along the sides. At the centre of the turntable is an iron bracket for a pole, for use with two horses. The horse shafts have been taken off and laid on the floor beneath the van.

Both vans have seating rails all the way round the sides and across the back above the tailboard. The driver's and passenger's seat of the green van is lying on the floor. The frame of the turntable has more ironwork and has complete ellipse leaf springs for the front wheels, but it has no bracket for a pole for a pair of horses.

Every farm in the Island had one van, and sometimes two, for carrying almost everything on the farm. The author's father had his van made when he started farming in Boulivot, in 1921. Some good old Jersey names appear among those who made Jersey farm vans, such as Boudain, Huelin, Jeune, Le Lievre, Mière, and Trachy; others well known in the trade were Gregory, Hunt, Lane and Underhill, and Grant. There were many skilled carpenters in the Island in those days, having served apprenticeships and learned their skills in the shipbuilding industry, which was in decline.

It was the law for horse-drawn vehicles and handcarts to have the owner's name and address painted on them, by a signwriter. On a van, it was painted on the outside of the first panel on the right. On a box cart, it was on the outside of the right-hand horse shaft, towards the back, often in white block letters. Often the owner of a handcart would use both sides, sometimes with large letters, to advertise the owner and his wares.

Carriages and traps

Group of three horse-drawn passenger vehicles, including a carriage (Samarès Manor collection).
The vehicle in front is known as a 'town cart', possibly dating from the 18th century; behind is an upholstered four-wheel carriage. Right at the back is a two-wheel trap with a substantial pram hood. They were all designed to be comfortable, with elliptical springs, upholstered seats, and cushions.

The author's father had a carriage in the 1920s and 1930s, which was used by the family to go to town, visit relatives, or for Sunday afternoon drives. A young French horse was purchased in the 1930s. During a carriage drive one Sunday afternoon with parents, grandparents, and children we began to climb the steep hill at Paul Mill. It was thought a strong young horse should be able to cope! However, after a few yards the horse found it too much and the carriage began to roll back. Quite suddenly the carriage jackknifed, having turned at right angles to the horse and front wheels. This was a vulnerable position to turn over and over it went, throwing the passengers young and old onto the road. Fortunately we suffered only bruises and shock! After walking up the hill the drive continued. To ascend a steep hill with a full carriage of people, the menfolk might have to descend from the carriage and walk up the hill!

Hand carts

The farm handcart has no springs; this one has two handles, but some had only one handle, with a T fitting, for both hands. They were used for carrying milk cans or fetching mangels from the mangel heap to feed the cows.

The farm handcart is made of wood with iron fittings and axle, twelve-spoke wheels, 3 ft (87 cm) in diameter, and an iron tyre, shrunk on. It has detachable 5-6 in. (12.6-15.2 cm) deep risers above the sides sloping outwards over the wheels; the tailboard can be removed but the headboard is fixed. Metal braces with flattened ends supported the legs. Usually painted grey or light blue on the outside and pink or red on the inside. Made by a local carpenter. Frequently seen in the days of hand-milking 'in the field' when cows were tethered outside during the summer. They carried the 6-pot milk cans, milking buckets

or pails, the milk strainer, box of filter elements, and lastly the milking stools to the field. This type of handcart would have been commonplace through the 18th, 19th, and 20th centuries. (Samarès Manor collection.)

This handcart made by Underhill & Sons, the vehicle makers was for their own use.

This handcart is a little different from the first ones; it might have been for use about town. It has no risers on the sides and both the headboard and tailboard can be removed. It has semi-elliptic leaf springs and the usual iron fittings. The bed is constructed with boards assembled across the cart with fixed sides. The dimensions of the bed are 3 ft 6 in. (175 cm) long and 2 ft 3 in. (83.5 cm) wide. (Steam Museum collection.)

Children's hand cart.

A small hand cart or child's toy made by a local craftsman in the 19th or early 20th century or earlier; it is a box cart with fixed sides, headboard, and tailboard. The bed is 2 ft 6 in. (91 cm) long and 19 in. (48 cm) wide. It has 19 in. (48 cm) diameter cast-iron wheels with rather narrow rims, confining its use to a firm surface. It was not unusual for children to have such toys on farms. The author recalls having a four-wheel van, approximately the same size as this cart, with fixed sides including the head- and tailboards. The front wheels could be steered with the handle to pull it. The children would play with it, one child pulling the other children about the

farmyard for a ride. (La Société Jersiaise/Jersey Heritage Trust collection at Hamptonne Museum.)

A water cart with a 12-gallon (55 l) galvanised tank (Steam Museum collection).

The water cart was manufactured by Whitlock. The tank has a diameter of 1 ft 3 in. (38 cm) and is 1 ft 7.5 in. (44 cm) deep, and it is on 15 in. (38 cm) diameter steel wheels. The carts could be supplied with a variety of tanks, large oval ones up to 40 gallons (180 l) and rectangular 65-gallon (300 l) food containers. Wheels were in various sizes, mostly 16 in. (40.5 cm) pneumatic-tyred wheels; even bigger wheels were available. The tank has lugs on the side to rest in open slots in the top of the frame. It could be pivoted by gripping the handle towards the bottom to tip water into a trough. They were useful for carrying water to the cows, both in the stable and in the field. The cart handles could be lifted up high enough to pivot forward for the tank to swing, remaining level and resting on the ground, and the cart could then be withdrawn. They were very heavy when full of water, which slopped out. A cloth cover was available, but a heavy wet sack thrown over the top did help!

Farmer's wheelbarrow

A Jersey farm wheelbarrow.

This Jersey farm wheelbarrow (*chiviéthe*) was made of wood with wrought iron by a local craftsman to a regular pattern for Mr. de La Haye, of Bushy Farm, Ruelle Vaucluse, St. Helier. Mrs. de la Haye is hoping to give it to the Société Jersiaise for their collection. The body is made of 0.75 in. (2 cm) thick timber, and the inside measurements of the load platform are 2 ft 6 in. (76 cm) long with a shallow curve at the open back, comprised of two boards both 9 in. (23 cm) wide at the back and 18 in. (45.5 cm) wide overall, tapering toward the front at 6 in. (15.2 cm) wide and 12 in. (30.4 cm) wide overall. The front headboard has a curved top, very often protected with a metal band screwed on but also to hold it together in the event of the timber splitting along the grain. There is a gap between the bottom of the headboard and the load platform, which allows water to drain out rather than have water accumulate in the bottom and cause the timber to rot. The sides are 9 in. (22.8 cm) high. The 20 in. (50.6 cm) diameter wheel is made of wood, with four spokes and four felloes with an iron tyre shrunk on. The wooden hub and axle has 0.75-in. (2 cm) diameter metal ends fitted into plain metal bearings. Very often painted light blue or grey on the outside and red on the inside. They were used for carrying everything and anything: a newborn calf from the field, a sack of cattle food. An old one was commonly used for carting the mixture of manure and straw bedding from the cow stables or horse stables to the manure pit after mucking out. Well looked after, they would go on for many years. Some barrows had the wheel replaced with a metal wheel and pneumatic tyre.

Farm lorries

Loading potatoes 'for town' with a lorry in the potato field.

A typical scene in the 1930s in the potato field during the potato season. The empty 'non-returnable' barrels are being unloaded and the full barrels loaded on; two men would work together to lift the full barrels onto the lorry. Note the green potato tops placed on the top of full barrels to keep the sunlight off the potatoes because they will turn green in sunlight. (Courtesy of Mr. Don Le Boutillier's collection.)

The barrels were known as 'non-returnable' because the previous barrels were expensive to return to the Island when they were empty. The non-returnables were lighter, made of plywood, and cheaper. They did not have to be returned. Farmers would buy them for their own use to carry potatoes to the merchants and on the farm. When delivering potatoes to a merchant, the farmer would empty his barrels into the merchant's barrels for shipping. There were minor differences between the barrels. Those used for export had lids and ropes around the top for tying down the lid. Farmers' barrels had no lids or ropes.

Just as farmers were required by law to have their name painted on their horse vans, many of them continued to do the same with their lorries, painting their name on the driver's door. Very often a farmer's lorry was his only motor vehicle, used to go to town and take his wife shopping. There were no parking problems in St. Helier in those days!

Farmers' lorries were often fitted with seating along both sides of the lorry, probably adapted from the horse-drawn van. They were frequently called upon to carry schoolchildren on a summer school tour around the Island, often with streamers flying and stopping at one of the beaches for a picnic. Jolly good fun they were too, for both pupils and teachers.

This lorry was manufactured by the International Harvester Company of Chicago in 1929.

The engine is a 25-hp, Lycoming, four-cylinder side-valve petrol engine with a four-speed gearbox. Load capacity 50 cwt (2.5 tons), 10 ft 10 in. (325 cm) wheel base. Four-wheel braking, very advanced for the time, the parking brake operating on the transmission. The chassis is no. SR 4506 and serial no. CT57895. The local supplier was Messrs. Richmond, Bath Street, St. Helier. The owner was Mr. Messervy. The vehicle has been beautifully restored by Mr. Sam Pallot of the Steam Museum. Many farmers considered the International to be ideal for their purposes.

A farmer's lorry manufactured by Dodge in the USA in 1931.
The Dodge was registered in 1932. It has a 21 hp petrol engine, four-speed gearbox, and a single-wheel back axle. Total vehicle weight is 4,480 lb and load capacity 30 cwt. Model UG 38 and chassis no. 8350338. It was delivered CKD (knocked down, i.e. partly dismantled for shipping) to Kew in London where it was assembled and shipped to Jersey. The local supplier was Stevenson's Motor Garage, Gloucester Street. The body was built by Mr. Vautier, The Yews, St. Peter. Sometimes the chassis was supplied without a cab, which was also built locally. The owner was Mr. Boléat of Valley Farm, St. Saviour, one of the last farmers to make cider commercially. It is displayed here at the Steam Museum on a Threshing Day.

This lorry was beautifully restored in every detail over many years by Mr. John Le Plongeon of Abbey Gate. His grandfather ran a haulage business in Dorset Street, St. Helier. He started with horses and wagons; his first motor vehicle was an army surplus Pierce Arrow lorry, from the US Army in France. Several of these vehicles came to the Island. In common with many motor vehicles of those days, it had a folding-down canvas roof, and can be seen in old photographs of the period.

A farmer's lorry manufactured by Chevrolet in 1931.
The Chevrolet has a 26.3-hp, six-cylinder petrol engine. The load capacity is 30 cwt and the back axle has single wheels. It has the serial no. 158364. Previous owner Mr. Adolphus E. du Feu. Chevrolet lorries were not manufactured after 1931 but were replaced by Bedford lorries produced at Luton. A manufacturer's plaque on the back of this vehicle draws the attention of drivers following it to the special feature of this vehicle: that it had brakes on all four wheels. It warns the following drivers that if they have brakes on only two wheels, they had better keep a safe distance as they will not be able to pull up as sharply as a vehicle with four-wheel brakes! Present owner Mr. Ken Taylor. (Samarès Manor Threshing Day.)

This lorry was manufactured by Dodge in the USA on 18 April 1933.
This Dodge is model UG 30 A; it has a 15-16-hp, four-cylinder, side-valve petrol engine. Load capacity is 30 cwt. It has single wheels on the back axle. The local supplier was Stevenson's Garage, Gloucester Street. The owner was Mr. F. R. Le Brun, of Pond View, St. Ouen (Steam Museum collection.)

Morris commercial lorry manufactured in the late 1930s; model no. NPFC 11856.
This Morris lorry carries the serial no. LC 8952. It has a 15.9-hp, four-cylinder, overhead-valve petrol engine. The load capacity is 30 cwt. It has single wheels on the back axle; the ratio is 6.57 : 1. The local supplier was Cleveland Garage, the owner Mr. C. O. Le Couteur, of Westlands, St. Peter.
Having hay ladders in place and loaded with sheaves of oats there can be little doubt that the above vehicle is a farmer's lorry! (Steam Museum Threshing Day in September 1997.)

This advertisement appeared in 1934; note the price.
The price of the vehicle in this advertisement gives a clear indication of the effect of inflation over the past seventy years!

This advertisement for Ford lorries appeared in 1934.

This Morris commercial lorry, model no. CVS/1140, was manufactured in 1939.
The Morris lorry has a 25-hp, six-cylinder petrol engine and twin rear wheels on the back axle. The local supplier was Cleveland Garages at Havre des Pas. First purchased by a utility company and used during the Occupation, then sold to Mr. G. Le Sueur after the war, who used it on his farm in St. Lawrence. Farmers would normally buy the four-cylinder model, but in the early years after the war, when farming was doing well, they were buying bigger, more expensive, long-wheelbase lorries, with the extra load capacity. They became popular; although this one is not a long wheelbase it is a good example of that period up to the 1950s. It now belongs to Mr. Le Gros, who ensured its preservation.

One of Mr. Vautier's converted army lorries, made from a 15 cwt Bedford army lorry.
This 15-cwt former army lorry was sold at one of the many auctions of army surplus vehicles after the war. It was purchased locally for farm use by the author's father Mr. Francis Billot of Beau Désert, St. Saviour, and converted by Mr. Vautier, in Rue à la Dame, at Five Oaks, St. Saviour. Originally it had iron hoops and a canvas cover over the load-carrying bed and a collapsible canvas roof over the driver. This particular bonnet shape over the engine was a common feature on all Bedford army lorries. It would have been manufactured at any time during the war, probably serving on the home front and perhaps in France after 1944. It has a 30-hp, six-cylinder, overhead-valve (OHV) petrol engine. It was converted in 1947 to a platform lorry with a cab and doors, etc. It had removable sides and tailboard, and screw tipping with crank handles. It could carry a load of 25 cwt. Originally painted khaki, it was resprayed grey after the alterations. (MRB collection.)

This Austin army lorry is a K3 model, type GS, manufactured in 1944.
The Austin army lorry has a 40-hp, six-cylinder, 3,460 cc OHV petrol engine and a four-speed gearbox. The rear axle has single rear wheels, like so many army vehicles. Imported into the Island in 1951 and probably sold at auction when many army surplus vehicles were disposed of after the war. Used for many years as a farm lorry by Mr. Roy Vibert, a tomato grower of L'Industrie, at Samarès, St. Clement. It would have required little, if any, alteration to carry tomatoes to town from the farm, for export, other than to remove the canvas cover and supporting frame. The vehicle has been restored to former army appearance by Mr. Denis Jean. Seen here at one of the Steam Museum shows.

A Commer lorry manufactured by the Rootes group in the early 1950s.
The Commer has a 30-hp, four-cylinder, petrol engine, twin rear wheels, and a load capacity of 3 tons. The picture was taken in 1957, in a hayfield, baling hay with a Jones stationary baler at La Pointe, on the farm of the owner, Mr. Percy Le Masurier, of St. Ouen.

Decorated for a day out with the Sunday school children.
It is a tradition to take the parish schoolchildren for a ride round the Island and a picnic. The lorry will have seating along the sides, which cannot be seen at this angle. The Commer lorry was popular with some farmers in the 1930s. They were manufactured by Commer Cars in England.

Bedford lorry, model MS, manufactured in 1952.
The Bedford has a 28-hp, six-cylinder OHV petrol engine, load capacity 3 tons, twin rear wheels, and synchro-mesh gears. It was originally owned by Mr. Cyril Le Vesconte, at Les Ormes, Trinity. The present owner is Mr. Stephen Hewlett, of Sorel. It is exhibited here at a show at the Steam Museum. The lorry has been fitted with seats, as used on the horse-drawn farm van for parish school outings and picnics and the Visite du Branchage (parish officials' tour of

the parish to check that hedges have been cut; failure to do so results in a fine).
Synchro-mesh gears were a new innovation on commercial vehicles at the time; they had been available on private cars since the 1930s. Second, third, and fourth gears were made with a male or female short cone, to enable the speeds to be synchronised before engagement, making gear-shifting easier, avoiding the need to double declutch when changing gear.

Transport boxes and tractor trailers

The original concept of the farm tractor was to haul cultivating implements and harvesting machinery at relatively low speeds on agricultural land. The pneumatic tyre made a tremendous difference to their use, as they could be driven on and off the road at will. As time went on in the late 1940s and 1950s, tractors and equipment were being designed to satisfy the demand for hauling materials over the farm and public roads, at higher road speeds. But tractor braking systems were still primitive, only suitable for use on the farm, such as a transmission brake or drum brakes acting only on the back wheels. Some tractors had two foot pedals to operate the rear wheel brakes, each pedal connected separately, one to the left rear wheel brake and the other to the right rear wheel. On other tractors they could be linked for road work, so that stepping on one pedal applied both brakes; on others there was a third foot pedal which operated both brakes. Having separate or independent wheel brakes for each wheel is to enable the application of the left brake when making a sharp 180 degree left turn on the headland, or the right hand brake to make a sharp right turn, that is to turn on the spot. They are necessary when weeding with a rowcrop tractor and mounted hoe, in rowcrop work when coming out of a row and entering the next row, without all the normal manœuvring.

Not all farm trailers had brakes, except perhaps a handbrake for parking. While adequate in the field and about the farm, they were not safe for high road speeds. All this was to change. The new generation of faster tractors towing farm trailers dispensed with the need for a lorry on some farms. Farm trailers came into being with 'overrun' brakes, which would come on automatically when the tractor brakes were applied. Tractors and the trailers have linked braking systems, very essential today with modern trailers with twin rear axles, carrying 10- or 15-ton loads being hauled at speed by 100-hp four-wheel drive tractors. One has to admit to having some anxiety about the ability of tractor drivers to control the tremendous loads they are hauling on our small public roads in the Island.

The transport box manufactured by Dnesvoys for carrying on the three-point linkage on the tractor (courtesy of Mr. A. Le Gallais, Cowleywood Ltd.) Transport boxes are made by many farm machinery manufacturers. The dimensions of this box are 6 ft (184 cm) wide and 2 ft 10 in. (86.10 cm) front to back, 2 ft (60.8 cm) deep headboard and 1 ft 2 in. (35.5 cm) at the detachable tailboard. The transport box is carried on the three-point linkage of the tractor for carrying a small load about the farm, such as a couple of hay bales to young stock in a field, or a water container to top up a water trough in the field, or a couple of bags of feed or fertiliser. Some boxes will tip to empty them if the tailboard is removed and the release tripped on the top link, or by simply detaching the top link and raising the lift, when the lower links will rise and tip the box. This box has its own top link with a release mechanism. Leaning against the front of the box is a Ferguson-type top link with a bottle screw adjustment to alter the length, essential for ploughing to adjust the pitch of the plough. Transport boxes were not all made to tip; many were designed to bring the box and the load in it as far forward as possible towards the centre of the tractor to reduce the turning moment and keep the tractor stable. The early Ferguson box was designed to fit between the lower links and the rear wheels. It is longer front to back, the front just clearing the back axle; it was very stable.

In today's world, dairy farms have large herds requiring much more water, and tanker trailers on big-diameter wheels with wide tyres are used. A galvanised tank of several hundred gallons may be carried on a farm trailer. Some tanks are adapted from some other purpose, or simply a new tank mounted on the back axle of a scrapped lorry and welded in place with a drawbar at one end fitted with a pick-up ring to serve the purpose. Tanker trailers with a capacity of 1,000 gallons (4,500 l) are made by a number of manufacturers. A water trough may be fitted to the back of the tanker with a ballcock for gravity-feed from the tank and parked in the field. Some farms will have the water piped to their fields and a galvanised water trough with a ball cock to control the level in the trough. Others may use an old bath, which is rather ugly, but practical.

A farm trailer made on the farm or by local craftsman about 1947. It is on two large-diameter wheels and hauled by a Ferguson tractor.

The wheels are at the centre of the load platform, which provides a balanced trailer and more responsive steering when reversing. Wheels fitted towards the back of the trailer would transfer some of the load onto the tractor to assist traction. The trailer in this picture has no sides, which would have made loading mangels difficult, because they could not be thrown on the trailer. That may have been deliberate, to 'show off' the well-stacked load of exceptionally large mangels, a load to be proud of. It must have been a bumper year at La Pointe, St. Ouen, for Mr. Percy Le Masurier, whose picture it is.

After the Second World War and the Occupation many blacksmiths and carpenters/coach and body builders were busy, like Mr. Vautier, in Rue à la Dame, at Five Oaks, converting army lorries to order for farmers. Others were busy manufacturing implements and converting farm equipment for the hydraulic lift on Ferguson and David Brown tractors. Mr. Farley, in St. Lawrence, made a very good farm trailer, using army surplus lorry wheels. It had a 7 ft x 5 ft (213 cm x 152 cm) platform with a fixed headboard, removable sides and tailboard, and a screw-jack tipping mechanism, with cranking handles. It was a very popular trailer. Mr. Francis Billot at Beau Désert and Mr. Elias Billot at La Porte, both in St. Saviour, had one each. Sadly there is not a trace of one of Mr. Farley's tractor trailers in the Island.

A Ford-Ransomes (F-R) trailer manufactured for Ransomes of Ipswich for their F-R range of equipment in 1966.

The F-R tractor trailer serial no. 11026 is a hydraulic tipping trailer with 3-ton load capacity. The price was £170 in 1966. It has two pneumatic-tyred wheels, size 7.50-16 fitted towards the back to transfer much of the weight of the load onto the tractor's rear wheels to increase traction. F-R trailers often had an adjustment for moving the axle for those who favoured having it, like the Ferguson trailer, right at the back. The body is 10 ft (307 cm) long and 6 ft (184 cm) wide, the headboard is 22 in. (55 cm) high, and the sides 18 in. (45 cm). The hay ladders are 4 ft 6 in. (138 cm) high above the headboard. The trailer has a dual hitch, a jaw for a drawbar and pin, and a ring for the hydraulically operated pick-up hitch. The trailer is designed for the Ford Dexta and the Massey Ferguson 35. The hydraulic hose for the tipping ram is coupled to an external hydraulic service connector, at the back of the tractor. The trailer can be tipped by the driver without leaving his seat. The owner of the Ransomes F-R trailer is Mr. Brian Ahier, of Surguy Farm, St. Brelade, and the local supplier was La Motte Street Garage. The tractor is a Ford 2000, which superseded the Ford Super Dexta.

Another view of the F-R trailer with the side down and resting on the parking jack fitted to the drawbar.
The trailer has a part load of empty potato boxes, having delivered a load of seed potatoes for planting.

Tractor trailer manufactured by Martin Markham of Stamford, Lincolnshire, in the 1960s.
The Martin Markham trailer is a 2-ton tipping trailer with a hydraulic tipping ram; the hose for connecting to the tractor external services can be seen hooked over the parking brake lever above the drawbar. The dual-hitch drawbar can be clearly seen; it has a jaw for use with a draw pin and a ring for a hydraulically operated tractor 'pick-up' hitch. The serial number is FJ 544; it has two wheels on 6.50-16 tyres and the wheels are set well back, to transfer the weight of the load to the tractor rear wheels to increase the traction. The load platform is 8 ft (283 cm) long and 5 ft (152 cm) wide. It has 15 in. (38 cm) high sides and headboard and 4 ft 6 in. (138 cm) high hay ladders above the headboard. It is in Mr. Vincent Obbard's collection at Samarès Manor.

18 Hand Tools on the Farm

Digging tools, spades and forks, etc.

A Jersey pattern spade: the modern digging stick!

This Jersey pattern spade was manufactured by Spear & Jackson in Sheffield, probably in the 1890s, one of the Neverbend range of tools. The wooden handle is riveted in a socket of a forged steel blade, 10.5 in. (26.55 cm) long, 9 in. (22.8 cm), wide, handle 34 in. (86.10 cm) long and T piece 5 in. (12.6 cm) wide. The owner was Mr. Elias Billot, La Porte, Maufant.

It has the initials EBL on the handle, the author's grandfather's initials. This spade was used regularly pre-war and early post-war, particularly during ploughing to dig 'the ends' of the furrows. To ensure the plough started and finished each furrow at full depth, the furrow ends were dug with a spade. The features of the Jersey spade are a long handle and a large blade, both are straight; with no bend between. All these features make digging much easier. A garden spade purchased in a modern garden centre will have only a short handle and small blade, and a bend between the blade and handle. A certain back-breaker!

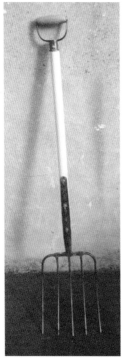

Known as a Jersey potato fork, this is in fact a general purpose fork used around the farm.

This Jersey fork is a Spear & Jackson Neverbend made in Sheffield. It originally had the initials EBL on the handle, but a new wooden and very white handle has since been fitted. The handle is fitted in a socket with three rivets. The fork has five spring steel prongs: they are 12 in. (30.4 cm) long and set at 2.25 in. (5.5 cm) centres, the handle length is 35 in. (88.60 cm) long including the 5 in. (12.6 cm) wide D handle. The original owner was Mr. Elias Billot, of La Porte, Maufant. The potato fork was used for many purposes such as handling FYM (farmyard manure), mucking out in the stable, manure spreading in the field, digging potatoes, and, for many years since then, in the farm garden.

A pitchfork for pitching or loading hay, or sheaves of oats, wheat, or barley.

This two-prong pitchfork was not mass-produced. This one is very old. It has particularly long 23 in. (58.3 cm) prongs, a 6 ft (184 cm) long handle, and is 8 ft (283 cm) long overall. It is an individual fork, probably made by a black-smith in the 18th or early 19th century before the days of the mass producers such as Spear & Jackson and others. This fork was unusually large by today's standards. Though similar in appearance, these forks were made in two main sizes. There are big ones with long prongs and the extra-long handle that enabled them to pitch hay or sheaves onto the top of high loads, when carrying from the hay or harvest field. The smaller forks with short, closer prongs and a shorter handle were for everyday use, for carrying hay about the farm buildings, stables, etc.

A tool for digging out docks (Jersey French *haledocque*).
Probably made by a Jersey blacksmith with the handle made from the branch of a tree to replace the original. A foot is placed on the bar or foot tread on either side to add weight to push it into the ground under the dock root, before prising down to lift out the dock with the root complete. The Jersey-French name implies it was for docks, but was that always so? The parsnip was a popular vegetable on the farm for both human and animal food before the potato, and the parsnip has a deep root, possibly deeper than a dock. One wonders if this implement was previously used for loosening parsnips before pulling them. It is a very popular tool, in every farmer's tool shed. (Mr. Vincent Obbard's collection of implements at Samarès Manor.)

Grappins and hoes

A grappin may have four or five tines.
The grappin handle is riveted in the socket and is 7 ft long, but handles and the prongs can vary in length. Newer grappins were imported, but older ones were made locally, very often with longer prongs. This one was made about the turn of the 19th/20th century. The original owner was Mr. Elias Billot, La Porte, Maufant. It was used regularly for several jobs, as a cultivating tool in rowcrops, such as potatoes on côtils, and in mangels. It was also used in January for pulling farmyard manure (FYM) off the cart when carting from the pit, to be spread on the land to be ploughed in. The grappin was also used for gathering vraic off the beach.

Vraicing grappin for hauling floating vraic or seaweed in the surf.
The vraicing grappin has four prongs 12 in. (30.4 cm) long. Made locally by a blacksmith in the 19th century, the tines were hardened by quenching in water, and it has a 7 ft (213 cm) long wooden handle fitted in a socket. This implement is a variation of the grappin used on the land. This one was used at St. Ouen's Bay. Originally owned by Mr. McGugan, of Le Val Vallon, Grouville, and currently by his son, Mr. Arthur McGugan.

Jersey-pattern draw hoe or flat hoe made in Jersey.
The hoe has a wooden handle in a socket and a hardened Sheffield steel blade and wrought-iron holder. To give the blade a keen edge it is beaten on the field anvil. This type of hoe is almost unique to Jersey and was made locally by many blacksmiths over many years since the 19th century. Some were made in England but this one was made by the late Mr. Clem Le Breuilly in the 1970s. They were in use all through the 20th century and earlier. There would be several in every farmer's tool shed. Owner Mr. M. Billot, La Porte, Maufant.

Cutting tools, sickles, and scythes

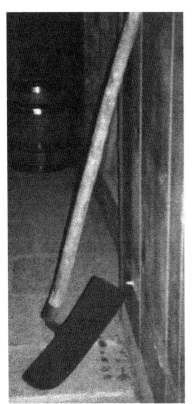

Root chopper and root-topping chopper.
This root chopper was probably made to order by a local blacksmith in the 19th century. The blade is 16.5 in. (42 cm) long and 4.5 in. (12 cm) across, and the handle is 3 ft (902 cm) long. Root crops such as mangels, swedes, and turnips were harvested by pulling them from the ground and laying them in double rows, with the crowns in line and the green leaf tops lying outwards. The tops are then cut off using this tool, or very often a long knife or an old sickle with the blade cut short. While the tops are still fresh, they are carted off and fed to the cattle. The root chopper would be used again to chop the roots into small pieces before they were fed to the stock. From the 1850s, root-slicing and pulping machines were being manufactured, but cutting the tops in the field continued. (La Société Jersiaise/Jersey Heritage Trust collection at Hamptonne.)

Left- and right-hand sickles and forked stick.
The sickle as a tool goes back to the Neolithic times but not in its present form, which goes back to the Iron Age. The modern sickle appears no different from its Iron Age counterpart! The curved blade has a tang which passes through a metal collar and the wooden handle; the end that protrudes from the outer end of the wooden handle is peened over. The sickles illustrated are right- and left-handed for right- and left-handed people (the right-handed sickle is on the left). The right-handed sickle is early 20th-century and the left-handed sickle was made in the 1970s.
The sickle is used for cutting hay and cereal crops, in fact any crop that has to be cut at harvest time. In Jersey farmers would cut green maize to feed to dairy cows when grass was in short supply, in summer. It is also used in Jersey for the branchage, cutting grass banks, and hedge-cutting. Sickles for cutting cereals, particularly wheat, had a broader, heavier blade but are slightly smaller overall than the lighter grass sickles. Locally, a small sickle about half the size of a grass sickle was specially made for cutting vraic off the rocks. The forked stick was used with the sickle for cutting grass and the branchage; it is held in one hand and the sickle in the other. The stick holds back the grass to expose the base to make cutting easier to see and perform. Sickles are manufactured by Messrs. Saut du Tarn at Saut du Tarn in France; others are made in Sheffield. The author owns these two, and the local supplier was Channel Industries Ltd.

Successful use of the sickle depended on keeping it sharp. One never went to work with a sickle without taking a whetstone and the holder filled with water. The holder was a small-diameter but deep tin can or a horn from a dead bull filled with water. It would be carried hooked in the waistband or propped up near the hedge. To achieve a sharp cutting edge, the blade is beaten thin with a special square-headed hammer and a small anvil and finished to a fine edge with a whetstone. Many farmers had a small field anvil for beating both the sickle blades and the scythe. They were also to beat the edge of a Jersey hoe blade, but it was not sharpened with a whetstone.

Two examples of the field anvil—in use since the Iron Age.
The field anvil for beating the cutting edge of a sickle and
scythe prior to sharpening with a whetstone or on a sandstone
wheel. They were made of cast iron by local foundrymen such
as Grandin. They were driven down to the curled stops into an
earth floor in the farm buildings in winter, to be used on a wet
day, but were also carried to the harvest field. The farmer or
farm worker would sit on a folded sack, legs astride with the
anvil between the legs, and with a square-headed hammer he
would beat the cutting edge of the sickles and scythes. It was a
slow, tedious job, which had to be done thoroughly to be
effective. (Steam Museum collection.)

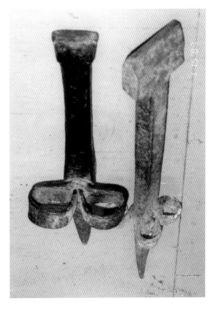

The scythe was first used in the first century AD with a
cradle to collect the sheaf. The cradle may take the form
of a metal or wooden bow fitted at one end to the handle
and at the other end to a hole made for the purpose in the
blade, several inches from the handle. Successful
mowing with the scythe depends on keeping it razor-
sharp. The cutting edge has to be beaten thin, like the
sickle, with a square-faced hammer on a small anvil
made for the purpose like those above. A man with a scythe will mow 2 acres, or 5 vergées, of oats
a day, but only 1 acre (2.25 vergées) of wheat, and the work is even slower in barley. It is slower
because the straw blunts the blade, so the mower has to stop work frequently to sharpen the blade.
The scythe will cut closer to the ground than the sickle and was a popular tool with the gardener
for mowing the lawn in the days before the lawnmower. The sickle remained the favoured tool for
wheat and barley until the horse-drawn reaper came along, followed fairly soon by the binder.
Sadly, the only scythes one can find today are either rusty, blunt, or damaged and sometimes all
three. One of the few remaining manufacturers in the early 1980s was Messrs. Saut du Tarn in the
south of France. There are three types of handle: first the popular curved wooden handle made of
willow with the two short hand grips; second a long straight handle, some made of wood and
some of metal, both having only one short hand grip; the third, used in Scotland, has a handle
which divides in two halfway up, supported by a crosspiece fitted between them. The two handles
are of equal length with the grips at the end of each one. Saut du Tarn import their curved
wooden handles from England.

A scythe with an English handle.
Mr. Vincent Obbard poses with a scythe from his collection. The
blade is 26 in. (63.3 cm) long and 3 in. (7.5 cm) broad at the
centre, tapering to a point. At the handle end it is wider at 6 in.
(15.2 cm). Some English blades tend to be narrower along their
length and slightly longer with a supporting rib riveted along the
back. The curved willow handle is English; it has two short hand
grips, the lower one clamped a blade length from the bottom
and the second length of the forearm above the first.
(Samarès Manor collection.)

A scythe with a straight handle.
Mr. David Levitt with a scythe from his collection. The blade may have been made during the 19th or early 20th century, probably in France. The blade is 33 in. (83.6 cm) long straight across and 35 in. (88.6 cm), measuring along the cutting edge. The breadth of the blade is 6 in. (15.2 cm) at the handle but at the centre this well-used, well-worn scythe is now only 2 in. (5 cm) broad, having probably been nearer 3 in. (7.5 cm) broad when new. From the centre it tapers to a point. The straight handle is 5 ft 8.5 in. (184 cm) long with one short hand grip, which is usual with the straight handle type. This one does have a slight curve and may have been made on the farm, using a suitable branch from a hedge.

A scythe made in western USA.
The scythe blade and handle are probably 20th-century. The blade is 32.5 in. (82.3 cm) long, the breadth is 3 in. (7.6 cm) at the centre and tapers to a point. Measuring the handle from the fitting at the bottom in a straight line to the top is 5 ft (1. 2 cm). The blade has only a very slight curve. A rib is riveted along the back to add strength and possibly add some weight. The rib curves up sharply at the handle to fit in the clamp in the handle. When new, the blade was painted green; some green paint is still in evidence on the blade today. The handle is beautifully curved and has two stub handgrips, which makes it a joy to use, so easy to swing with the body. It is held here by its owner, Mr. David Levitt.

Threshing and winnowing

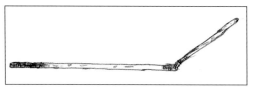

The flail for threshing wheat, oats, or barley.
The flail is a very old implement going back to the earliest days of growing cereals. It is made with an ash handle attached by a loose swivelling joint to a beater that is shorter than the handle but made of a heavier timber of thorn or holly. The swivelling arrangement was made up of ash or yew steam bent to the appropriate shape, forming a loop and lashed in place to the staff or handle. A piece of leather is also formed in a loop on the beater and a leather thong is woven around the loop and 'sewn' in place. It may seem remarkable that such an arrangement would stand up to the constant beating of heads of grain on a wooden floor. Flails were made for many centuries to be used by both men and women and continued to be used in the 20th century! The handle was held in both hands, raised above the head, and it was brought down on the heads of cereals: wheat, oats, or barley. It was a slow business. One man could produce between 6 and 8 bushels a day; to thresh the harvest required a large labour force. It is not surprising then that men feared for their jobs when the threshing machine first appeared and the Tolpuddle Martyrs marched in protest, only to be shipped out to Australia as convicts. Some became successful sheep farmers and another returned to England, settling in East Anglia, where he became a successful farmer.

The threshing table.

The threshing table has a curved, slatted top, was probably made in the 18th or early 19th century by a local carpenter and measures 3 ft 4 in. (110 cm) long and 2 ft (60.8 cm) across, front, to back. It is 27 in. (68.3 cm) high at the front rising 2 in. (5 cm) in a curve to 29 in. (73.3 cm) at the highest point. The crossbars or slats are 3.5 in. (8.9 cm) across and 2 in. (5 cm) deep with 1.75 in. (4.3 cm) clear space between them. Other tables were larger, measuring 2 ft 6 in. (76 cm) across and 4 ft (122 cm) long with the same curved top and at the same height. The heads of the sheaves were laid on the crossbars of the table and flailed. The grain fell through the space between the crossbars. It was an alternative to threshing the grain on a wooden floor, particularly if the straw was to be preserved for thatching. (La Société Jersiaise/Heritage Trust collection in the store at Augrès.)

A winnowing basket.

The basket is made of willow on ash, sewn with cane around the front lip and edge to reduce wear. The handles were made of ash. The basket is approximately 4 ft (122 cm) wide at the front lip, 3 ft (92.5 cm) deep, and 12 in. (30.4 cm) high along the back. They were used for many centuries before the winnowing machine came into use in the late 18th century. Winnowing baskets were used in the threshing shed or barn after the flail had threshed the sheaves of

grain and the straw was removed. Then the remaining loose grain and chaff was collected up and passed through a hand-held sieve and shaken to let the grain fall through, after which the remaining grain, chaff ,and husk was shovelled up in the winnowing basket. Across the threshing shed floor, between two open large doors, on each side, to generate a draught, the contents of the winnowing basket were cast aloft, and forwards. The lighter small straws and chaff would be blown to one side in the draught and the separated grain fell to the floor. The system allowed for some grading; the best-quality grain, being heavier, would travel further and the seconds of shrivelled or damaged grain, being lighter, fell short, closer to the thrower's feet. A slow, tedious process, done in the winter.

Harvesting rake

Hand-held hay and harvest rake.

Before the horse rake came into being in the late 19th century, the large hand rake was used in the hayfield and in the harvest field, in the days of the sickle and scythe, and it is said it was also used for gathering vraic on the beach, torn from rocks during storms. The rake had been in use for many hundreds of years but this design became popular in Jersey and on both sides of the Channel. The tines are 10 in. (25.3 cm) long and curved, and the overall width of the rake is 4 ft 10 in. (148 cm) wide. This one is in the Steam Museum collection.

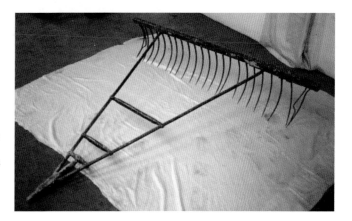

Cultivating implements

A hand harrow, made in Jersey.

Hand harrows like the one above were made during the 19th and 20th centuries, and possibly earlier. The dimensions are: length 3 ft 10 in. (117 cm), width 3 ft (910 cm), the tines are 3 in. (7.5 cm) long under the beam, in five rows at 8.5 in. (21.5 cm) centres. Eight tines at 5.5 in. (14 cm) centres on each beam total forty tines. The drawbar is made of wrought iron. Some hand harrows were slightly fan-shaped. In work the hand harrow is pulled from one corner, the harrow adopting a diamond shape on the ground. This is to ensure the tines do not line up one behind the other but are spread to cover the ground. However, the work has to overlap on each lap across the field to get an even coverage. The hand harrow was pulled by one man in the field for light cultivation: preparing a seed bed or harrowing in seeds that have been sown broadcast by hand, cross-harrowing early potatoes just after they have emerged, before the days of plastic! The harrow pictured here is the property of the Billot family, at La Porte, Maufant.

Two-man wooden potato scarifier.

Two-man potato scarifiers were made in the 19th century, before the 1880s, by local blacksmiths and carpenters. After the 1880s the iron scarifiers were produced. Potato scarifiers are fitted with three tines and a rolling crumbler at the back. The usual arrangement: a front tine with an arrowhead point and two tines behind, staggered on either side with a half-arrowhead on the inside. The implement is held and controlled by the two handles at the back, while the crossbar handle at the front is held by the person pulling the implement, who faces forward with his hands behind his back, gripping the cross-handle. Potatoes were scarified after planting for weeding and cultivating between the rows before banking, in small plots and on côtils. This implement has a metal frame to carry the tines and crumbler; very often wooden implements have a timber frame supporting the tines and crumbler. (La Société Jersiaise/Jersey Heritage Trust collection.)

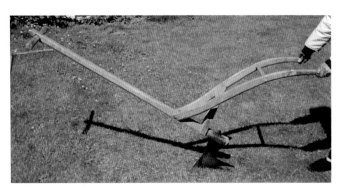

Two-man wooden potato banker.

Wooden potato bankers were made by a local carpenter and blacksmith in the 19th century before the 1880s. The banking body is 12 in. (30.4 cm) wide, wing tip to wing tip, and approximately 12 in. (30.4 cm) deep. They are operated in the same manner as the scarifier, one man in front and one behind for banking potatoes in small pieces of ground, côtils, etc. There are several examples of this implement in the various museum collections. (Courtesy of J. Arthur, La Pompe, St. Mary.)

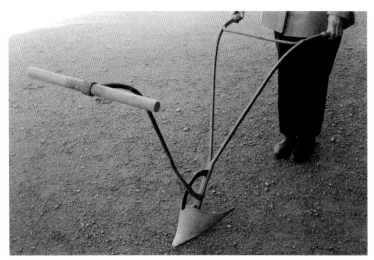

Two-man iron potato banker with an adjustable front handle.
The banker was made by a local blacksmith after the 1880s. Very much the same as the wooden banker but a little more sophisticated! The front handle for pulling the implement is adjustable for height, which also affected the pitch, i.e. the angle of the point to the ground, a facility not available on the wooden implements. The implement is of wrought iron except for hand grips. Used exactly as the wooden implement in small pieces of land, in short turns, i.e. short rows, and on côtils. (La Société Jersiaise/Jersey Heritage Trust collection at Hamptonne.)

Hand barrow

Two-man hand barrow.
The hand barrow was a most useful tool. They were made by a local carpenter and measured 2 ft 3 in. (65.8 cm) wide with five or six crossbars. Two men, one at each end, would take hold of the handles and hold it horizontally, one man facing it and the second facing the way ahead. The hand barrow was placed flat on the ground to load it. It carried boxes of seed potatoes, first to load the van or lorry from the shed and then to unload the van in the field, then to distribute the boxes over the cultivated land, to avoid driving over the freshly prepared seed bed. They were seen on every farm. (Steam Museum collection.)

Drilling machines and hoes

(*right*) Reeve's two-wheel seed drill
The seed drill was manufactured in the 1920s or earlier by R. & J. Reeve & Son Ltd., Bratton Iron Works, Westbury, Wiltshire. It is a brush-feed drill. The rotating brush is driven by the wheels, which are adjusted for width by sliding along the axles. The size of feed hole is adjusted with a sliding plate and clamp for drilling root crops and brassicas etc. The heelers to cover the seed were available as an extra. It has been modified with Planet heelers and a split roller in an effort to close the furrow made by the seed spout and the roller, to firm the soil over the seeds. To be effective, it needs to be held firmly in place, with a gentle downward pressure, which this modification does not have. (La Société Jersiaise/Jersey Heritage Trust collection.)

The American Planet JR seed drills and cultivators were only a small selection of the many machines manufactured by the company, which also manufactured a range of inter-row horse-drawn cultivators with a number of different tines and hoe blades. They produce a range of simple single-wheel push-hoes, for weeding between the rows of crops, and fertiliser spreaders. They were popular among Jersey farmers and went on being used from about the turn of the last century through to the 1950s and probably the 1960s, until tractor-mounted precision seed drilling machines appeared in the late 1950s and early 1960s. The agent in Jersey in 1914 was John Jones, an ironmonger at 1 Mulcaster Street.

Planet Junior push-hoe fitted with two L-shaped hoe blades.

Detail of the hoe blade adjustment.

This Planet push-hoe is fitted with one steel wheel. Planet hoe blades vary in width and can be set to different widths. The maximum width is 12 in. (30.4 cm). The blades are riveted to an iron casting, which has a threaded bolt; in turn each bolt is fitted into a slot in a cast-iron bracket on the push-hoe. The blades can be slid along the two slots to adjust to the appropriate width for the row to be weeded. The slots can be seen in the picture on the right. It is a common feature to have a cast-iron spanner housed in a bracket at the top of the handles on Planet machines for making the adjustments, or very often they are tied to the handles with binder twine. (La Société Jersiaise collection at Hamptonne and the Steam Museum collection.)

A fertiliser placement distributor manufactured by Planet of the USA.
The Planet Junior no. 220 has one steel wheel with a smaller 8 in. (20.30 cm) diameter ring at the centre with ten stubs set horizontally at regular spaces around it, which pulled a rod to open the feeder at regular intervals. A control on the handles regulates the discharge from the galvanised 1-bushel hopper which supplied six delivery chutes. The feed gate can be adjusted to fill all the tubes, or just the centre tubes, or to fill only two or three tubes. The tubes can be adjusted to spread from 4 in. (10 cm) to 30 in. (75.8 cm) wide. This is a two-man machine: it is pushed by one person on the handles and pulled by another hooked to the drawbar at the front. (Steam Museum collection.)

JOHN JONES

General and Furnishing Ironmonger .   .
Zinc and Tin Plate Worker, Locksmith, &c.
MULCASTER STREET, JERSEY.

Lawn Mowers, Ploughs, Harrows,

Chaff-Cutters, Pulpers, &c., &c.,

And all kinds of Garden Requisites.

REPAIRS OF ALL
KINDS BY . .
EXPERIENCED
WORKMEN.

Colza Oil, Paraffin, Linseed and other Oils, Turpentine, Paints, Colors,
Varnish, Pitch, Oakum, Tar, Resin, Brushes, Mats, Zinc, Lead, Wire, &c.

This advertisement appeared in the RJA & HS journal of 1911

The American Planet JR seed drill and cultivator.
John Jones's advertisement above Illustrates the range of cultivating attachments available for use with it, including a banker, weeding tines, and hoe blades. It is quite different from the Planet drill on so many Jersey farms, illustrated on the next page. The seed box is mounted in the hub between the two wheels. As the wheels rotate, the seed box rotates, dropping the seeds as the feed hole reaches the bottom. The size of the feed hole is adjustable for mangels, turnips, swedes, maize, brassicas, etc. (Steam Museum ref. 2003.)

The Planet Junior seed drill was very popular with farmers in Jersey

Planet Junior and its row-spacing marker.
The Planet Junior still has its uses today. Using one of several fittings in the feed mechanism, it is capable of sowing a variety of seeds, maize, mangels, turnips, swedes, fodder beet, and brassicas. It is not a precision drill as we know them today but the Planet Junior was the best there was at the time. It would sow in what Planet called 'hills', that is it dropped a small group of seeds together. It has a wheel at the front and a roller at the back. The front wheel has a small gearwheel which operates the feeder. The rear roller is split in two sections to press the soil lightly down onto the seed. An adjustable marker for marking the next row could be lifted over to either side of the machine. The wooden handles are varnished, the seed hopper with a hinged lid is painted green, and the wheel and roller are black. This drill was eventually superseded when seeds were treated before being sold, to be more easily handled by tractor-mounted precision drills, which made their appearance in the 1960s. (Steam Museum collection.)

A seed drill manufactured by R. Hunt and Co. Ltd.
This Hunt two-wheel drill has a seeding tine beneath the seed box. The two wheels are adjustable for width of track on a very long axle with square-headed clamping bolts. The lever beside the handle will lift the top gearwheel off the lower one, to disengage the drive to the seeding mechanism. The large-diameter wheels will make it easy to push and are adjustable for width. R. Hunt & Co. Ltd., at Earls Colne, in Essex were agricultural machinery manufacturers in the 19th and 20th centuries.

Reeve's wheelbarrow-type brush seed drill.
Reeve's brush-type broadcaster for grass and clover seed. Rotating brush and shutter type, driven by a shaft from the wheel with spur gears. The large-diameter wheel has wooden spokes and hub with a metal rim. The drive to the feed brushes was engaged by a lever on the handles, which moved the driveshaft crown gear sideways to engage the teeth on the shaft in the 12 ft (381 cm) long hopper. To regulate the rate of seeding, copper slides, later replaced by zinc slides, are set by two small racks and pinions. Discs with various size holes covered the holes in the wooden hopper. A later model was made to fit onto the front of a tractor. (Steam Museum collection.)

Two old hand-push drills.
The drill on the left was manufactured in England in the 19th century and can be seen in agricultural museums in England. The one on the right is rare and may be French.

A view of the detail of the machine on the left of the group shown at the foot of the facing page.

The machine on the left is a rowcrop drill for turnip seed and other root crops. The turnip was a popular root crop for human consumption for many years and for feeding to cattle. In the wooden frame is a seed box, or hopper, with rotating agitators in the bottom; it has a rotating brush, to feed the seed through a hole in a disc. The disc has a selection of holes that can be rotated to the selected hole size over the feed chute to suit size and type of seed. A gear-driven shaft from the front wheel drives the agitators and rotating brush feed. A manually controlled cam moves the gear sideways away from the gear on the front wheel to stop work. The two wheels have wooden hubs and spokes, but iron rims; the front wheel has a diameter of 22 in. (55.7 cm), and the rear wheel a diameter of 18 in. (45.5 cm), and is on an adjustable stalk, to adjust the height of the seed chute.

Detail of the hopper of the drill on the right with the rotating disc and pegs and adjustable hatch; probably French and made in the 18th or 19th centuries.

The wooden disc in the bottom of the hopper has sixteen metal pegs (two are missing!) around the periphery, which suggests that this drill was for sowing coarse material, possibly guano, but for sowing sparingly down the row rather than broadcast. The wooden barrel-type hopper has a 14 in. (35.5 cm) internal diameter and is 13 ins. (32.9 cm) deep. The pegs are both agitators and feeders to deliver the material to an adjustable shutter through which the guano passes, to descend the single front chute which has a diamond-shaped wooden block divider. On each side are 17 in. (43 cm) diameter steel wheels, mounted on an axle with a gear, which rotates a large-diameter ring gear on a shaft keyed to the feed disc in the hopper. (La Société Jersiaise/Jersey Heritage Trust collection at Hamptonne.)

The Aero fiddle-type seeder.

A portable broadcast sowing machine. Described as the Aero model DLK with serial no. 125 4 567 8910. It was otherwise known as a fiddle broadcaster, because the action is to push and pull a wooden handle towards and away from the machine to operate the broadcasting mechanism. These machines first appeared in the late 1940s and became quite popular. The machine consists of a canvas bag hooked around the operator's neck above a wooden hopper, to hold the seed. In the bottom is an adjustable feed gate, through which the seed falls onto a disc beneath. The disc has five shoots, like the spokes of a wheel pointing outward, with open ends, from which the seed is thrown as the disc is spun. The disc is spun with a bow as on a violin, but the gut is a leather thong with one turn around the shaft/axle below the disc. The bow is moved to and fro as on a violin and drives the disc around, first in one direction and then in the other.

Mostly used for grass seed but it could be used to broadcast cereals, rape, kale, and turnips. A useful and popular tool in its day. (Courtesy of the Arthur family, La Pompe, St. Mary.)

Hand roller

The early hand roller was made with a solid timber roll and timber frame and plain metal bearings with iron stub axles. The roller had a diameter of 10 or 12 in. (25.3 or 30.4 cm) and was 4 ft (115 cm) wide with an iron collar on each end of the roll. Some rollers were made in two halves, separated in the centre for easier manœuvring. Hand rollers were relatively easy to pull and were suitable for small areas.

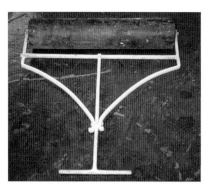

Hand roller.
The roller illustrated is similar in appearance to the earlier wooden rollers but it has a wrought-iron frame and roller made with a pitch-fibre drainpipe 7 in. (17.7 cm) in diameter and 2 ft 10 in. (85 cm) long, filled with concrete. The frame was made by a local blacksmith, probably post-war. It is heavy and the small diameter of the roll would make it difficult to pull in soft going. (Steam Museum collection.)

Knapsack sprayers and dusters

A group of four knapsack spraying machines.
On the right are two Vermoreil machines made at Villefranche; those on the left were made by W. T. French & Sons and were known as the Mysto. All four have a capacity of 2 gallons. The pump under the tank is operated by a lever that is raised and lowered continually to get up the pressure and maintain it. The tank is made of sheet metal, copper alloy, and bronze for the pump fittings and nozzles, and reinforced rubber for the hose to the lance. Pumping continues until the tank is empty. The spray lance has a T piece on the end, to which are attached the two spray nozzles. A tap is fitted to the lance to shut off the supply, as at the end of a row. They were used from the very beginning of the copper sulphate spray known as Bordeaux mixture, to spray potatoes and tomatoes against blight and the Colorado beetle in early post-war years, as well as on weeds around the farm. The agent in Jersey in 1903 was Messrs. H. Becker at 13 Beresford Street and at the nursery at Five Oaks. (Steam Museum collection.)

Knapsack and breast dusting sprayers like these two replaced the wet sprayers in the 1940s and 1950s.
These two machines applied dry powder against blight in potatoes and tomato crops. They were a great saving in time and labour, as it was no longer necessary to cart large quantities of water to the field. The powder was just as effective, and a programme of regular spraying could be set up.
The yellow machine is a lever-operated blower, a knapsack made by Vermoreil, model 64, that came into use in the late 1930s and 1940s. The blue machine on the right is a breast-mounted dusting machine, of the middle to late 1940s. It has a crank handle operating a rotating fan blower, replacing the yellow knapsack, type of machine. Used on the beaches for dusting vraic against the Colorado beetle after 1945. (Steam Museum collection.)

States of Jersey Department of Agriculture staff dusting against Colorado beetle on seaweed on the beaches in 1945 at Rozel.

An interesting story of the German Occupation. In the background of the picture of Rozel is the author's family beach hut on the pier. It was built by the author's father in 1935 and it was the only beach hut on the pier to survive the German Occupation. Charlie Blampied, the harbour master at Rozel, who lived in the harbour master's house in the foreground, insisted the Germans should not take it for firewood as they did those on either side of it. It has since changed hands.

Billhooks

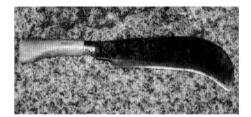

Billhook: a lopping tool.

The billhook is made in a variety of shapes and sizes, as illustrated in Elwell's catalogue of the late 1940s, to suit the needs of the various hedge-laying techniques used in different counties in England and Wales. It is an excellent form of maintenance and for making a hedge stock-proof. Unfortunately, Jersey farmers do not practice hedge-laying. The sight of a recently laid hedge out in the countryside is attractive. In Jersey, hedges were originally grown tall to provide shelter from the wind for the many cider orchards. In view of today's changing farming practices, dairy herds of over a hundred or two hundred cows are spending almost all their lives outside; it is therefore important that shelter belts be planted for cows and heifers in open fields.

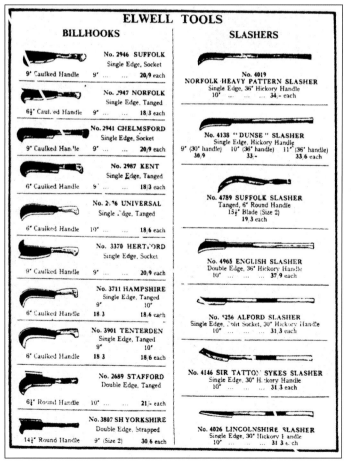

Elwell's tools catalogue. The popular billhooks in the island appear to be the single-edge Universal and the double-edge Stafford illustrated above.

Whetstone grinders

Wet sandstone wheel and trough.
Two examples of whetstone grinders made of sandstone for sharpening the cutting edges of sickles, scythes, axes, billhooks, etc. The top wheel has a diameter of 23 in. (58.4 cm) and is 4 in. (10.1 cm) wide. (La Société Jersiaise/Jersey Heritage Trust collection at Hamptonne.)

The second wheel has a diameter of 24 in. (61 cm) when new and is between 3 in. (7.6 cm) and 4 in. (10.1 cm) thick. (Steam Museum collection.)

The stone is more effective when wet, so the wheel runs through water in a wooden trough beneath it. They were commonplace on farms up to the 1940s but they required two people to operate them. While one sharpened the blade another person had to turn the stone with the crank handle. Sandstone is a very fine-grain stone quarried in France, where the wheels were made. They produced a beautifully smooth cutting edge to any steel blade. A local carpenter made the frame and trough.

These whetstone grinding wheels were to be found in every farmyard, and every blacksmith had one. On the farm, a farmer's boy or farmer's wife would turn the handle, while the farmer held the blade to the stone, sharpening his sickles and scythes. The blades will have been beaten first on the anvil to produce a thin edge. The author often turned the handle for his grandfather at La Porte. The trough had to be drained in frosty weather; apart from ice damaging the trough, the stone would freeze and shatter the part in the water, leaving a very lopsided stone that was rendered useless.

A hand-held, sharpening whetstone is carried to the field with the billhook, sickle, or scythe to keep the cutting edge sharp. Some stones have a wooden handle and may be used dry; there were also whetstones that were carried in a discarded domestic tin—a long narrow cylinder filled with water in which the stone is carried to keep it wet. The tin had a small hole pierced at the top, through which a piece of wire shaped into a hook was fitted so that the man could carry it on his belt.

The electric bench grinder has taken the place of the whetstone. The bench grinder starts at the press of a button and does not need two people to sharpen a blade.

19 Miscellaneous Items around the Farm

Water pumps

Fresh-water hand pump above a well.
A fresh-water pump, probably late 19th or early 20th century. It has a 3-in. (7.6 cm) bore and 8-in. (20.3 cm) stroke, operated with the usual hand lever. It is mounted very conveniently for the farmhouse, by the back door, on a wooden wall board. Even so, it is outside, which is not so convenient in inclement weather. Wells or pumps may be beside a scullery sink in some farmhouses, while others are not always so conveniently placed and may be across the farmyard or in a nearby field. These pumps were almost always installed with a grey/blue granite water trough alongside. This one is at Hamptonne in St. Lawrence, a National Trust for Jersey property. It was the late Mrs. Joan Stevens who alerted La Société Jersiaise to this unique property, with its many stages of development. The Société, in co-operation with the Jersey Heritage Trust and the National Trust for Jersey, acquired the property, so we have the present-day museum for all to enjoy. It was originally the property of the Emmanuel family.

Fresh-water lever-action hand pump, operating a plunger or piston with a simple flap valve, erected above a well at La Val Bachelier, St. Ouen.
These lever-action hand pumps operate a reciprocating piston, with a simple flap valve to lift the water. As the piston descended into the water, the flap valve would open, allowing water to pass through and onto the top of the piston; as the piston was lifted, the flap would close under the weight of water, so lifting the water to an outlet pipe. They were installed in the 19th and early 20th centuries, and probably earlier, before the dangers of lead poisoning were understood. In spite of that scare, many farmers lived into their nineties. This type of lead pump attached to a wooden post is quite common on the Jersey farm, usually over the well. The post is often painted farm-red or pink and the lead is usually unpainted. Some have a small hole in the top of the curve of the spout for drinking by placing the lips over the hole and sucking water through it while pumping the handle. (Courtesy of Mr. Alfred Le Boutillier, La Val Bachelier, St. Ouen.)

The lever-action pump is also used for pumping liquid manure, often seen on top of the surrounding wall of a farmyard manure pit. Under the pit is a masonry tank into which the liquid manure from the cow and horse stables will drain. This system of collecting liquid manure from the stables is unique to Jersey. It was the idea of a dairy farmer in the early years of the 19th century, was encouraged by the Royal Jersey Agricultural and Horticultural Society and became established practice.

The liquid manure chain pump.

The chain pump was a popular pump with farmers in the 1930s and 1940s. Normally they are operated manually but they could be adapted to be driven by flat belt from a petrol engine or electric motor. The pump could lift liquids 15 ft (457 cm) and it could cope with solids. The lift-pipe was available in 2 in. (5 cm), 2.5 in. (6.3 cm), and 3 in. (7.6 cm) diameters and was 12 ft (365 cm) long; the lower part is made of wrought iron and the remainder is of cast iron. A horizontal pipe with a slight fall could be fitted to the outlet for delivery some distance from the pump. It is said to be easier and quicker to operate for a boy than a lever pump. The chain made a cheerful clinking sound in the pipe when it was being operated.

The hydraulic ram fresh-water pump.

Placed in a fresh-water stream or brook, the pump operates on the principle of the hydraulic ram. Water enters through the large-diameter stub pipe at the bottom on the right and is delivered through the small-diameter pipe beneath the pressure vessel above, on the top.

Any property with a stream flowing through it can abstract water with this type of pump. It depends on a steady flow of water in quite a small stream or brook to operate, requiring no other source of power, so it is economical to run. The pump operates on a simple system with a non-return valve allowing water to flow into the pump. Then with a diaphragm and pressure vessel, the water is moved in pulses up a pipe. It is the ram effect of the water running into the pump that provides the power to push the water along. Water can be delivered over quite a long distance and up a steep incline to a tank. It will deliver between 100,000 and 500,000 gallons a day, depending on the size of the installation and the flow in the stream. A hydraulic ram was installed in a brook in Swiss Valley to supply water to Roselands Farm in the 20th century.

Windmills

There were several windmills in the Island before electric power was available in rural areas.

This windmill operated a fresh-water pump over a well at Beau Dèsert.

This windmill was manufactured by the Climax Company in the West Country in England in the early 20th century. It was erected over a deep well to operate a water pump. The windmill fan has an overall diameter of 8 ft 6 in. (259 cm) approximately, with eighteen blades. The tower is constructed of galvanised steel on an 8 ft 2 in. (249 cm) square base, on four 6 ft (184 cm) long angle-iron struts grouted in concrete. Galvanised risers of 2.5 in. (6.3 cm) angle-iron and 1.0625 in. (2.7 cm) flat-straps with horizontals of 1.25 in. (3.1 cm) angle-iron set at 58 in. (147.3 cm) centres, of which there are six, the last section coming almost to a point, to support the platform. The height of the platform is approximately 34 ft (10.36 m) above ground. The mill drives a piston pump with flap valves to lift the water 50 ft (15.24 m) from below ground to the tanks.

The windmill was working efficiently in the late 1950s and probably well into the 1960s, but sadly it has since been neglected. Most of the connecting rod is missing. It was composed of timber sections joined by galvanised metal straps on opposite sides and bolted through. Also missing is the ground-level control lever, which was connected by a heavy-gauge wire rod to the windvane to enable it to be swung round, to rest alongside the fan, which had the effect of turning the fan away from the wind, so allowing it to freewheel off the wind, i.e. switching it off. This was advisable in high winds or when the tanks were full. The wooden control lever was approximately 18 in. long and worked on a ratchet with a lock. Water was pumped into two tanks, inside a wooden shed constructed above a corner of the granite wall surrounding the garden and two further granite walls on the inside, to form a rectangular building which doubled as a garden shed beneath the two tanks. The pitched roof over the tanks was made of wood covered with galvanised iron sheeting. Standing inside the shed under the tanks, one could hear the water being delivered in spurts into the tanks.

The height of the tanks provided a substantial head of water for the farm buildings and the house. The system supplied sufficient water for the whole farm, i.e. the family, the farm staff, a dairy herd of twenty-five head of milking cows, ten or twelve followers, two horses, a number of pigs, and finally a dairy supporting a large milk round in St. Saviour. The well is 55 ft deep but it was not a straight shaft. The pump was mounted at the foot of a shaft directly beneath the windmill about 10 or 12 ft (366 cm) down. From the pump, a granite-walled tunnel carrying the water pipe extended northwards, horizontally for approximately 10 ft (305 cm), to the top of the actual well, which was a further 40 ft (12.19 m) down to the well bottom. The author went down the well and along the tunnel in the 1950s. It was also necessary to go down to maintain the pump, and to climb the ladder of the windmill to the platform to lubricate and maintain the windmill. The windmill tower and fan are still there today at Beau Désert, St. Saviour.

Drinking bowls and poultry feeders

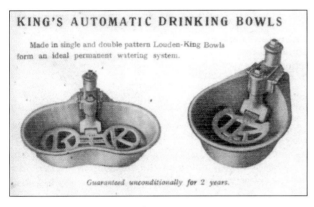

Automatic drinking bowls for dairy cattle.
Automatic drinking bowls manufactured by Louden King and supplied by the CGA, formerly on the Esplanade in St. Helier. They were made of cast iron and galvanised with bronze fittings and aluminium lever plates. They were installed in cow stalls in the cow stables and collection yards. Cows drink large quantities of water and it is important to keep them well supplied. The animal pushes down with its chin on the plate (with the letter K) in the bottom, which opens a valve and lets more water in. The animals soon learnt how to do it. It is a very efficient system and saved carrying water to the cattle. Drinking bowls were made by a number of manufacturers.

Poultry-feeding equipment

Equipment for poultry-feeding is quite simple and so efficient that it has remained unchanged for decades. The equipment is made by Eltex, which fabricates them with sheet metal, and then they are galvanised.

A water fountain on the left and a food trough on the right.
The long rectangular food trough should have a wire guard over it, to prevent birds other than poultry feeding from it. Both the water fountain and the food trough are manufactured in a range of sizes; those illustrated are rather small and are intended for just a few birds. These are in the chicken run at Hamptonne. The line drawing on the following page illustrates the simple design of the water fountain.

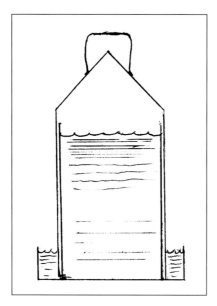

Drawing of the water fountain.
The outside cover of the fountain has a coned top and a loop handle which, when it is lifted off, will reveal a cylinder welded to the bottom. The cylinder has a small hole in the side at the bottom. The cylinder is filled with water, which flows through the small hole into the annular trough. When the cover is put back on the cylinder, it is a loose fit but it covers the hole, restricting the flow of water. The water in the trough effectively seals the bottom of the cover, preventing air getting in and water running out. As the poultry drink the water, the level goes down, breaking the seal and allowing more water to flow into the trough. A couple of clips in the bottom of the trough will grip the cover when it is given a small twist. That will enable the whole assembly, filled with water, to be carried using the loop handle at the top.

Irrigation equipment

Irrigation has featured in agriculture for over 3,000 years, beginning with irrigation canals in Egypt. Local farmers with irrigation equipment water vegetable crops, the Jersey Royal early potato, and grassland in a drought year. The problem is finding a source of water. Many farmers constructed reservoirs to collect and store water until it was needed. The only satisfactory method is a combination of borehole and reservoir, because of the consumption rate.

In more recent times in the British Isles irrigation systems were in use, pre-war, in horticulture, with 1.5 in. (3.8 cm) internal diameter steel pipes with brass spray jets every 2 or 3 ft (61 cm or 91.5 cm) supported on specially designed stands to support the pipes and spray jets above the crop. The pipes are joined with a square flange on one end of each pipe and a flange with ledges at the other end. The ledges are at right angles to the flange and slotted to accept two wedges to clamp the pipes together. A rubber gasket between the flanges formed a seal.

A water motor, driven by water pressure at one end of the line of pipes, rotates the pipe slowly back and forth through 90 degrees. Each stand has a small rail with a stop at each end, to both support the pipe and allow it to roll back and forth without rolling off. The area sprayed was rectangular, measuring the length of the pipeline, making the area to be irrigated easy to manage. These systems are relatively small for high-value vegetable crops such as lettuce. The manufacturer was Bomford Bros. Ltd., near Evesham in the West Midlands.

In the post-war years, when aluminium became more readily available, making the equipment lighter and easier to handle, and high-capacity pumps and high-powered tractors with the PTO were manufactured, it was possible to consider irrigation on a field scale. In Jersey, irrigating potatoes and grassland during periods of severe drought became possible. The land must be given a good soaking, but it must not be done too fast. Half an inch in two or three hours is desirable to give the water time to soak in and not run off. However, irrigation on this scale uses vast quantities of water, demanding a good source of supply, a high-capacity pump, and a powerful engine or electric motor. The average farm well will go dry during a long drought with normal use, so would be quite unsuitable if used for irrigation. There are exceptions, such as a deep well in an area that has a permanently high water table. A deep borehole and submersible pump is a frequent source, and even better when used together with a reservoir which is filled when water is plentiful. This is an important consideration in an island with a limited supply of water, although that view is now disputed. A farm reservoir must have a lining with a material that can be cut and welded on-site so that it is tailor-made for the reservoir.

The water is applied to the land through lengths of 2 in (5 cm) diameter aluminium piping with a coupling arrangement, to join the lengths together with a break at regular intervals to fit a riser and a rain gun. The water is pumped to the distribution system through large-diameter flexible pipes at pressures of 30 to 50 lb per square inch (or psi). The bigger rainers may require up to 80 psi. Water is pumped from a reservoir with a tractor-mounted centrifugal pump driven by the tractor PTO. The centrifugal pump is ideal for this purpose, as it is flexible to handle different quantities of water at different pressures to suit the area to be irrigated. The area will vary to suit different-size fields and layouts of pipe work.

The rainer, or sprinkler nozzle, is designed to use the water pressure to rotate the sprinkler to deliver water in a circular pattern. Some sprinklers have two jets set 180 degrees apart. One jet has a longer range, delivering water towards the periphery of the circular area being irrigated, and the other a shorter range to cover the inner area of the circle. Having saturated an area, then the system has to be shut down, the pipes uncoupled and moved to the next area to be irrigated.

A more recent innovation consists of a large-diameter hose on a mobile hose reel with a rain gun. A water motor drives the reel over the area to be irrigated, away from the water supply. This system is proving useful on grassland. A variation of the system that can deal with dirty water is used for spreading liquid manure on the land.

The best-known manufacturers of irrigation equipment in the 1950s and 1960s were Wright Rain and Farrow.

Irrigation pipeline, with standpipes and sprinklers irrigating brassicas.

Water is drawn from a farm reservoir nearby, pumping with a centrifugal pump driven by a powerful tractor with a power take-off (PTO). The reservoir is filled first from a borehole, using a portable generator to drive a submersible pump.

Detail of Wright Rain standpipe and sprinkler.
In front of the jet, on the sprinkler, is a deflector and hammer: the jet of water forces the deflector to one side which loads a spring, which in turn forces the deflector back onto the jet outlet, which makes the hammer strike an anvil on the jet assembly, moving the jet around through a few degrees, so changing the direction of the sprinkler. This action is automatic and continuous, constantly changing the direction of the jet rotating the sprinkler right around through 360 degrees. The local suppliers for Wright Rain are the Jersey Farmers' (Trading) Union Ltd. (JF(T)U), trading first at Olympia on the Esplanade, up to the late 1960s and later at Commercial Buildings, with a depot in St. John.

A mobile irrigation pump coupled to a tractor pick-up hitch and PTO shaft.
The pump is a centrifugal pump driven by the tractor's PTO. The suction hose is coupled to the open inlet at the back. Above the pump is a hand-lever-operated diaphragm-priming pump. The outlet is on the right, with a handwheel to operate the valve.

A selection of suction pipes to connect the pump to the water supply and the delivery hoses.
The delivery hoses connect the pump to the water supply and to the line of sprinklers. The amount of water applied will be measured in thousands of gallons an hour, depending on the number of sprinklers, the capacity of the pump, etc. Pressures can vary between 35 and 50 psi. depending on the equipment and condition. (Courtesy of Mr. J. Le Gallais, Roselands, St. Saviour.)

Sheep shearers

A sheep shearer made by R. A. Lister.
The original sheep shearer was made in Australia in 1868 by the son of a clergyman on his brother-in-law's farm. The shearing machine was not a great success until 1877. It was first manufactured in the United States by the Chicago Flexible Shaft Company and marketed in the UK as the Cooper and Cooper Stewart. A single, hand-operated sheep shearer requires two operators, one to turn the handle and hold the machine steady and another person to operate the clipper. The crank handle operates a gearbox that increases the rpm and operates a shearer on the end of a flexible shaft. The shearer has clippers similar to those in a barber's shop, but the shearer's clippers are bigger and wider. In Australia the operators worked in groups, travelling the sheep country as they had with hand-operated shears. They would operate up to eight or ten units at a time, the machines driven by overhead shafting. This changed again when electric generators were produced and shearers were powered by electric motors, one motor driving two flexible shafts and shearers and up to ten motors being installed.

In due course in England sheep shearers were manufactured by the Wolseley Sheep Shearing Company and R. A. Lister & Co. in the 1880s and 1890s. They were produced in large numbers for export to many parts of the world, notably Australia, for the wool industry. Here in Jersey there were sheep in the Island in those days, but with the advent of the Jersey Royal potato, the tomato, and the success of the Jersey cow, sheep disappeared from the Island. However, the shearer still had its uses in the Island for trimming the coats of horses and preparing cows for agricultural shows. The clipper heads are changeable: a coarse clipper can be removed and a finer clipper fitted. There is a separate clipper for the coats of horses and cows.

Herbert Austin, later Lord Austin, began his career with the Wolseley Sheep Shearing Company, becoming the chairman. The company continued manufacturing the shearers into the 1960s. Lord Austin eventually started his own company, manufacturing Austin cars and Austin tractors. In due course Wolseley began the manufacture of the Wolseley car and changed again to become Wolseley Engineering, manufacturing the Wolseley Merry Tiller rotary cultivator. That was to change again when eventually Wolseley's garden machinery business was taken over by Qualcast Group.

Electric fencing

The electric fence is a valuable and essential piece of equipment for the control of livestock on the farm. An electric fence stretched across a field provides an excellent temporary fence to contain the stock within a particular area. It is useful in Jersey, where a field may be divided into two areas, with grass on one side and potatoes on the other. An electric fence stretched along the edge of the grass to be grazed will prevent the cows trampling over the potatoes. Another use is to control the amount of grazing available to the cattle, by 'folding', as it is sometimes called. Each day the fence is moved forward to give the cows a fresh strip of grazing. It is particularly useful in the spring and early summer, when there is plenty of fresh grass which must be rationed. This system is much more practical than in the old days, when the cows were each pegged or tethered and had to be moved at least once a day, which was time-consuming.

The fence wire is supported on plastic or ceramic-coated insulators fitted to the top of light metal posts that are simply pushed into the ground, holding the wire some 24 in. (61 cm) to 30 in. (76.2 cm) above. The insulators are often in the shape of a pigtail, which enables the wire to be detached quickly and easily. This will be sufficient to control cows and heifers. Two wires at 12 in. (30.5 cm) and 18 in. (45.5 cm) above the ground are required for pigs and sheep.

To operate the system, an electrical fencer unit is placed at one end of the fence and connected to the fence with an insulated wire and a clip to attach it to the fence wire. The fencer unit is contained in a metal or sturdy plastic box, with two six-volt dry batteries, to which it is connected. Some farmers use a twelve-volt accumulator. The fencer unit is mounted on a metal post or tripod pushed well into the ground to provide a good earth, which is necessary to complete the circuit. The batteries supply a low-voltage current through a contact breaker to a primary coil that creates a small current of high-voltage by induction in a secondary coil. The high-voltage current lasts a fraction of a second, passing along the fence wire roughly every second and providing a short, sharp shock to any animal or person who touches it. Nothing must touch the wire, such as a weed, as this will earth the current and render the fence quite useless. Batteries would last for ten or fourteen days and the fence would be effective for up to 15 miles.

The fencer unit, power supplied by a 12-volt accumulator rather than two dry batteries; the unit is clipped to the fence wire.

The electric fence post and pigtail insulator wire-holder, illustrating the flexibility of the electric fence.

Probably the most popular electric fencer was manufactured by Wolseley Engineering, who made both battery-operated and mains-electric fencers. The mains units were not as popular as the battery unit because they had to be near a mains supply which usually meant near the farm buildings. Otherwise a long lead would be necessary, which would not be practical or safe for long and frequent use. Many people will remember the red aluminium cover on the Wolseley battery fencer with the 'on-off' switch underneath.

A more permanent electric fence using wooden stakes and plastic insulator holders nailed to the post.
This picture illustrates the confidence the farmers have in the electric fence to keep animals from straying out of a field and onto a road.

Incubators

An incubator cabinet for hatching chickens, made and patented by Hearson.
This incubator, described as the Champion, was manufactured in the early 20th century, and possibly sometime before that. The heater is an oil lamp with a single yellow flame. The eggs are arranged in the drawers, and as the chicks hatch out they are transferred to a separate heated unit, providing heat and shelter with feeding trays and water troughs alongside. The author's father had incubators of this type in the 1930s, using them for many years. It was a delight to open up from time to time and watch the young chicks breaking out of the shell, eventually climbing out and standing unsteadily and staring about. They were then transferred to another galvanised sheet-metal cone on the ground, with a central heater. It had 6 in. (15.2 cm) deep curtains all around the periphery which enabled the chicks to run in and out. They would come to feed at troughs nearby and go back under the curtain to keep warm. (La Société Jersiaise/Jersey Heritage Trust collection at Hamptonne.)

Balance scales

W. & T. Avery balance scale.
Balance scale manufactured in the late 19th and early 20th century. It has two cast-iron wheels and two handles with which to move it. It is made with cast-iron components and stout timber load and weight platforms. It may have been used with either cast-iron weights or on a farm with local stone weights.

A 19th-century balance scale, older than the scale above.
The load platform on this balance scale appears to be on top, but one of a pair of brackets remains towards the bottom, which suggests they may have supported a load platform in the usual place. With the platform being high, the users were able to get a bag on their shoulders more easily. The handles fold back out of the way when not in use. It has 5 in. (12.6 cm) diameter cast-iron wheels each with six spokes. It may have been used in a mill. (National Trust for Jersey collection at Moulin de Quétivel.)

Stone weights

A selection of stone weights with the weight cut on each stone.
Stone weights were made with granite pebbles off the beach. The bottom of each stone was chipped away to make a flat base for it to stand upright. Many had their weight cut into the stone. They all had a hole in the top, into which a small ring with a tang was inserted. Attached to it was a larger ring by which the stone could be lifted. The Weights and Measures Department of the States checked the weights, filling a small hole in the top with lead. The lead brought the weight of the stone to the exact amount, and they were marked with the department's marks.

Cross-cut saws

Cross-cut saws: they require a man at each end to pull on each end in turn.

The dimensions of these two cross-cut saws are 5 ft 4 in. (162 cm) long and 4 ft 6 in. (137 cm) long; the teeth at 1 in. (2.5 cm) centres are 0.5 in. (1.3 cm) deep. There are variations along the same theme. Some slighter shorter saws have the pistol-grip handle at one end, like a carpenter's saw, with a vertical handle a few inches along above the blade. A second detachable vertical handle may be fitted at the other end, but the blade is deeper to prevent the blade bending when it is pushed in work when used by one man. (Steam Museum collection.)

A circular saw by Dening of Chard.

Circular saws were popular on those farms with plenty of timber. They are manufactured in many types and sizes; the only common feature is that they all operate in the vertical plane mounted on a horizontal shaft. Some saws protrude through a slot in a flat cast-iron table: the log is placed on the bench at 90 degrees to the saw and pushed towards it. The bench size varies according to the diameter of the saw. A bench 36 in. (91.5 cm) long by 18 in. (45.5 cm) wide for an 18 in. diameter saw and up to 4 ft (122 cm) long by 2 ft (61 cm) wide for a 2 ft diameter saw. Another type of circular saw is mounted on the end of a shaft, at the end of a frame, with no table. The log is placed in a cradle, on a frame, pivoted at the bottom of the frame. The cradle, complete with log, is pushed toward the saw, and the cut log falls to the ground. The usual farm saw might have a diameter of 2 ft up to 3 ft (100 cm), sufficient to cut up logs from a fallen or felled tree on the farm. They have two flat-belt pulleys: one will drive the saw while the second will freewheel, controlled by a sliding-belt guide to stop the saw when changing a log, etc. The saw is driven by a stationary engine or tractor, with the necessary pulley.

A saw mill driven by a diesel-powered tractor using a flat-belt pulley.

A rack saw mill driven by an early post-war Fordson Major Industrial tractor with a Perkins P6 diesel engine. The circular saw has a diameter of 4 ft 8 in. (142 cm); the carriage runs on rollers mounted on a bed controlled by a rack and pinion operated manually, supported on brick-built pillars. Two men operate the machine for sawing planks from the log. Power is delivered by a flat belt and a pulley on the tractor. It was manufactured about the turn of the 19th/20th century, imported second-hand from the West Midlands and installed at Westlands, St. Brelade, to saw up the many trees lost on the property by Dutch elm disease and the Great Storm of 1987. (Courtesy of Mr. Charles Le Couteur.)

The chainsaw

Power saws have been manufactured since the days of steam power, but a portable power saw could not be made until small reliable engines and suitable sawchains became available. The post-war years have seen a rapid advance in the design of chainsaws. One big problem was weight. At first, British manufacturers looked for a small engine such as the Villiers 98-cc and 125-cc two-stroke engines, types which were popular on lightweight motorcycles and lawnmowers in the early post-war years. These engines had carburettors with float chambers, which by their very nature could not run when turned on their side. To be of any use the saw had to be designed to enable the guidebar and chain to cut both vertically and horizontally. To do so the guidebar had to be turned through a right angle, relative to the engine, so the carburettor could remain vertical and the fuel supply uninterrupted. The problem was further complicated by the need to maintain the power train from the engine to the chain on the guidebar at whatever angle was necessary. To overcome that problem, various swivelling arrangements were devised, but they tended to make the saws heavy and clumsy to handle.

The arrival of the diaphragm carburettor, which both pumped and metered the petrol into the airstream, drawing the fuel through a wobble pipe in the fuel tank, allowed the engine, complete with guidebar and chain, to operate at any angle. The 'wobble' pipe was simply a small-diameter flexible rubber pipe with a sintered bronze filter at the free end, which was also a weight, heavy enough to ensure it always fell, or 'wobbled', into the lowest point of the fuel tank, to pick up fuel.

With the problem of operating a chainsaw at any angle solved, they became more compact and lighter. Eventually, the leading manufacturers, like McCullock, produced a saw that could be held and operated in one hand.

The single-cylinder two-stroke engine makes use of the crankcase as part of the induction process of transferring the fuel and air mix into the cylinder. In order to lubricate the crankshaft bearings, the connecting rod, and piston rings, oil is mixed with the fuel and so drawn into the crankcase. For many years this was done by adding normal lubricating oil to the petrol at a very high rate of usually 15 to 20 per cent, which could in certain circumstances lead to difficult starting. Lubricating oil is heavier than petrol, and if the mixture is left to stand for even quite a short time, the oil will separate and sink to the bottom of the fuel tank or the float chamber of the carburettor. To prevent that, if the engine is stopped the machine has to be shaken before starting up again. If not the engine will never start until the carburettor has been drained and the fine fuel ways are washed clean.

It was a hard lesson to learn for all who operated machines with two-stroke engines, whether a chainsaw, a motorcycle, or a lawnmower. The author can remember going through that agony with a new motorcycle in 1951. Having stopped at a filling station to refuel, those few minutes were long enough for oil in the float chamber to sink to the bottom, and the new bike failed to start. Advice from a kindly filling station attendant was simple—close the fuel tap as one approached the filling station, allowing the carburettor to empty and the engine to stop as it was starved of fuel, and give the bike a shake before starting up to mix the fuel in the tank.

Many years later, McCullock, a well-known and well-respected American manufacturer of a wide range of chainsaws, produced the answer. They produced that wonderful, vegetable-based, lightweight lubricating oil which, when mixed with petrol, remained in suspension in the fuel. While expensive, it required only a 40:1 mix of fuel and oil, which compensated for the high price. It was also coloured a deep red, to ensure at a glance that the fuel being put in the fuel tank was a mix and not neat petrol. In due course these oils became more readily available.

When the author first heard of this oil in 1970, it seemed it would obviously be a winner with all his customers with two-stroke engines. At first it was only supplied in 40-gallon drums from the McCullock distributor in England. It was outrageously expensive at £340 for a 45-gallon barrel. That was a lot of money for lubricating oil, and the freight was about £30. On top of that a special import licence had to be obtained from the Customs Department at the Weighbridge in St. Helier. In those days everything a merchant or trader imported into the Island had to be cleared through Customs by form filling and parting with a cheque before collecting the goods from the freight carriers.

To sell the oil, McCullock supplied a large cardboard box of small 200-cc plastic containers with a screw top and a roll of labels to go on each. Whenever any of the staff in the workshop had an idle moment, they used the time to fill these little containers. We had to sell them at 50p each, which hardly bore comparison with conventional oil selling at 25p or 30p a pint. Private customers would buy them one at a time, whereas contractors would take two or three. In due course, when customers discovered how good it was, the contractors would buy it by the pint but had to provide their own containers. It proved extremely difficult to find a supplier of pint or litre containers at a sensible price.

Thankfully, Oregon, the sawchain and accessory manufacturers, improved the supply side a few years later when they came to the market, offering a similar oil at the same sort of price but in 1-litre and 5-litre containers. By this time all the customers were asking for it and it became more widely available in the Island.

Another step forward in the lubrication of chainsaws was the introduction of sawchain oils. These oils were designed to stick to the chain and not be thrown off, as the chain rapidly changes direction when it passes around the driving sprocket and the nose of the guidebar. It is easy to identify by simply dipping your fingertip into it. Normal lubricating oil will fall from your fingertip in drips, but sawchain oil will stick to your fingertip and stretch in a thin string as high as one can reach.

Today, many manufacturers do not make their own sawchains and guidebars, preferring to use those developed by experts in that field. The best known and most popular are manufactured by Oregon in the USA, in the state from which the company takes its name, where logging and timber extraction is big business. They have a high demand for high-quality sawchains. After many years of development, Oregon were almost alone in manufacturing a range of high-quality sawchains and guidebars, with chains varying in type and size of link and tooth to suit large powerful chainsaws with guidebars to match, from 3 ft 6 in. (110 cm) long down to domestic electric saws with 12-in. (35 cm) guidebars.

Early sawchains had a scratch-type sawtooth, which was simply the old cross-cut sawtooth riveted onto a power-driven chain. It was slow and made a lot of sawdust. The great breakthrough came with Oregon's first truly successful chipper chain, in which each cutting link peeled or sliced off a thin sliver or chip of wood. The cutting edge was a minute version of the blade in a carpenter's plane, but is angled to aid entry into the timber as it planes off a thin, narrow slice of wood, so thin it falls away as a curled chip. The teeth are right- and left-handed, fitted alternately on the chain, which enables the saw to maintain a straight cut. It is important that both left- and right-hand teeth are equally sharp; if not, the saw will tend to cut at an angle. Two popular chains were chipper and microbit, the latter a slight variation on the chipper. Microbit chain suited most people's needs.

The chains and guidebars have to be lubricated while in work; this is essential, or wear to both components will be rapid. Chain oil is carried in a tank, often beside the fuel tank on the saw. On early chainsaws it was delivered to the chain by a manually operated pump, usually by continually depressing and releasing, with the thumb, a spring-loaded lever or plunger mounted near the throttle control or the support handle. Some modern domestic electric saws retain this feature. When automatic pumping systems came into use, many of the old hands were suspicious of them, maintaining that while they kept pumping a manual lever they were confident that the oil was getting onto the chain. They could detect from the pressure on the lever when the oil tank was empty and work had to stop to replenish it. On automatic saws the oil tank capacity is so designed that the fuel tank will run out of fuel before the oil tank, thus ensuring the chain will not run dry.

Chainsaws have an automatic clutch using centrifugal force to engage, the force increasing as the engine gains speed and acts on two weighted shoes, retained by return springs. The two shoes move out to engage on the inside of the skirt, on the clutch drum. The chain sprocket is fitted directly to the clutch drum; that was common practice on all chainsaws and continues today. Modern saws have a safety brake, which tightens a metal band onto the outside of the drum skirt, forcing the chain to stop instantly if an accident occurs. It is operated by a guard or shield in front of the top handle of the saw, which is pushed forward by the operator's wrist, in case of an accident.

A British chainsaw manufacturer which began life in post-war England in the London area was Danarm. Later they moved their operation to Stroud in Gloucestershire, trading as Danarm Ltd. They produced the DD 8 F model chainsaw, using a Villiers two-stroke engine mounted in a frame to which they fitted a guidebar and sawchain. It was a big saw with a slow-running engine, using a massive 0.625-in. (1.5 cm) link sawchain, but it was portable and popular with farmers in the Island, who always spoke highly of them. Many farmers were still using them in the late 1970s.

It was followed by Danarm's 110 and 125 models introduced in the 1960s, the model numbers indicating the size of engine in cubic centimetres or cc. The Danarm 110 was offered with a choice of guidebars with lengths of 16 in. (40.6 cm), 20 in. (50.8 cm), or 2 ft (61 cm), and the 125 with a choice of 28-in. (71.1 cm) or 36 in. (91.5 cm) bar and a 0.375-in. (1 cm) chain. Danarm chainsaws were imported into the Island by Channel Industries Ltd. in the 1960s, 1970s, and 1980s.

The Jersey Farmers' (Trading) Union Ltd. imported the American-made Remington chainsaws, which were popular with Jersey farmers, as were the McCullock and Teles chainsaws. Nowadays chainsaws are on sale everywhere, in ironmongers, garden machinery dealers, and other merchants. Other popular manufacturers are Dolmar and Stihl of Germany, Husquvarna and Jonsered of Scandinavia, and a range of manufacturers in Japan.

Chainsaw manufactured by Danarm Ltd. of Stroud. The Danarm model 1-71-SS chainsaw in 1977 has a 71-cc, single-cylinder, two-stroke engine and 21-in. (53.3 cm) guidebar. It has a recoil starter, the fuel used is a petrol and oil mix, and it has automatic oiling of the chain by an internal pump. The saws were offered with 16-in. (40.6 cm), 21-in. (53.3 cm), and 25-in. (63.5 cm) guidebar lengths. The handles were fitted with dampers to isolate the vibration from the engine. The local supplier was Channel Industries Ltd.

The introduction of this chainsaw was timely, at the time when Dutch elm disease was at its height. The saw was well designed, at the leading edge of the technology of the period, and as a medium-weight saw it was light, with a high-speed engine with rapid acceleration, It was also quiet. The engine was mounted in a sprung frame, which dampened the vibration for the operator, said to be the cause of a condition known as 'white finger'. The sawchain was smaller and narrower than previously, having a narrower guidebar, so the cut was narrower, using less power, and contributing to reduced weight. However, within months it was improved, having a chain brake designed to stop the chain instantly, so reducing possible injury in an accident. When the chain strikes something hard or loose while in work, the saw might leap upward unexpectedly, the guard will strike the back of the operator's wrist, which will make it trip and apply the brake. It was a useful development which quickly became a legal requirement. Danarm also manufactured the more powerful 1-91-SS, almost identical in appearance but having a 91-cc motor and a 28 in. (71.1 cm) or 32 in. (81 cm) guidebar and sawchain. A lightweight chainsaw in the Danarm product line was the Danarm 55, having a 55-cc motor with a choice of 16-in. (40.6 cm) and 21-in. (53.3 cm) guidebar and sawchain and automatic oiling. Finally, an ultra-lightweight, branded the Danarm 1-36, with 36-cc motor and 12-in. (30.5 cm) guidebar and sawchain. It could be carried in one hand but the rear handle was too far back, making it difficult to operate in one hand. They did not manufacture it; it was imported.

A small chainsaw which was well made, beautifully balanced and was possibly the first of these lightweight saws to be manufactured was the McCullock. It came on the market in 1969 and 1970 with a 40-cc motor and a 12-in. (30.5 cm) guidebar. This excellent little saw was popular with tree surgeons but was rather expensive for the farmer or private user. McCullock were among leaders in the field of chainsaw design and manufacture.

A group of different makes of chainsaw.

All these chainsaws have a recoil starter, a two-stroke engine, and use a fuel mixture of petrol and oil. They are the property of Mr. Ken Godel, Bel Air, St. John, who is a contractor.

At the top is a Remington model SL11.773, serial no. 772378, manufactured in the late 1950s and early 1970s. It has a 21-in. (53.3 cm) guidebar with 0.375-in. (1 cm) microchip chain.

Second from the top is a Jonsered chainsaw, manufactured in Scandinavia in 1980 and an advanced design in its day. Like the Danarm 1-71-SS illustrated above, it is an anti-vibration saw with sprung handles, 65-and 70-cc motor, 18-in. (45.5 cm) guidebar, and 0.375-in. (1 cm) microbit chain with automatic oiling.

The yellow chainsaw in the centre is a Pioneer Model 650 with a 65-cc engine and a 20-in. (50.8 cm) guidebar manufactured in the USA. An earlier design of the 1960s. It has a $^3/_8$-in. (1 cm) chipper chain and manual oiling with the oil pump lever beside the back handle for thumb operation.

The orange saw next to the Pioneer is a Homelite, serial no. 7E 2150088, 35-cc motor, and 12-in. (30.5 cm) guidebar, manufactured in the 1980s. It has automatic oiling and 0.25-in. (0.6 cm) chain. One of the then new lightweight small saws, it is well balanced and can be operated with one hand.

Nearest to the camera is another Remington. Another modern and popular chainsaw in the Island not illustrated here is the Dolmar, manufactured in Germany.

In the 1970s a hazard to regular, daily chainsaw users, such as forestry people and tree surgeons was a medical condition known as 'white finger', referred to above. The blood flow to the affected fingers is reduced. It is caused by the vibration from the two-stroke engine. To overcome the problem, chainsaw manufacturers have attempted to isolate the engine and so prevent the vibration affecting the handles. Some have assembled the handles to the saw using rubber or coil-spring dampers. Others have mounted the engine alone on dampers, the handles being part of a frame with the fuel and oil tanks and guidebar; others use very sophisticated dampers. They have all effectively reduced the vibration previously transmitted to the handles and so to the operator's hands.

Accidents while using chainsaws in Jersey have not usually been caused by the chainsaw itself but as a result of the tree or branch falling on the victim (not necessarily the saw operator). Great care must be taken when a tree is being felled or a heavy branch being taken off; the operator must ensure nobody is in the area where the tree or branch is expected to fall. It is dangerous to use a chainsaw in poor light, as the author knows from his own experience, when he was asked to clear a fallen tree blocking a road after dark on a stormy night. Nobody was hurt except the author's pride and an item of clothing that was damaged.

Wheel jack

A wheel jack for a cart, van, or carriage. It would have been found on many farms and in every wheelwright's yard.
Jacks made after the last decades of the 19th century were made of steel and galvanised. This jack is made of wood with wrought iron adding to its strength and reducing wear. The hook is placed under the axle and the lever pushed down and then hooked to a chain to hold it in place. They have a vertical line of holes in order to adjust the height of the hook up or down, to suit different vehicles with different diameter wheels. Cart and van wheels had to be removed from time to time, to grease the axle. The wooden wheels ran on plain bearings. (La Société Jersiaise/Jersey Heritage Trust collection at Hamptonne.)

Spokeshave bench

A recreated wheelwright's spokeshave bench.
Not quite farm equipment but the equipment of those craftsmen who supplied services to farmers such as wheelwrights, carpenters, and mill owners. This wheelwright's spokeshave bench is a simple device. The work piece is held in place by a clamp that is itself kept in place by the craftsman's feet. It is quickly released so that it can be rotated or turned from end to end as work proceeds. They are being manufactured today for third world countries. Not so many years ago every carpenter's tool bag would contain a spokeshave, which had so many other uses apart from making spokes for wheels. (Samarès Manor Threshing Day.)

Gear wheels

Beautifully profiled teeth on a section of a wooden gear wheel in a water mill
The construction of the gear teeth is interesting and more sophisticated than might appear. Each tooth is individually made and fitted into its socket on the rim. Note the shape. The profile is both tapered and rounded, carefully worked out geometrically, to give the tooth the correct shape to slide into mesh with its neighbour on the driving or driven wheel, to reduce the friction and so minimise the loss of power and the wear as the load is transferred from one wheel to the next.

The wooden tooth is continued with the cast iron wheel, for safety and to reduce damage in case of accident. If the load is too great the tooth will snap, saving more serious damage elsewhere. A broken wooden tooth is quickly and cheaply replaced rather than replace an expensive complete iron gear wheel. The same applies as components become worn: to replace a set of worn wooden teeth is cheaper. The ends of the teeth can be seen protruding through the inside of the rim. This is done deliberately in order to make it easy to tap out the tooth with a mallet if it has to be replaced. (National Trust for Jersey collection, Moulin de Quétivel.)

Two gear teeth: one is profiled and the other is a blank.
The tooth on the left has been shaped and profiled as described above and been used. On the right is a blank, i.e. a spare tooth that has to be shaped or profiled and the stem also has to be tapered to fit.

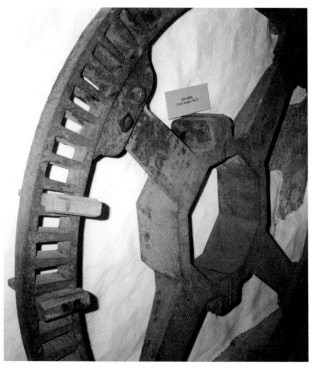

An iron gearwheel cast in three pieces; the rim can be detached from the four spokes. The wooden teeth have been removed, leaving two loosely fitted.

Farm containers

In this group of containers are a barrel on the left, a measure in the centre, and a non-returnable 1 cwt potato barrel. In the foreground is a picking basket for potatoes and tomatoes.

The black container at the centre is a measure and it is heavy! Mr. John Norman of Norman Ltd. who were coopers says it is probably a 4 cabot measure. It is conical with metal handles at the side; normal barrels do not have side handles. It is particularly well made, most likely by a local cooper in the 18th or 19th century.

On the left is a 1 cental potato barrel, made by local coopers such as Norman Ltd. in their early days. Some coopers travelled around the farms repairing barrels. These barrels were used in the potato fields and only left the farm to carry potatoes to town for export. The barrels were emptied in the merchant's packing shed and put back on the farmer's van for return to the farm. The potatoes were then packed in similar but smaller barrels for shipment to mainland markets.

On the right of the group is what was known in the 1930s as the 'non-returnable', 1 cwt barrel. It was considered by the merchants to be uneconomical to send away potatoes in the old barrels and have them returned empty. So a cheaper barrel was produced in vast numbers by merchants such as Norman Ltd., who specialised in making containers for shipping produce. They were in use in the 1930s, 1940s, and 1950s. Made of plywood, they were 2 ft (61 cm) deep with a plank base and 1 ft 3 in. (38.1 cm) in diameter. Those used by the merchants had looped ropes threaded around the top to tie down a circular plywood top. Having carried the potatoes across the Channel the barrels were not returned. A plain version, without ropes or lids, was used by farmers in the fields for carrying the potatoes to town for export, and like the old cental barrels these were the farmer's property. They were used for a variety of purposes on the farm for carrying things about: carrots, apples from the orchard, etc.

In the foreground of the group is a Jersey potato basket used when picking potatoes in the field, but also used in season for tomato picking. Like the barrel it had many uses on the farm. (La Société Jersiaise/Jersey Heritage Trust collection, at Hamptonne.)

Coopers making barrels at Norman Ltd., in the 19th century.

Potato boxes for carrying seed potatoes to and from the fields.
It was a job on a Jersey Royal potato grower's farm, every October and November, to stand the Jersey Royal potatoes in the potato boxes. There they were stored in a loft or shed through the winter to allow the shoots to grow upright. In the early spring they were carried to the fields for planting. The boxes were used again later to collect the seed potatoes from the field after

'digging for town' (export). They were supplied by timber merchants as complete boxes or in pieces for assembly on the farm. The merchants, and some farmers, would assemble boxes when their workers were less busy with normal farm work. A similar box with double sides and ends was used in the fields for outdoor tomatoes, carrying them to town to pack for export. Picking baskets, like the one on the left in the picture, were used for picking the tomatoes, which were then tipped into the boxes.

20 Some Occupation Innovations (1940–1945)

Some of the effects of the Occupation on farming

The German wartime Occupation of the Island affected Island farming greatly. June is the busiest month of the potato season; the arrival of the German forces brought it to an abrupt end. The United Kingdom markets for agricultural produce, Jersey Royal potatoes, and tomatoes were closed off and the world markets were also closed for the Jersey cow. Importing foodstuff for the population was also closed except from occupied France. The Island would have to feed itself! There was an urgent need to concentrate on growing cereals, vegetables (including maincrop potatoes), and later a certain amount of tobacco. Experiments to grow cereals in glasshouses were carried out without much success; the crop grew very tall, making a lot of straw, according to a photograph taken at the time.

Farm mechanisation had not really taken off by 1939. There were a number of Fordson model F and N tractors on steel wheels, perhaps two or three of them on pneumatic tyres; Ferguson-Brown tractors were also on steel wheels. A few of the new Ford Ferguson 9N tractors were on pneumatic tyres. There were several models of International on steel wheels and a small number of John Deere tractors, of which only was one on pneumatics. Steel wheels restricted tractors to field work; a few were hauling tractor ploughs with a self-lift but many were still hauling the traditional horse plough, with its large forecarriage, and requiring a ploughman on the handles. Some machines originally designed for horse draught had been converted for tractor draught. Some of those may have been changed back to horse draught in the altered circumstances and shortage of fuel.

Wheel-bands had to be fitted to tractors with steel wheels and lugs to go on the roads. Tractors were not used for hauling trailers; indeed, there were very few if any trailers. Farmers used a lorry, a horse and van, or a box cart for hauling loads on the farm and on the road. There were two exceptions, when tractors with rubber tyres were available in the mid-1930s: one was Huelin, the builders' merchants, and the second was Le Gallais, the furniture people. Both purchased Fordson tractors on rubber tyres, to haul their previously horse-drawn harbour wagons, to carry their imports to their various stores about the town and in Huelin's case to Five Oaks. Another exception was Le Cappelain, who moved their threshing machines to a different site with their tractors, on steel wheels and road bands. In fact, farm trailers did not come into use until a new generation of tractors on pneumatic tyres started coming into the Island in the late 1940s after the war. So, in 1940, the horse-drawn box cart and the van were still in use. Horses were not necessarily dispensed with on many farms with tractors. That was just as well, because as time went on fuel became so short that horses had to do the field work, ploughing, and field cultivation. Mr. Egré, of St Mary, was one exception. He told the author that during the Occupation he was asked by the Constable of St. Mary to do the ploughing around the parish, because his twin-cylinder John Deere was so economical on fuel. Mr. Egré ploughed with the traditional Jersey big plough; a second man held the handles.

The States were faced with the difficulty of obtaining fuel oil during the Occupation. Due to the petrol shortage, the States imported Gasogene charcoal-burning equipment from France, for fitting to lorries, vans, and tractors. A number of the few rubber-tyred tractors were commandeered to be converted to run on 'town' gas. Some of the tractors were converted in France, others were converted in the Island. The conversion resulted in a small reduction of power. Mr. Don Pallot converted one at his works to operate more efficiently and this improved the performance.

The process of mechanisation was not only halted, but went into reverse! Many good horses were confiscated by the Germans, making things even more difficult. Labour on the farms soon doubled, which was just as well in view of the fact that so many people were without work. There being no tourism industry, no export of produce meant very little work at the harbours, the airport, hotels, tour coaches, etc. Some of these people were no doubt glad to get work on the land, but were also well placed to get certain items of food to feed their families. As time went on, food became very short for townsfolk, especially in 1944 and 1945.

Maincrop potatoes were grown and dug with horse-drawn potato diggers and spinners. The potatoes were stored in clamps, organised by the States. It was common practice in England but unusual in Jersey, and lessons had to be learned to ensure the crop remained healthy in the clamp and did not go rotten.

Traditional methods continued for haymaking; it was before the days of the pick-up baler. Hay was cut with horse-drawn reapers and made with horse-drawn tedders, and horse rakes gathered it into windrows. It was heaped into haycocks with hay forks and, when thoroughly dry, it was bundled. To bundle hay, it was drawn from the haycock, gathered into an armful and folded to form a bundle on the ground; then, putting a knee on it to compress it, a handful of hay was taken and twisted into a rope and passed around the bundle, drawn tightly and the end simply pushed under. It was done very quickly and most farm workers knew how to do it. Bundling hay made it much easier for loading onto the van, rather than handling loose hay. Furthermore, it was easier to get down from the loft to feed the animals, etc.

Wheat, oats, and barley continued to be cut with the binder and with sickles. Obtaining binder twine must have been a problem. The crop was gathered in the traditional way, neighbours working together. During the war and Occupation church bells had to remain silent and were only used as an alarm, so the stooks stood for three Sundays, but with no bells.

Tobacco was a new crop to be grown on a field scale and Ching's tobacco factory were no doubt more than pleased to process the dried tobacco. It was often hung and dried on the farm. There was money to be made from it, and in late 1945 it was still hanging to dry in farmers' sheds and lofts.

There are many stories of how farmers got around their difficulties during the Occupation. Hedley Le Quesne told the author how he mixed sump oil with paraffin and heated it up before pouring it in the fuel tank of his Standard Fordson tractor. The engine ran on it after starting it in the usual way with petrol first, then switching over as for kerosene. The Fordson tractor had a vaporiser, heated by the exhaust manifold, for kerosene or TVO (tractor vaporising oil), and the vaporiser did its stuff with his mix of oil and fuel. As mentioned elsewhere, the sump oil in the Fordson had to be changed every fifty hours because unburnt TVO would run down the cylinders and dilute it. The fuel mix did not seem to do his Fordson much harm, for he was still ploughing with it in 1947 at La Retraite, St. Saviour. After the Occupation farming quickly reverted back to Jersey Royals and tomatoes for export; cereals continued to be grown for cattle food for some years.

Occupation innovations

Grindstone

A grindstone thought to have been made in 1940 after the start of the German Occupation.

Mr. Alfred Le Boutillier of Val Bachelier, St. Ouen, made the grinder using the lower part of a lady's cycle. The cycle frame was cut through in a line about 12 in. (30 cm) above the pedal and sprocket shaft and turned upside down and fixed to a piece of timber as a mounting. The cycle chain to the rear wheel was left in place, but the rear wheel was replaced with a circular grindstone. He went to a lot of trouble to fit a shaft and bearings to the stone and one wonders from where the perfectly shaped stone originated. A water tank surrounds the lower half of the stone. The pedal and crank were completely removed from one side, but on the side of the sprocket, only part of the pedal was removed, leaving the shaft, to which a wooden handle was fitted. It looks rather forlorn having been left outside, as grindstones often were, but it still works perfectly with less effort and with greater periphery speed than the old big-diameter stones in wooden frames and water trough. It would have been a useful piece of kit on any farm before the electric motor.

The threshing machine

A power-driven, home-made threshing drum.

The exact year this threshing machine was made and who made it is unknown, except that it was during the German Occupation 1940-5. The threshing drum is 20 in. (50.8 cm) wide and has a diameter of 11 in. (8 cm). The beaters were made of four lengths of angle-iron operating in a simple concave and all fitted in a purpose-built plywood-panelled box. A 7-in. (17.7 cm) diameter flat pulley on the drum shaft would have been driven by a stationary engine or a tractor. Running at 400-500 rpm, it would have required about 5-6 horsepower. The machine made little attempt to separate the straw; this was done manually. The loose grain and chaff would have been passed through a winnowing machine.

The 20-in. (50.8 cm) wide and 11-in. (8 cm) diameter threshing drum.

Mr. L. C. Pallot's mobile engine

Mr. L. C. Pallot, of the Central Motor Works at Sion, refused to undertake work for the Germans during the Occupation, stating that he was too busy repairing farm machinery. He had a difficult time keeping the threshing machines going; the main problem was obtaining the right fuel.

He finally decided to build a mobile engine to drive his threshing machine. He found a suitable engine at St. Saviour's Hospital. It was a 20-hp Ruston & Hornsby, single-cylinder, compression ignition diesel engine with a 15-cwt flywheel, manufactured in 1923. Mr. Pallot purchased it for £5. The engine was part of an electric generator and was grouted to the floor with six bolts. It was normally started with a compressed-air system.

The engine, complete with accessories, was dismantled and transported to the works at Sion. Meanwhile, with the assistance of the Harbour Works, two 12-ft (366 cm) girders were obtained from a disused crane at the harbour; they were marked out and holes were drilled in them. They were then welded to form a rigid frame. The back axle of a 7-ton Commer lorry was assembled under one end of the frame and the front axle of a Fordson tractor was fitted under the other end, together forming the basis of a chassis. To this was mounted a 10-hp Citroen engine and a Chevrolet four-speed gearbox to complete the transmission to the Commer back axle. A Morris steering column was assembled to the chassis and the Fordson front axle to provide the steering. A handbrake to the back wheels, the foot pedals, and a driver's seat completed the chassis. The Ruston & Hornsby engine was mounted on the chassis, and a Fordson radiator was fitted to cool it, complete with a Fordson fuel tank. All that remained was an arrangement for the Citroen engine to start the Ruston & Hornsby engine and the outfit was ready to be driven from site to site for the next threshing season.

A threshing scene with Don Pallot's Ruston & Hornsby mobile engine driving a threshing machine (captured on canvas by Edmund Blampied).
The painting hangs at the Steam Museum. Edmund Blampied recorded many activities during the Occupation years, quite apart from his set of currency notes and postage stamps. (Courtesy of the Blampied family.)

Pat Gruchy's mill for making potato flour

During the Occupation years, flour was in very short supply, so people experimented with potatoes, endeavouring to find a way to make potato flour. One young man at the time, the late Pat Gruchy, built a machine in order to help with this. His machine was in effect, a mill, and very similar in operation. Pat was evidently kept busy with his machine, making flour for friends and neighbours. It was a way of earning a living in those uncertain times.

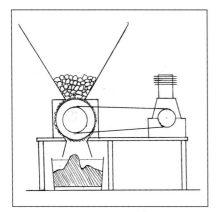

A line drawing of Pat Gruchy's potato flour mill. Not to scale, but simply drawn following his description to the author.

The hopper is on the top of the mill on the left with the potatoes in it. On the right is the air-cooled Villiers engine, with a flat belt between the engine and the mill to drive the roller under the hopper. The potatoes were fed onto a roller underneath. The wooden roller was covered with sheet metal, which had previously been pierced to create a rasplike surface. To achieve that the sheet metal had been pierced with hammer and nails. As the roller rotated, the rough surface shredded the potatoes into a pulp, which dropped into a galvanised bath beneath the roller. The pulp was tipped out of the bath, spread and levelled off, then water was poured over it, to a depth sufficient to cover the pulp. In due course the pulp would rise, enabling it to be skimmed off, leaving the flour, which had sunk to the bottom of the bath. The water was strained off and fresh water poured over the flour to wash it clean. It was then strained off again. This process was repeated for several washes. Finally the clean flour was spread in pans in a greenhouse to dry. In due course Pat mounted an engine with a belt to drive the roller. The Villiers engine was air-cooled but needed a continuous draft of cooling air to prevent the engine overheating. To achieve this, Pat had to make a cooling fan and cowling to blow cold air over the cylinder. He made the fan by cutting sheet metal into strips and shaping them into fins. The fins were then riveted onto the periphery of the flywheel of the engine.

The problem then was finding the fuel, no doubt siphoning it from the petrol tanks of the vehicles of their unwelcome visitors. This became quite common practice among the young lads out to 'put one over' on the Germans.

This type of machine worked well and other people made similar mills. Mr. Le Boutillier, of La Gabourelle at Portinfer, St. Ouen, was one of them. Sadly the technical details of the mill are not known. There were probably many other innovations about which we know nothing.

21 Blacksmiths, Engineers, Machinery and Tractor Dealers, and Agricultural Contractors

For centuries the country blacksmiths were the 'wayside garages' of their day. They attended to a loose shoe on a horse and shoeing horses, repairing the wheels of carriages, farmers' carts, and vans, and repairing implements. Some of them provided other services in addition, such as chandlery, ironmongery, farm implements, and machinery. Some became better known than others if they were both good businessmen and good technicians, producing what the farmer wanted, making ploughs, cultivators, hand tools, beating a new point or edge on plough shares, fitting new handles to spades, etc. The more business-minded imported implements and machinery, selling them at the right price; they became popular and well known: people like Messervy, Grandin, Le Cappelain and sons, the Maretts and sons, Thérin, Clem Le Breuilly, Ozouf, and Don Pallot and family, to mention only some. As we shall see, many blacksmiths were much more than that: they were successful engineers and businessmen, quite remarkable when one considers their skills were developed from an elementary education and a five-year apprenticeship at the forge and anvil.

Other suppliers of farm machinery were merchants and dealers, such as the Jersey Farmers' (Trading) Union Ltd. (JF(T)U Ltd.), who as agricultural merchants sold cattle foods, fertilisers, hay and straw, and David Brown tractors, Alfa Laval milking machines, and a range of implements. The Country Gentlemen's Association (CGA) were, like the JF(T)U Ltd., selling all sorts of agricultural goods. The CGA sold Gascoigne milking machines, Wolseley electric fencers and tillers, among other implements. Both businesses were also potato merchants, packing and shipping Jersey Royal potatoes. A number of garages sold machinery: Colback's were agents for International tractors, Renouf at St. Mary Garage sold Coleby two-wheel tractors, and La Motte Garage sold Fordson, Ford, and Ransomes MG tractors and implements. Ransomes equipment was previously handled by T. F. Pirouet of Beresford Street, St. Helier, which became Mr. Le Marquand's business and sold farm machinery including, Nicholson's fertiliser spreaders until he retired. Another agent who has disappeared was John Jones, who sold the very popular Planet seeders and weeders. St. Helier Garages sold Ferguson tractors and implements.

Grandin

The Grandin Iron Foundry was founded by François Jean Grandin in 1850 at Commercial Buildings in premises to the south of no. 27, and traded as Francis J. Grandin. After two years of trading, and in need of more room, he moved to no. 27.

François Grandin was born in 1819, the son of a Mr. Grandin of Trinity, a shipwright with a shipyard in St. Aubin's Bay, located on the west side of Clark's shipyard. In the Census of 1841 François was living at Seaton Place working as a blacksmith. In 1851 he was living at no. 18 Pier Road employing six men and four boys in his foundry and blacksmith shop. By the 1861 Census he was living 'over the shop' at 27 Commercial Buildings, employing sixteen men. In due course he was joined by his sons, Francis Phillip who was born in 1842, John Elie, born in 1849, and Andrew William, born 1857.

At that time the Grandin family had shipping interests, owning various ships. The eldest son Francis wrote from St. Malo in 1869 to his new wife, expressing concern that one of their ships, the *Ellen*, was still loading coal in St. Malo.

Among the products for the foundry for which they were probably best known was the 'Jersey' kitchen cooking range, a solid-fuel burner, some with a large copper water tank mounted on one side for heating water. They also manufactured a wide variety of goods ranging from anchors and

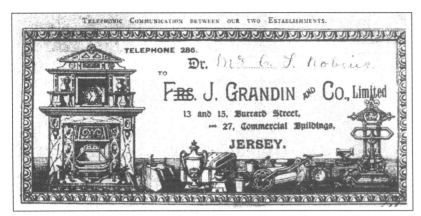

Grandin's bill head illustrates their products.

manhole covers to castings for ploughs and cultivators, mostly for Le Cappelain. One of their monuments is the Westaway Monument at the foot of Mount Bingham, where their name is cast in one of the flukes of the anchor. It was rare to see their name appearing anywhere on any of their products except on their road gratings for drains and manhole covers, which can still be seen about the town today.

In 1898/9, having purchased the castings and components from Benz in Germany to build a car, the employees set about making use of the company's facilities to fettle and machine the castings and forgings, completing the many components which had been supplied as blanks, i.e. unfinished castings and forgings from the German factory. In due course the work was done and the car assembled and driven along the Esplanade. It was the first and only new car to be produced in Jersey, and no doubt good publicity for the company. The author understands that, at the time, Benz in Germany were tooling up to produce a later model car.

In due course there was a name change to F. J. Grandin & Co. Ltd. Having started as foundrymen and blacksmiths, they also had a machine shop and now were general engineers, then retailers with shops and ironmongers, and lastly they were iron and steel stockholders. They had premises at 13 and 15 Burrard Street, 27 Commercial Buildings and 34 Bath Street, and they took over Le Marquand's foundry at 58 Don Street. They continued to manufacture a wide variety of goods, including domestic items as well as their traditional products.

In 1874 a steam engine was installed to drive shafting to operate machine tools in the machine shop, the foundry, and tinsmiths. By 1881 changes had taken place: François Jean had died, leaving a widow and Francis Philip was living at no. 27 with his wife. The business and foundry were still flourishing under the supervision of the three sons, employing eighteen men and three boys, but like Messervy at Faldouet in the 1880s and 1890s, there was a change of direction due to the demise of the shipbuilding industry. Their advertising in the local almanacs indicates a concentration in domestic goods and other lines.

In addition to these activities, the company was also erecting and maintaining windmills and water pumps. Windmills went on being offered up to 1939, and were often displayed at the Royal Jersey Agricultural and Horticultural Society's summer show at Springfield.

The year 1903 had seen a change in policy when the family decided to sell shares in the company, offering them at £5 each. They continued to expand with the acquisition in 1909 of G. Le Feuvre, the iron founders of Bath Street and Belmont Road. Following the death of Francis Philip Grandin at the age of 80 in 1922, the remaining brothers, John and Andrew, continued to run the business with the assistance of A. F. Gallichan, a nephew who married one of the sisters. However, 1928 saw another change following the deaths of the two remaining brothers. The business carried on trading under the supervision of the younger sisters and A. F. Gallichan who in due course became the company chairman.

F. J. GRANDIN AND CO., Iron Merchants, Ironmongers, and Founders.

OFFICE—
THE LIGHT & HEAT DEPÔT,
13 & 15, BURRARD STREET.

✴ JERSEY. ✴

WORKS—
27, COMMERCIAL BUILDINGS.

Invite attention to the undermentioned Goods, of which they have a choice assortment:—

ABBOTSFORD GRATES
AMERICAN STOVES
AMERICAN HARDWARE
ANGLE AND TEE IRON
ANCHORS
AXES AND HATCHETS
AXLES, CRANKED OR STRAIGHT
ASBESTOS

BAR IRON, NETHERTON BEST ♔
BAR IRON, L.W.R.O. ♔
BATHS, ALL KINDS
BACKBANDS AND TRACES
BELLS
BIVALVE REGISTERS
BLIND ROLLERS AND FITTINGS
BLOCK TIN
BOILERS
BOILER PLATES AND RIVETS
BOLTS
BORAX
BRASS COCKS
BRASSFOUNDRY
BRASS TUBING
BRASS WIRE
BRITANNIA METAL GOODS
BROUGHTON HEARTHS & KERBS
BROOMS AND BRUSHES
BUILDERS' IRONMONGERY
BUCKETS
BUTLER & CO.'S CUTLERY

CABIN STOVES
CAFETIÈRES
CANDLESTICKS
CARPENTERS' TOOLS
CART SPRINGS
CASTINGS
CHAFFCUTTERS
CHAMOIS LEATHERS
CHAINS, SUPERIOR QUALITY
CHANDELIERS
CHEST HANDLES AND HINGES
CIDERPRESS SCREWS, WITH BRASS
    NUTS
CINDER SIFTERS
COAL VASES AND SCOOPS
COACH BOLTS AND NUTS
COACH SCREWS
COMBS
COMPO. TUBING
COOKING STOVES
COFFEE MILLS
COPPER DOORS AND GRATINGS
COPPER KETTLES
COPPER RODS, NAILS, AND WIRE
COTTON WASTE
CRUETS
CUTLERY

DAIRY SCALES
DOOR FURNITURE
DOULTON FIREPLACES
DOULTON MANTELS
DOULTON KERBS AND HEARTHS

EDGE TOOLS
E.P. SPOONS AND FORKS
ELECTRO-PLATED GOODS

ENAMELLED WARE
ENAMELLED CHIMNEY-PIECES
ENGINEERS' TOOLS

"FARRINGDON" PUMPS
FELT
FENDERS
FILES AND RASPS
FIRE BRICKS AND CLAY
FIRE LUMPS AND BALLS
FIRE BASKETS
FIRE BRASSES AND IRONS
FIRE DOGS AND STOPS
FIREPROOF SAFES
FOOT SCRAPERS
FORKS
FORGE BACKS
FRYPANS
FURNACE BOILERS, DOORS, &c.

GALVANIZED BARS AND BOLTS
GALVANIZED CISTERNS
GALVANIZED CORRUGATED ROOFING
GALVANIZED WIRE NETTING
GARDEN ENGINES AND BARROWS
GARDEN HOSE AND FITTINGS
GARDEN TOOLS
GARDEN SYRINGES
GAS BRACKETS
GAS STOVES
GAS TUBES AND FITTINGS
GATES AND RAILINGS
GAUGE GLASSES
GENUINE WHITE LEAD
GLUE
GRATES
GREASE, ENGINE AND CART
GRINDSTONES
GREENHOUSE WORK
GUTTERS

HAMMERS
HINGES
HOT-WATER WORK
HOOP IRON
HOLLOW-WARE
HEATING STOVES

INDIA-RUBBER SHEET AND TUBING
IRON
IRONING STOVES

KEYS AND BLANKS
KITCHEN RANGES
KNIVES AND FORKS
KNIFE CLEANERS
KNOBS, IN WOOD, CHINA, GLASS,
    BRASS, &c.

LAMPS AND ACCESSORIES
LAUNDRY BOILERS, VARIOUS
LAUNDRY REQUISITES
LAWN MOWERS
LEATHER BELTING AND LACES
LINSEED OIL
LOCKS AND LATCHES

MACHINERY
MARBLE CHIMNEY-PIECES

MARBLE KERBS
MATS
MEAT SAFES
MEASURING TAPES AND RULES
MILLWORK
MOPS
MUSGRAVE'S SLOW - COMBUSTION
    STOVES

NAILS AND SCREWS

OILS AND PAINTS
ORNAMENTAL CASTINGS
OVEN STOCKS

PATENT PULLEY BLOCKS
PERFORATED ZINC
PETROLEUM COOKERS
PETROLEUM OIL
PICTURE RODS
PIG TROUGHS
PILLARS
PLASTERERS' TOOLS & BRUSHES
PUMPS

RAINWATER GOODS
RANGES
REGISTERS

SASH WEIGHTS
SASH LINES
SCALES AND WEIGHTS
SHEET BRASS, COPPER, LEAD, AND
    ZINC
SIEVES AND RIDDLES
SKIDMORE'S PATENT FIRE - PROOF
    SAFES
SMITHS' TOOLS
SPADES AND SHOVELS
SPOONS
STAIR RODS AND EYES
STABLE FITTINGS
SMITH & WELLSTOOD'S STOVES
STEAM FITTINGS
STEEL—BLISTER, CAST, DOUBLE
    SHEAR, AND SPRING
STOVE PIPES AND ELBOWS

TEA POTS
THERMOMETERS
TILE STOVES
TILE HEARTHS
TIN GOODS
TOILET SETS
TRAYS
TRAPS
TRUNKS
TURPENTINE

UMBRELLA STANDS

VARNISHES
VENTILATORS
VICES

WASHERS
WATER - WHITE CRYSTALLINE
    BURNING OIL
WEIGHING MACHINES
WHISKS
WIRE GOODS
WRINGING MACHINES

Turning, Planing, Boring, Drilling, Grooving, and Screwing by Steam.

The list of products manufactured and imported on the back of their invoices in 1884 and 1894 reveals a wide range of goods. Of particular interest to our story is that in 1894 the list indicates they were importing farm and garden equipment including chaff cutters, pig troughs, and lawnmowers. They were not slow to move into the new technology of the day, offering a service for internal combustion engines. These were probably stationary engines. As soon as Dr. Otto's four-cycle engine technology was understood and the patents ran out, small engines of up to 5 hp were being produced in the UK, Europe, and the USA, and sold in large numbers to farmers and rural dwellers to drive water pumps, mills, and electric generators.

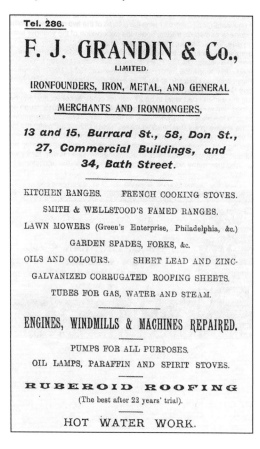

Tel. 286.

F. J. GRANDIN & Co.,
LIMITED.

IRONFOUNDERS, IRON, METAL, AND GENERAL

MERCHANTS AND IRONMONGERS,

**13 and 15, Burrard St., 58, Don St.,
27, Commercial Buildings, and
34, Bath Street.**

KITCHEN RANGES.   FRENCH COOKING STOVES.

SMITH & WELLSTOOD'S FAMED RANGES.

LAWN MOWERS (Green's Enterprise, Philadelphia, &c.)

GARDEN SPADES, FORKS, &c.

OILS AND COLOURS.   SHEET LEAD AND ZINC.

GALVANIZED CORRUGATED ROOFING SHEETS.

TUBES FOR GAS, WATER AND STEAM.

ENGINES, WINDMILLS & MACHINES REPAIRED.

PUMPS FOR ALL PURPOSES.

OIL LAMPS, PARAFFIN AND SPIRIT STOVES.

R U B E R O I D   R O O F I N G

(The best after 22 years' trial).

HOT WATER WORK.

The Grandin advertisement in 1914 for engines and windmills, as well as domestic and industrial equipment.

In 1926 the company were appointed agents for Morris Cars working from the original premises at no. 27 Commercial Buildings. In 1930 they acquired the Premier Garage in St. Peter. This was to be the last acquisition before the business finally closed in 1934. Mr. Gallichan retained the Morris Car agency, continuing to trade at no. 27 as a garage. Later in the 1930s Morris Cars were sold by Cleveland Garage in Cleveland Road.

As a schoolboy, the author often went to no. 27 with his father to collect their Morris Cowley car after it was serviced. He recalls that while waiting he stared up at the high, rough, and rather bleak granite walls at the back of the premises. In those days servicing a car often included 'decarbonising' the engine every few hundred miles. That involved removing the cylinder head, cleaning off the accumulated carbon, 'grinding in' the valves and setting the tappets.

So when the young Le Cappelain went to Grandin's to serve his apprenticeship, he joined a well-established and highly respectable firm of ironfounders. Like his own family's business, the Grandins had among their many activities strong connections with the agricultural industry.

Le Cappelain, St. Peter's Iron Works

Le Cappelain at St. Peter's Iron Works was founded in 1859 by T. J. Le Cappelain. Trevor Gavin Le Cappelain is the present-day proprietor. The works are in La Rue des Landes, St. Peter.

List of managers and directors since 1859

Théophile John Le Cappelain	founder 1859–1882	23 years
Georg Philip Le Cappelain	1882–1929	47 years
Théophilus George Le Cappelain AIBAE	1929–1959	30 years
Cyril George Le Cappelain SIBAE	1959–1984	25 years
Trevor Gavin Le Cappelain	1984–	

The products have changed over the years with the changing way of life and farming. At first it was wooden ploughs and cultivators with iron fittings, shares, and mouldboards, followed by iron ploughs and implements, and then operating and maintaining threshing machines and steam engines. Then the company operated a district electricity service in the parish of St. Peter. Electric generating sets were installed on farms and private houses, and imported implements, tractors, and milking machines were sold, followed by combined harvesters, potato harvesters; they are now producing wrought-iron work, balustrades, and repairing implements etc.

Century of directors 1859–1959

"CENTURY"
DIRECTORS
OF
ST PETER'S IRON WORKS
1859 — 1959

THEOPHILE JOHN LE CAPPELAIN   ∨
FOUNDER 1859 — 1882
GEORGE PHILIP LE CAPPELAIN 1882 — 1929
THEOPHILUS GEORGE LE CAPPELAIN A.I.B.A.E.
1959   ∨
CYRIL GEORGE HELLIER LE CAPPELAIN S.I.B.A.E.
1984
TREVOR GAVIN LE CAPPELAIN
1984

GARAGE ESTB⁰ 1936

STAFF 1959

FOREMAN   CHS. ED. MORRIS
FORGEMAN   JOHN DE C. VIBERT
ENGINEER   ARTHUR W. MICHEL
ASSISTANT   LOUIS CHS. VILLETTE
CLERK   WILLIAM GEO. LATTER   ∨

Quod erat demonstrandum
Quod erat faciendum

Théophile J. Le Cappelain was born at Pont Marquet in 1828 and served his apprenticeship at a shipyard in Gorey before becoming a blacksmith in Pont Marquet and then moving to the present site in St. Peter. The business was well established by 1871, when Mr. Le Cappelain entered in the machinery and implement trials with his threshing machine and steam engine at the Royal Jersey Agricultural and Horticultural Society's Channel Islands Exhibition and demonstrations of machines at work held at Victoria College. In 1873 a group of Jersey farmers got together on 19 April to present a 'self-acting screw- [thread] cutting lathe', costing £90 sterling, to Théophile J. Le Cappelain for introducing steam threshing machines and straw elevators into the Island. The presentation is recorded in a framed testimonial with all the contributors' names. The original testimonial was a grand affair and was the size of a poster, framed and mounted on a wall, but unfortunately it was damaged following a leaking roof. It has been restored professionally as far as possible but it is too big to reproduce here. The photograph of the lathe was also damaged and cannot be restored.

The lathe was not only for cutting threads; it had a long bed, which was a necessary requirement for machining the crankshaft bearings on the straw walkers of threshing machines. The lathe was driven by a flat belt from overhead shafting in those days, and is still in use today in the machine shop, driven by an electric motor.

The early years of the business were the days of the wooden plough. The business was busy building wooden ploughs with iron mouldboards and shares, wooden-frame cultivators with iron tines, corn ploughs, breezing ploughs, deep-digging ploughs, *la grande tchéthue* (the big plough) and the very light potato-planting plough, wooden-frame potato scarifiers and bankers.

The business having been established in 1859 leads one to ponder on the young enterprising Théophile John Le Cappelain; he may well have travelled to the Great Exhibition of 1851 at the Crystal Palace in London. He was 23 at the time, and it was a time when young men grew up fast. (The captains of many Jersey sailing ships at that time carrying on trade across the world were in their early twenties.) Records indicate that many manufacturers were giving demonstrations of equipment at work on the site and in many other areas of London, including Hyde Park. Among the many British exhibits were portable steam engines, traction engines, threshing machines, and a variety of agricultural machinery and implements. This was at a time when England was the world's engineering workshop, leading the world as a manufacturer of both industrial and agricultural machinery. Companies such as Marshalls of Gainsborough and Ransomes of Ipswich were the first to manufacture portable steam engines, traction engines, and threshing machines, and John Fowler was producing ploughing engines and associated equipment, working with Ransomes, who made the ploughs.

In 1875 St. Peter's Iron Works had a full-page advertisement in the Royal Jersey Agricultural and Horticultural Society's *Annual Report and Year Book* published in that year. In that advertisement they offered portable steam engines and threshing machines for sale and for hire,

Ile De Jersey

[In this space was a photograph of the lathe, due to the damage it cannot be copied]

Nous les Sousignés, membres du Comite nomme par un grand nombre des
Agriculteurs de cette Ile, afin d'offrir en leur nom, Testimonial a
Mons. Theophile Le Cappelain
lui presentons cette adresse accompagnee d'une gravure, representant le
"SELF ACTING SCREW CUTTING LATHE"
de la valeur de £90 Stg
qui forme l'objet du dit Testimonial et ce comme preuve de leur estime et en
reconnaissance des services par lui rendu à L'Agriculture tant comme l'un des premiers
artisans du pays que comme introducteur des

"STEAM THRESHING MACHINES et STRAW ELEVATORS"

Jersey
ce 19me jour d'abril 1873
——————-"——————

Thomas Howard Ecr. Président

John Pinel Ecr. Trésorier	Philip Neel Ecr. Secrétaire
Fred Le Quesne Ecr	John Duval
Pierre Le Sueur	Pierre Blampied
John Vigot	Aimable Le Heron
John Horman	John Le C. La Jerche
John Hacquel	Charles Vigot
Philippe Quenault	Elie Nicolle
John Le Masurier	William Alexandre
Philippe Le Masurier	Charles Mourant
William Nicolle	Louis Barrot
John Mauger	Arsene Le Goubey
Edward Gilley	John De Lecq Le Montais
Jules Manoury	François Horman
Marcel Le Masurier	John Gibaut
James John Ahier	Elie Hubert
John Luckarift	Frémont Ozouf

A copy of the testimonial presented to Mr. Theophile Le Cappelain.

manufactured by Marshalls of Gainsborough. They also offered to service steam engines and
threshing machines, and offered a range of cultivating implements for sale, some of which they
manufactured.

In those years the Island continued to grow many vergées of cereals, so there was a widespread
demand for the threshing machines. So much so that, while they had their own 'threshing field' at
St. Peter's Iron Works, it was company practice to store their threshing sets in different parts of
the Island. They were all busy in their various locations for three months of the year. One was
kept in Guernsey and was operated by a Mr. Norman at St. Peter-in-the-Wood, and another was

kept in Portbail in France. Each set consisted of a portable steam engine and threshing machine, both being Marshalls with a Hornsby trusser. The sets were for hire or contract work and were set up where and when required. Many farmers in the Island, such as Mr. Holly, stacked their harvest in a rickyard on the farm, and when they was ready to thresh they would get on to Le Cappelain and, with the assistance of the farmer's horses, the set would be hauled to the farm, placing the threshing machine right alongside the rick. Alternatively, they would arrange to set up in a farmer's field for what might be described as 'public use'. Farmers in the district were invited through advertising in the press to bring their loads of sheaves to be threshed when the crop was ready to carry. The threshing set might stay on a site for three or four weeks or remain on site working continually for up to three months until all the farmers in the district had finished threshing.

T. LE CAPPELAIN,
AGRICULTURAL ENGINEER,
ST. PETER'S IRON WORKS,
JERSEY.

Agent for Steam Engines, Thrashing Machines, Chaff Cut...,
Single and Double Action Root Pulpers and Slicers, Horse
Gears, Mowing and Reaping Machines, &c., &c.

Portable Engines and Thrashing Machines, from 4 to 6 Horse
Power, to Let on Hire; also Steam Engines, for Thrashing,
Pumping, Chaff Cutting, and Sawing, &c , &c.

Manufacturer of Ploughs, Harrows, Carts, Scarifiers, and all
other Agricultural Implements.
Steam Engines, Chaff Cutters, Pulpers, &c., &c., efficiently
repaired.

An advertisement in 1875.

One of Le Cappelain's threshing sets at work beside a rick in St. Ouen in 1912.
Two box carts with casks of water are backed up to the portable steam engine to keep the boiler supplied with water. The horse waits patiently while the van is loaded with the threshed grain. The labourers on the ground have time for a chat while waiting for the cameraman to compose and take a picture. That was not usual around a threshing machine, where there was always plenty to do, shifting the cavings from under the machine, one man attending to the grain bags, changing them over as they fill and weighing

them and loading them onto the van. There were moments while waiting for a bag to filled, or the cavings to build up, but no time to stop for the men feeding the sheaves into the machine.

In 1882, Théophile retired with a reputation for having built hundreds of wooden-frame ploughs in his lifetime. So George Philip Le Cappelain took over the reins. Born in 1859, George left Boyer's School at Beaumont at 15, working first for Mr. C. Vautier at St. Peter making wooden plough frames. He then served a seven-year apprenticeship at F. & J. Grandin's iron foundry and machine shop at Commercial Buildings. Returning to St. Peter, he continued to produce many wooden ploughs but, having trained as a foundryman and blacksmith, he moved away from wooden ploughs into manufacturing the first ploughs of iron and steel. His castings were made at Grandin's foundry, and the rest of the metalwork, the blacksmithing, and machining was done at St. Peter's Iron Works. In the 1895 RJA & HS implement trials held at Le Hague Manor on 17 August, his plough earned praise by winning in its class. Following this success he commenced manufacturing an all-iron, horse-drawn, twin-furrow breezing plough. This again was a first in the Island. When tractors appeared some thirty years or more later, it was suitable for tractor draught with some modifications for the tractor driver only to operate. These successes were quickly followed with another first, the light, 'all-metal' Jersey potato-planting plough that sold for £4 10s. (£4.50). This was timely with the recent arrival of the highly successful Royal Jersey Fluke, the now famous early potato.

Details about the business in those days, and of George Le Cappelain who managed it, are to be found in a red leather-bound pocketbook. Embossed in gold on the cover are the words 'Where is it?' Letters of the alphabet alternating in black and red appear on tabs on the edge of the pages, there being some half-dozen pages under each letter, as in an address book. Inside the front cover, in pencil, is the price, 1s. 3d. One can only imagine the book was probably purchased as a gift for a birthday or Christmas. As the entries in it cover the period 1916 to 1932, we can assume it belonged to George Le Cappelain, who retired in 1929.

It was both a private notebook, with some interesting entries of a personal nature, and for business. The book was not used regularly and entries are not in any particular order. An entry in one year may be followed by another on the same page several years later, all the entries clearly handwritten in ink.

This entry, copied here as it appears in the pocketbook, concerns cash earned for threshing:

> 1919
> Amount thrashed by No 4 at Douet Rue
> > £356 - 2 - 2
> > £247 -11- 4
> > £180 - 2 - 4   leaving £100 net for Jeff
> Wages

Those figures total £783 15s. 10d., a lot of money in those days. George probably recorded it as a bumper year. Unfortunately there is no indication whether this was for a private job or a 'public' threshing in the district of Douet Rue, probably Douet de Rue in St. Mary, when farmers brought their loads to the machine. This is most likely, as the way the money is listed suggests it is probably cash taken over three weeks, showing the amount for each week. The £100 net for Jeff and 'wages' is confusing: wages were only £2 or £3 a week at that time. The expenses, apart from the wages for the driver/operator of the steam engine, were for fuel and possibly water for the boiler. The fuel was coal or wood, more likely the latter supplied by a farmer 'off the farm', and water would be from the nearest well, incurring little or no expense. When working in a farmer's rickyard, the farmer traditionally had to supply both fuel and water.

At the turn of the century in 1900 Le Cappelain was interested in potato diggers. Bamfords, the agricultural machinery manufacturers of Uttoxeter in Staffordshire, produced the first of the Jersey Lily potato diggers, followed in 1905 with an improved model 'no. 2'. However, due to the skilled and hard-working Breton, who knew how to handle a potato fork in the field without damaging the crop, there was not a great incentive to buy a horse-drawn mechanical digger. Furthermore, there was a certain anxiety that the Jersey Royal potato was too delicate and suscep-tible to bruising, which would spoil its attraction to consumers, so it had to be handled as gently as an egg. The exception was among the more wealthy, forward-thinking farmers, and when men were eventually conscripted in the First World War, taking every able-bodied man off the land, mechanisation was the only way to get the crop dug, and Bamford's Jersey Lily was purchased in greater numbers.

An entry in the pocketbook on Friday, 22 September 1916 concerns the fuel consumption of a Ford car:

Ford Car
Friday Sept 22/16
2 gallons petrol were put into tank
Registering 8644 miles 2 galls of Petrol
25th   8684   2 galls of Petrol
Oct 7th   8726   2 galls of Petrol
Oct 14th   8788   2 galls of Petrol

Other dates were entered when 2 gallons were put in the tank, but not the mileage. Where the details are complete, it seems the Ford car was returning 18 to 20 miles per gallon.

An entry in 1918 deals with private financial details of Post Office Savings accounts in London and modest amounts of interest received over a period of several years up to 1932. In another private entry, George makes a note of advice from his doctor or a pharmacy:

Syringe out the ears with a tumbler full of warm water containing a teaspoonfull of Bicarbonate of Soda.

The author recalls spending time in and out of workshops and complaining to his doctor about the frequent need to have his ears syringed, sometimes twice in the same year. The doctor explained, that it was a hazard of working in a foundry, forge, or almost any workshop: where there is dust, the ears will make a lot of wax.

Again, like Messervy with his 'pied à terre', George grew early potatoes:

Clos de La Forge and Clos du Roi in 1918
amount of potatoes sold £91–0–0.

Another entry concerning the sale of land:

Clos de La Forge July 5th. 1920 was measured by Adv. Le Brocq.
1 Vergée 32 perch 11 feet
and sold to Mr Mesny 60£ a vergée
or £108 – 13 – 0

It was found to have a Romeril apple tree.

Then we come to entries dealing with the affairs of the business. These were the days when St. Peter's Iron Works built many iron ploughs and implements. An entry dated 28 February 1918 concerns a stock order for malleable castings and mild steel:

In stock to Dec. 31/17   Mall 150 lbs   mild steel 3 cwt
material ordered 1917 Permit and not yet received—
                                    500   do do   1000 (lbs)
[Mall = malleable]

It was in the later part of the First World War, when many young men would have been called up to join the forces. We know from the Year Book of the Royal Jersey Agricultural and Horticultural Society that farmers were short-staffed, employing women and buying machinery.

A list of orders from his customers in the autumn of 1917:

Week Ending Oct 16th.
3 One Horse Wheat Plough   3
Week ending Nov. 10th.   To be made
One 2 Horse Twin Plough   1 30
Three 1 Horse Wheat do.   3   7 Th. Coutanche, H. Wakeham, C. Sumner

There are further references to permits from the Defence Committee for materials, which indicates the frustration experienced by the business over obtaining materials in short supply due to munitions production during the First World War. Yet another entry records an order for materials followed by a long list of orders for a variety of different cultivating implements. There are orders from farmers, a butcher, (no doubt with his 'pied à terre'), and from Western Farmers (a farmers' co-operative in the South-West of England, where early potatoes are also grown).

The fact that this list of orders is the only one in this special little notebook leads one to wonder why. Was it a bumper year for orders, perhaps, like the entry above for cash taken for threshing? St. Peter's Iron Works may well have been short-staffed and George Le Cappelain felt it necessary to keep a close eye on progressing these orders through the works.

1/2 ton of malleable casting through Defence Committee

	Week Ending June 2/ 1917—
1 Self lifting Scarifier	Hubert, Gorey
1 Planting Plough	Bree Th.
	Ending June 9/17
1 Pot [potato] Scarifier	Gautier, Bagot
1 Banking Plough	Western Counties
	Ending June 16
1 7 Tines One Horse Self Lifting Sca [scarifier]	J. Bree
1 One Horse Pot Scarifier	J. Richard
	Ending June 23rd
1 One Horse 3 Furrow Banking Plough	
1 Two Horse Self Lifting Scarifier	J. Hamon
1 Two Horse Self Lifting "	Pirouet
	Ending June 30th
1 Two Horse Self Lifting Sca	Theo. Seale
1 One Horse Planting Plo	Dav. De Gruchy
1 One do Pot Banking Pl.	Pirouet
	Ending July 7th
1 1 hand banking Plough	Mr Coutanche
1 Potato Planting Plough HP2W	J. Marie Butcher

		Made to date
Week Ending July 14th		"Pirouet" 5
1 One Horse Banking plough		Pirouet 4
1 One Horse Planting Plough		

after a break on the same page starting again in October:

Week Ending Oct 16th.			
3 One Horse Wheat Plough	3		
Week ending Nov. 10th			To be made
One 2 Horse Twin Plough	1		30
Three 1 Horse Wheat do.	3		7 Th. Coutanche, H. Wakeham, C. Sumner
Week Ending Nov. 17th.			
3 = 2 Horse Twin Ploughs	4		26 J. Fish, Th. Le Feuvre, Moore.
Week Ending Nov 24th.			
3 = 2 Horse Twin Ploughs	8		23 Godfray, Luce, E. P. Le Brun

2 = 1 Horse Wheat Plough	5	5
Week Ending Dec 1st Review 6	8	23
Week Ending Dec 8th		
6 2 Horse Twin Ploughs	14	17
Week Ending Dec 15th		
1 One Horse Self Lifting Sca	6	8 Guernsey Western Association
Week Ending Dec 22nd Review	7	7
1 2 Horse S.L. Sca.	7	8 6 A. T. Moore
Week Ending Dec 29	6- 9	5 Ph. Le Feuvre
1 2 Horse S.L. Scarifier ?		

and on the following page

	Review	Made to date	to be made	
Week Ending Jan 5/18				
One two Horse Scarifier	5	10	4	
One Two do Deep Digging				Jean Allo [deep-digger plough]
Week Ending Jan 12				
1 Twin Plough	1	15	16	Nicholson Gurney Not Sent.
3 Four Horse Deep Digger Plo 3		3	9	

July 13/18, Ministry of Munitions of War 5 cwt of steel to temper in water 65/cwt.

So the entry ends. To be helpful to the reader, the details and illustrations of these implements and machines above will be found in Chapters 6 and 18.

A Le Cappelain two-furrow breezing plough for horse draught, 1918/1919.
The cast-iron legs on the breezing plough have Le Cappelain's name in the casting. The legs and frogs are cast in one piece, either at Grandin's foundry at Commercial Buildings, or at Le Cappelain's works, when they had their own foundry for a time. The mouldboards are the shallow-digger type to break up the soil, and the shares are one-piece steel shares, 12 in. (30.5 cm) wide, providing for a 12-in. furrow width. Under-beam clearance to share tip is 17 in. (43 cm). The furrow wheel diameter is 17 in. and the landwheel 22 in. (55.75 cm).

So between 2 June 1917 and 12 January 1918, in just thirty weeks, George received orders for fifty implements, two of them for delivery outside the Island: quite remarkable for a country blacksmith who could justifiably be regarded as a small manufacturer. It is no wonder George felt it necessary to note the details in his private pocketbook so he could keep an eye on progress.

How were these implements produced? The little red notebook gives us some idea. A record of yet another order for materials in January 1918:

Jan 10/18 Ordered from Iron Stores

12 bars 2 1/4 x 1/2	12 bars of 2 1/4 x 5/8
6 bars 1 3/4 round	12 bars of 1 1/2 x 3/8
12 bars 1 3/4 x 5 1/16	6 bars of 1 3/4 x 5/8

An entry in 1921 helps us:

December 14th 1921
Material & time on a small 2 H. JD plough
to suit J P Plough carriage.

106 lbs of wrt iron at /4	1 - 13 - 4	
one cast iron body 12/,	12 - 0	
One slade	7 - 6	
2 men 31 hrs each at 3/,	4 - 13 - 0	
one pair wood handles	3 - 0	
One No O malleable head	10 - 0	
15 bolts & two 5/8 studs	4 - 0	
Drilling and tapping holes	10 - 0	
Draft collars	2 - 2	
	£8 - 15 - 0	

[A two-horse Jersey digger plough
to suit a customer's plough carriage.
106 lb of wrought iron at 4s.—
to attach the mouldboard and slade
(another name for a landside)]

The wrought iron was probably required for fabricating the beam and handles. There is no reference to a skimmer, so presumably just as the customer's carriage is being used, so perhaps a skimmer from a disused plough is being adapted. We begin to get some idea of the time and cost of producing some of these components and assembling an implement.

Details of an entry in 1924 throw a little more light:

Self Lifting Scarifier 1924

Weight of Wrought iron 189 lbs
two angle iron brackets
4 Malleable   ”
3 Road wheels
One Malleable latch
One sheave
7 MDI tines
Time = Ernest 40 Hrs. Charlie 40 1/2 Hrs
5 Hrs drilling
Painting 3 hrs
22 Bolts

The MDI tines were probably imported to get a higher tensile strength and resistance to bending, and they may have been cheaper to buy from the UK, where they were produced in quantity. The tines were fitted with hardened steel points that were both reversible and replaceable. These may well have been forged locally, toughening them by plunging them first into linseed oil and cold water. When the point was worn the single countersunk bolt was taken out and the point turned end for end. When both ends were worn, the point was replaced.

Lizard Pot Scarifier 1924
Forging above Ernest 20 hrs. Charlie 20 hrs.
Roller Front wheel
Weight 43 lbs
2 No 13 Clamps   £5 – 10 – 0 Cash

[Pot = potato]

Light Pot. Scarifiers mini wheel

weight 30 lbs	0 – 10 – 0
Ernest & Charles 15 hrs	3 – 0 – 0
Roller 6 lbs	0 – 10 – 0
6 bolts 3 Ash handles	5 – 0
	£4 – 5 – 0

Front tines 6/- side tines 4/- each banking hoe attachment 6lbs
Ern & Chas 3 hrs.

The surviving forge, which would have been a hive of industry in the 1920s when there were three blacksmiths. Above right can be seen the large leather bellows and a hood over the forge to gather the smoke to go up the chimney. The leather bellows is now redundant; an electric blower has replaced it.

St. Peter's Iron Works had their castings made at François Jean Grandin's iron foundry at 27 Commercial Buildings, where as a young man George Le Cappelain had served his apprenticeship. To have his castings made at Grandin's was a natural and obvious thing to do. The castings were many and varied: there were wheel hubs for steel wheels for ploughs and cultivators in which the spokes were made by the blacksmiths at the St. Peter's works, then taken to be cast in the cast-iron hubs in the foundry. These were returned to St. Peter's, where the blacksmiths had the hoops or rims made ready. The rims were shrunk onto the spokes and the spokes' ends peened over where they protruded through the rim. These were made in batches probably sufficient for the year, along with the frogs for plough bodies and the many cast-iron fittings for the stalks on cultivator frames, draw hitches, and many other components.

It should be noted that there was a time when St. Peter's Iron Works had their own foundry.

Charlie Morris started work as an apprentice at St. Peter's Iron Works in 1928. He was known as Jim at the works because one of the blacksmiths, an older man, was also named Charlie, so to avoid confusion he was told he would be called Jim. The customers knew him as Jim to the day he retired, many never knowing his real name.

Charlie recalls that Ernie Walters was one of three blacksmiths at St. Peter's Iron Works between the wars: he was highly skilled, turning out beautifully finished work. He was quite a humorous character and had served in the Royal Flying Corps (later the RAF) during the war, but he was a hard taskmaster who stood no nonsense from apprentices, including Charlie. The blacksmiths were assisted by a striker, usually an apprentice. The apprentice also had to operate the bellows and use a sledgehammer, and when heavy work was required, two men with sledgehammers worked together. They would strike alternately in a well-practised rhythm. Welding was done at the forge and anvil and was a highly skilled operation in the days before gas and electric welding. Woe betide the striker if he missed a strike while the iron was hot, from which comes the old saying 'strike while the iron is hot'.

The directors of the business evidently held Ernest, or Ernie as he was known, in high regard, as we see in an entry in the red pocketbook calculating a bonus paid to Ernest Walters:

Paid to Ernest Walters up to April 30th 1921
Paid at the rate of 50 Hrs per week at /2 an hour at 2d an hour = 8/3d per week
Paid bonus = £7-1-8.

and again

Paid Ernest Walters up to Dec 25/21 From June to Xmas
for 6 month bonus at /2 per hour 54 Hrs per week
£11-13-4 for 6 months
/2 = 2d

Ernest Walters's bonus was the only one entered in George's red book, and it was paid twice each year, up to the last entry in June 1928.

Plough mouldboards, sometimes known as covers or breasts, were made by laboriously cutting them out with hammer and chisel from mild steel sheet. Today they would be cut with gas profile-cutters. When sufficient had been cut for the year, they were heated in a coke furnace, laid on coke and stacked six high at a time, each one separated with blocks of wood. When ready, they were taken out one at a time and placed in the press, between cast-iron moulds, for pressing into shape. Grandin's in Commercial Buildings had cast the moulds. Before going to the expense of having the moulds cast, many hours must have been spent forming the original template to obtain the right curve to the turn or twist of the template, so that the finished mouldboard would throw the soil correctly to produce a well-turned furrow. The moulds for the wheat plough mould-boards and the big deep-digging plough had to be particularly well-shaped to produce well-turned furrows.

Production improved when the company had the mouldboards cut out in batches in England, using a template that had been sent over. The blanks were delivered to St. Peter's to be pressed.

Steel shares were made from 0.625-in. (2 cm) mild steel plate and cut and shaped at the forge. The edge was drawn out by heating in the forge and beating on the anvil. A Jersey cider cask cut in half was filled with linseed oil and another with water. The shares were tempered by plunging them into the barrel of linseed oil, followed immediately by plunging them in cold water. All these operations were timed and had to be finished by a particular time of day. The early days of 'time and motion'!

Care had to be taken when tempering shares in linseed oil: if they were too hot, the oil would catch fire! The oil companies eventually produced tempering oil. Individual worn shares were taken by farmers to the blacksmiths in those days to have the worn edge and point drawn out and sharpened. The author remembers taking plough shares to Jack Marett's forge at Five Oaks to have them beaten out and sharpened; sometimes he was allowed to stay and watch it being done. The blacksmiths were not past having a bit of fun if they had an audience, spitting on the anvil before placing the red hot iron on it, then hitting it with the hammer, causing a loud explosion which made everybody jump, especially nosy little boys!

The next change came about with the arrival of tractors. Locally produced shares and mould-boards were fine with horses and the wear and tear was tolerable, but tractors having more power and speed imposed greater loads on the plough, resulting in increased wear on mouldboards and shares. To overcome this, the life of shares was improved by welding a hard, wear-resistant steel to the cutting edge of the share, not with gas or electric welding as it might be done today, but at the forge and the anvil! Eventually, Ransomes and Oliver mouldboards were imported, the former from Ipswich and the latter from the USA, and fitted to locally produced ploughs. Ransomes' mouldboards were made from 'case-hardened steel' at their own factory, the Steel Case Company in South Wales. Oliver's were known as 'soft-centre steel', which is the same thing.

Electric generating sets were also installed in many country properties. The first reference to electric plant appears on the heading of an invoice dated 1911 which reads:

Geo. Ph. Cappelain & Son
St. Peter's Works, Jersey
Agents for Stella Electric Plant (installed at moderate charges)

An entry in the red notebook in 1919 notes:

The first charge on the accumulator
at Westlands was given on Oct. 2nd./19
It took 37 hours charging at 12 AMPS
to get 76 volts & 1220 Gravity.

Charles Le Couteur, who preserves old tractors, implements, and machinery at his property, Westlands, recalls this installation. It had a Petter engine, and an item in his grandfather's accounts at Westlands for 1919 shows he paid £150 on account to Le Cappelain for the electric generating set.

There was a similar generating set at La Hougue Bie in the late 1920s for lighting the house, tea room, and the tunnel to the burial chambers in the dolmen. As a child at this time, the author often visited the Clement family at La Hougue Bie to play with their son. Mr. Clement would allow us into the shed beside the entrance to the dolmen to see the generator and the large, open, glass accumulators, while he checked the gravity and sometimes started the engine. Each jar was three-quarters filled with acid, and two rods stood loosely, leaning against the side of the jar; each had a terminal at the top connected by wire to a rod in the neighbouring jar.

The next entry in the red book is particularly interesting. It is concerned with a comparison of reapers or mowers of four well-known names in the industry—measuring the revolutions of the crankshaft driving the knife and the distance travelled for one complete rotation of the landwheels.

Speed of Massey Harris's   [revs. equals revolutions]
    Mower no. 16 is 27 revs. to one turn of road wheel
    on an 8 ft 6" [258 cm] length of run

Speed of Mc Cormick
        New big 4 27 Rev.

Speed of Bamford's
        top gear 32 Rev.
        low gear 25 do

on an 8 ft 6" length of run

Speed of Albion top Gear 32 Rev
    "   "   "   low Gear 25 Rev
on a 8 ft 6" Length of run

The length of run was a common factor, and the revolutions of the crankshaft were common to the American machines, at 27, while on the two British machines they were 32 and 25. This is probably due to soil and climatic conditions producing a heavier crop, particularly hay, in the British Isles.

By way of explanation, the reciprocating knife in a mower's cutter bar on horse-drawn mowers was driven by one or both of the two land (or road) wheels as a pair of horses pulled the mower along. The revolutions of the crankshaft could be measured by placing a revolution counter on the crankshaft, or simply by jacking up the wheel and rotating it by hand and counting the number of revolutions of the crankshaft. Obviously, the distance run was the circumference of the wheel. Power was transmitted to the crankshaft through a crownwheel and pinion, usually assembled in a cast-iron gearbox with an oil bath and a hinged lid.

The first two machines were American; indeed C. H. McCormick manufactured the first-ever reaper, receiving a patent for his design in 1834, and produced it in quantity. It swept the Midwest when it first came on the market in the nineteenth century. It was eventually copied; all the reapers and mowers were almost identical in appearance, only the details being different. The Bamford and the Albion were British-made, with British conditions in mind. Massey Harris became Massey Ferguson and McCormick is part of Case-International. Today, the JCB digger is a Bamford machine produced by the same family in Uttoxeter. Albion produce specialist vehicles today.

At times Le Cappelain & Son provided general engineering services to civil engineering contractors. The portable engines, including a smaller Tyzack portable steam engine, were not only used for threshing, but were hired to quarrymen for driving stone crushers. The business operated and maintained steam cranes, steam condensing pumps (pulsometers), and traction engines with building contractors. One contractor was Charles Le Quesne, who was engaged in the construction of the seawall at Millbrook and the seawall at St. Ouen.

In 1929 George retired, and his son Théophilus George Le Cappelain took over the management. He had trained as a blacksmith and spent two years at Petters of Yeovil in England, the engine manufacturers, at a time when they were developing diesel engines. In the same year Le Cappelain was asked to supply an electricity service to the district. The parish gave its blessing to the project and work began in due course, installing and supplying electricity to many properties running their own generator, until an act of the States formed the Jersey Electricity Company, which took over the business.

In the 1920s an International 10/20 tractor was purchased, which was used to haul the threshing sets. It was described as a 10/20 model because the engine developed 20 hp at the pulley, which was standard equipment on American tractors in those days; the 10 indicated the horsepower at the drawbar. The 10/20 had its limitations for roadwork. Tractors pre-war were on steel wheels with spade lugs bolted to the rim on the rear wheels to obtain traction on the land, but on the road the lugs would damage the metalled surfaces, so they had to be removed or steel road bands fitted over the lugs. This was fine for moving the tractor on its own or with a light load, but towing a heavy threshing drum was quite different. It was difficult to get a good grip with smooth steel bands. The tractor would slip and slide alarmingly when going downhill, especially on a concrete surface. Climbing steep hills was equally hazardous, as the wheels would sometimes spin. On the these occasions, Théo, or Taffy as he was fondly known, would turn up with his 'bullnose' Morris and hitch it to the front of the tractor, so assisting with the tow up the hill until they reached the top.

Driving a threshing set with a tractor had its problems. To start rotating the heavy drum with a steam engine required close attention. As the steam valve was opened, the engine would begin rotating, taking up the load and slowly rotating the heavy drum and the many moving parts, the elevators, straw walkers, sieves, and fan all moving together from rest and accelerating up to speed together. Starting all this equipment with a relatively fast-running petrol/paraffin engine with a clutch on a tractor was very much more difficult. The whole lot had to move from rest and start rotating and accelerate up to speed much more quickly! So, however slowly the clutch was engaged, sometimes it would result in the flat belt being thrown off the pulleys. It was made easier as ball and roller bearings began to replace the old plain bearings on newer threshing machines, and when using a tractor with hand-operated, over-centre clutches.

Charlie recalls a threshing set driven by a Marshall portable engine kept in the St. Martin area, which was looked after by one of Le Cappelain's men who lived in St. Martin. All five threshing sets were still in use after the Occupation in 1945.

Trevor Le Cappelain, the present proprietor, remembers his folk talking about having a threshing machine set up for a time at Messrs. Peredés's, at Fairview Farm, Prince's Tower, in 1947/8. The author's father and his neighbours all worked together threshing there for one or two summers, carrying each other's harvest to the thresher and celebrating with a big midday dinner at each farm on the day they worked there.

In 1938 the company imported the new Allis Chalmers model B, a lightweight rowcrop tractor; implements were centre-mounted or hauled by hitching to the swinging drawbar at the back of the tractor.

During the 1930s the company sold Medland tractor-trailed, self-lift ploughs. In some cases the frame was imported and a stock or leg fitted, to which a locally made digger body was fitted. In the autumn this single body was dismantled from the plough and twin bodies were fitted for breezing, i.e. light or shallow ploughing.

In the 1960s the author discussed Melotte business in conversation with Théophilus Le Cappelain, just after he retired from managing the business but was still going into work each day. At the time the author was Melotte's sales manager in the UK. Théophilus recalled St. Peter's Iron Works selling Melotte cream separators when he was a boy. There was quite a big demand for cream separators in those days when butter was made on the farm. This was in the 1890s and the early years of this century, when the RJA & HS was promoting clean milk production among its members. Melotte products are described in Chapters 11 and 16.

Charlie Morris remembers helping relatives on the farm as a boy, turning the handle of the cream separator, and the barrel-type butter churn mounted on a wooden frame upon which the barrel turned end over end. He is amused by today's world when he recalls how farmers sent milk to the dairy and the dairy would send back the skimmed milk to the farms for feeding to young livestock. Our mothers would never dream of buying skim milk for home consumption, but today we buy the stuff to drink in blue packs and green packs! The author's father always had skimmed milk sent back from the dairy, which was mixed with other ingredients and fed to the calves. When the author was a schoolboy he used it mixed with meal to feed his sow and the young pigs.

From 1957, Fahr combined harvesters replaced the threshing machines. They were used extensively for ten or twelve years. One was last licensed for the road in 1967 and the second in 1968, by which time agriculture had changed and only a few farms grew cereals. However, farming is changing again, and some dairy farms are growing barley, linseed, etc. for cattle food. Charles Le Couteur has preserved one of the Fahr combined harvesters, which he uses on his farm at Westlands each year. A second lies partly dismantled, supplying spare parts to keep the working machine going.

One of Le Cappelain's Fahr combined harvesters at work.
The Fahr combined harvester is a bigger model MDL 1, serial no. 72 318, manufactured in 1957. It has a 6 ft (180 cm) width of cut. First used for many years by Le Cappelain, originally for contract work; at present owned by Charles Le Couteur, of Westlands, St. Peter. Further details are in Chapter 7.

Unfortunately Cyril Le Cappelain was sensitive to smell, and when he was installing new milking machines the smell of the cows upset him. When a horse was having new shoes, the blacksmith offered the hot shoe to the horse's hoof to check the fit, and the hot shoe singed the hoof, which gave off clouds of pungent-smelling smoke which again upset Cyril. So here was a man who was really in the wrong business! However, his father, who had not yet retired, insisted that they continue to do both because they were good business. Charlie Morris recalls installing many milking machines. Cyril was much happier working with tractors and field machinery. The last time the author met him he was happily working with his men in his workshop, modifying a potato harvester.

Cyril George Le Cappelain took over the management of the business from his father in 1959.

He imported Wühlmaus potato elevator diggers and potato harvesters from Germany. Modifications had to be made to them to suit Jersey's narrow potato rows, and this extra work carried out in their own workshops rather restricted the number they could sell in any one year.

Wühlmaus potato harvester; they had to be modified to suit Jersey's narrow rows.

In the 1960s the company imported French-made Staub two-wheeled tractors, to which they fitted their own large-diameter steel wheels with lugs for potato planting, scarifying, and banking. They were also quite useful for general cultivations on small areas. These tractors, powered by a Staub 7-hp four-stroke, single-cylinder, air-cooled engine, were started with a crank handle.

In 1984, Trevor Gavin Le Cappelain carried on running the business. Unfortunately in this ever-changing world with so few farmers in the Island today, there is no longer the business to be done that his grandfather enjoyed, and the works, staff, and business have been reduced accordingly.

Charlie, known in the works as Jim, with his Staub two-wheel tractor and toolbar.

Much of the story was compiled with the help of Mr. Charlie Morris.

L. C. Pallot & Sons Ltd.

Accompanying the illustrations in this history are frequent references to the Pallot family, their museum collection, and their products. One of Jersey's well-known and much loved characters was the late L. C. 'Don' Pallot, of the Forge and Garage at Central Motor Works, Sion, and at Rue Béchelet in the parish of Trinity. This short history is taken from Don Pallot's story, written by the family but not yet published.

Lyndon Charles Pallot, better known as Don Pallot, was born in 1910 at Le Vert Pignon, Trinity, the son of a cobbler who later turned to farming at Rockmount Farm, Trinity. Travel in those days was by horse and van or carriage, the bicycle or on foot. There were cars about but they were expensive and few and far between. To get around it was every boy's ambition to have a cycle; Don was no exception and enjoyed tinkering with them, so much so that he was repairing cycles for cash in his schooldays.

Like many schoolboys at that time he liked to watch the blacksmiths in the district at work, and recalls one of them, Henry William Gough. He was renowned for his skill; his forge was on the site of the present-day Trinity Arms. Don was amused by the man's tremendous thirst, which was quenched at the former British Hotel, located on the site of the new wide entrance to the States Experimental Farm. One of his employees was the late Clem Le Breuilly, who later set up in business at Victoria Village.

The recession in the 1920s before the crash of 1929 was bad for farming and his father got out and went back to shoemaking. He tried to get Don apprenticed to a garage, but cars were not selling and garages had no vacancies for apprentices. Young Don carried on his cycle business, selling the cycles he had overhauled and motorcycles and accessories from the new home at Temple View. Don found a way to stove-enamel freshly painted cycles. An overhauled cycle sold for between £4 and £5.

Don's grandfather, John Pallot of Mont Pellier, Trinity, was keen to see Don apprenticed and arranged for him to fill a vacancy with the Jersey Railway and Tramway Company, who operated the railway from the Weighbridge to St. Aubin and Corbière. This was a successful spell of training where he learned much that would stand him in good stead for later years. In his spare time he amused himself tuning and racing motorcycles. He also purchased a second-hand Fiat car, overhauled it, and used it for a time before selling it on.

In 1931 he started in business on his own, repairing lorries and cars. When the family moved to new and bigger premises, it gave him more room and the business developed further. In 1932 he was selling Austin lorries and cars, taking on employees to help him. He was a sub-agent for International Harvester, selling the W12 and W14 tractors and F12 and F14 rowcrop tractors, with adjustable track width, and Fordson tractors and Oliver ploughs.

In 1933 he married Dorothy Mourant, of St. Saviour. Shortly after, he borrowed £500 from a relative, with which he bought a plot of land at Sion and built a shed on it, completing the premises with petrol pumps, etc. This was to be the Central Motor Works. In 1942 he built a bungalow alongside.

During the Second World War Don decided he and his family would remain in the Island but the Occupation would mean a change for the business. Farmers lost their market in England for Jersey Royal potatoes and tomatoes, and the export of cattle to the rest of the world. They would have to make changes. It did not take long to realise the Island would not be able to import goods, especially foodstuffs. Everything would have to be home-grown as far as possible. This would mean growing cereals (mostly wheat, some oats and barley), maincrop potatoes, and in due time sugar beet. The local authorities took control: local inspectors were appointed to supervise and the German forces also had their own inspectors.

Don decided to go into agricultural contracting. The tractors he had taken in part-exchange were overhauled in readiness for a busy autumn and winter of ploughing, cultivating, and sowing.

In the summer there would be hay to cut and cereal crops to be harvested and threshed. He acquired equipment where he could find it, begging, borrowing, and buying on a 'make-do-and-mend' basis. People in those days were accustomed to this approach to life, many having lived through the shortages of the First World War, followed by the recession in the late 1920s and 1930s.

When Don was approached by the president of the Motor Traders' Association and told he would have to repair and maintain German forces' vehicles, he declared he was far too busy repairing and servicing farm tractors and machinery. This was accepted. However, he clashed with a German officer on one occasion, refusing to repair his bike, but felt it wiser to relent when pressed a second time. German soldiers could sometimes be helpful: Don was having a problem with an ignition system and a German soldier offered him a Bosch magneto that served the purpose.

When petrol was in short supply the States imported Gasogene charcoal-burning equipment from France for fitting to lorries, vans, and tractors. There was a loss of power as a result, but 'needs must', and many were converted, including all the Pallot tractors and some nineteen Fordson model N tractors, all on rubber tyres, which the States had commandeered. Don was sufficiently concerned with the loss of power that he fitted one himself, setting up the filter to operate more efficiently, thereby effecting an improved performance.

He had purchased a Bamford mower with a reaping attachment; it was able to cut hay, and at harvest time, with the reaping attachments, it would reap cereal crops. The attachments comprised an extra seat over the wheel on the cutter-bar side to carry a second operator. Behind the cutter bar a slatted wooden frame was attached, upon which the cut wheat, barley, etc. would fall. When there was sufficient to make a sheaf, the operator drew the cut material towards him using a wooden sweep, then swept it off the back ready for the sheaf makers working behind. All mowers and reapers were on iron wheels, converted from horse draught to tractor draught. Don's tractors were also on iron-spade lug wheels, which meant road bands had to be fitted each time the equipment was moved from site to site.

Advertisement for Central Motor Works and the services offered.

Don was desperate to move more rapidly from place to place during haymaking and harvesting. He purchased a 10-hp Citroen car for £10 from an uncle at Millbrook. The bodywork was stripped off, the chassis shortened, and a drawbar fitted at the back. To improve traction in the field, the rear-wheel tyres were changed for tyres more suited to off-the-road surfaces, and a second gearbox

was fitted in the transmission train. Meanwhile, a rubber-tyred transporter was made up, with two ramps up which the iron wheels of the mower were pushed to carry the Bamford mower. So the much-modified Citroen towed the mower from job to job; at the site, the mower was hauled off its transporter and towed by the Citroen around the field, mowing hay. A year later, in 1942, this was further improved by fitting the cutter bar to the side of the Citroen's chassis. This was more complicated than one might expect, because a power drive had to be made up from one of the gearboxes to provide the reciprocating motion to the knife. This must have been the first car with a PTO and the world's first motorised mower!

In the same year, Don purchased an almost new International McCormick binder for £90 for the harvest. There was a shortage of binder twine, so Don set about making and adapting twine from whatever he could find, mostly using tomato-tying twine which had to be unwound and then rewound, using a lathe to spin the bobbin. This was a bold move as the knotter on a binder is fickle at the best of times, so using adapted twine must have had its problems at harvest time.

In 1941 two Unis Français threshing machines manufactured by Société Français at Veirzon, France, and two wire-tying balers (the tying was done manually!) were imported by the States Buying Commission. One of the French machines was issued to Don and the other to J. E. Colback. Don, used an International W12 to haul the threshing set and drive the drum and baler at the start of the 1941 season. However, fuel was always in short supply, so in October power to drive the threshing set changed when a Merlin portable steam engine requisitioned by the States was made available with a supply of coke from the gasworks. (Before the war the author used to go with his father with the horse and van to the gasworks to collect a load of coke for the kitchen range.)

In 1942 things would change again for the threshing season, when the Department of Agriculture warned Don that only diesel fuel would be available. This meant more innovations as there were very few diesel tractors in Jersey at that time and Don was hard-pressed to find a way out. This story in full will be found in Chapter 20. He heard of a Ruston & Hornsby stationary diesel engine that had become redundant at St. Saviour's Hospital (called the Asylum in those days). Don bought it for £5, dismantled it, and took it to Sion. Using two 12-ft girders from the Harbour Works, and with their help, a chassis was made and completed at the Central Motor Works. A Citroen car engine was fitted to it with a gearbox, steering, etc. using a Fordson tractor front axle and a Commer lorry back axle and brakes; the Citroen engine also served as the starting engine for the Ruston & Hornsby engine mounted onto one end of the chassis, so this skeleton-like vehicle transported the stationary diesel engine from one threshing site to the next.

Farmers were pressed to grow as much wheat as possible, and when it was harvested and threshed it was taken to a grain store in town. The price was £1 8s./cwt. Although there was always a German soldier on the site while threshing went on, his main task seemed to be to keep a count of the bags of grain. However, the sentry could be distracted for a few moments from time to time when a bag or two was snatched by the farmer.

And so the Occupation dragged on until the Liberation on 9 May 1945.

Vehicles were in short supply in the early post-war years but there was a demand for lorries. Bedfords were suitable, but in short supply; Austins were available, but were too long for Jersey, so Don set about shortening them, taking 2 ft 8 in. (81.2 cm) off the chassis length and shortening the body to suit. They had to pass both the States' and the insurance companies' inspectors, who examined them thoroughly. Suffice to say they passed the test and work proceeded. Each vehicle took three days to complete and the cost was £500 a time.

It was a busy time for farmers, as it was for the rest of the country, with full employment. Farms were still small compared with today but were profitable nevertheless. The popularity of light tractors with the highly successful hydraulic three-point lift system, such as the Ferguson and

David Brown, led to a demand for mounted implements, particularly ploughs and cultivators. A local requirement peculiar to Jersey was the labour-saving, last-furrow plough, which was a mounted plough with a wide frame at the front of the plough. It had an arrangement to enable the body (the share and mouldboard) to be moved to one side of the plough's frame, relative to the tractor, to enable the 'last furrow' to be ploughed out, right up to the hedge or fence at the edge of the field. Otherwise the last furrow had to be dug with a spade and then levelled off, a job at which the author spent many a laborious hour. Land was considered too valuable to waste an inch.

The demand for the last-furrow plough was such that Don saw fit to engage a draughtsman to provide the necessary drawings before it went into production, priced at £50. Over time, a range of farm implements including a quarter-turn mounted one-way plough (as pioneered by Clem Le Breuilly just before the war) went into production. It was followed by an elevator potato digger.

Because the imported elevator-type potato diggers were generally too big and too wide for our narrow 18-in. (45.5 cm) to 20-in. (50.8 cm) potato rows, a mounted PTO-driven elevator potato digger with a narrow share and elevator chain was designed and produced, selling for £115. Later, a shaker attachment was fitted to improve the separation of the potatoes from soil and tops.

On the earlier ploughs, Oliver mouldboards and other components were bought in from Clem Le Breuilly, but as there was so much business, it was decided to install a press and extra capacity in the forge to make mouldboards for both the digger body and the skimmer. Moulds in two halves, top and bottom, were duly cast using an Oliver mouldboard to get the right shape, especially the 'turn' of the board, which is the secret for turning a good furrow. So the business turned out their own mouldboards as Le Cappelain had done many years before.

The Island's steep côtils facing the early-spring sunshine warmed up quickly. These côtils were Jersey's earliest and highly profitable potato land. They were too steep for a tractor, so they had to be dug by hand. It took several weeks in the winter months to dig these côtils and, as labour became more expensive, a more economical way was essential. While a tractor-mounted winch was not new, what was new was the design to meet another need peculiar to Jersey, although the crofters in the West of Scotland had a similar problem. Don devised and developed a way to make and mount a winch on the Ferguson tractor to haul a light plough up the steep côtils of Jersey, which in due course was yet another product to be manufactured. This subject is discussed in Chapter 19.

There was also a demand for second-hand Ferguson tractors and a few Bristol tractors, which were purchased at the Cambridge Tractor and Machinery Auction Sales. The Cambridge auction sales became a well-known institution in England in the 1950s and 1960s. There were some good bargains to be had as British dealers tried to 'unload' their inventories of second-hand tractors. These had been taken in part-exchange, with plenty of life left in them as the British farmers took advantage of the generous machinery subsidies available to them in the UK. The joke in the UK tractor trade was, 'if the ashtray is full, get a new tractor!' The tractors were shipped to Jersey, taken to Sion, and, after they had been reconditioned and resprayed, offered for sale: business was brisk.

The contracting business continued to be busy with haymaking and harvesting, so busy in fact that virtually all the Pallot family and employees would be busy driving tractors, some of them in the evening after school!

J. E. Colback had taken over as the importers for International Harvester equipment and tractors from Messrs. Richmond of Bath Street and continued to supply Don Pallot, but when Colback got out of agricultural machinery and went into the travel industry, the Renoufs of St. Mary's Garage became the International agents. However, in the early 1950s IH, like Ford in the UK, did not have a suitable tractor for Jersey, having only the British-built Farmall BM. When International introduced the lightweight B250 with three-point lift, and later the improved B275 with draught control, they had a tractor which competed directly with the Massey Ferguson 35 and the Ford Dexta. Don Pallot was now in a position to offer new IH tractors. The IH B275 proved be popular, and in due course Don acquired the agency for International Harvester.

In the 1950s a number of companies were manufacturing tractor-drawn PTO-driven combine harvesters and PTO-driven pick-up balers. International Harvester were among the more successful manufacturers with their PTO-driven trailed combines and the B45 pick-up baler. These machines were used in Jersey, but only by the agricultural contractors.

Other products sold included the British-made Allman tractor-mounted, PTO-driven, low-volume spraying machine for herbicides and pesticides, used mostly against blight in potatoes and outdoor tomatoes. The pump was actually fitted onto the PTO shaft and they had all-metal tanks. More recently, the more modern French Caruelle mounted sprayers with plastic tanks and the pumps mounted under the tank of the sprayer frame were offered for sale. They had the usual, universal, jointed shafting for fitting to the tractor PTO.

One of many of Mr. Pallot's advertisements.

Mr. Ozouf, of Augrès Garage, introduced the Samro potato harvester into the Island. Early deliveries were modified by the supplier to suit Jersey conditions. This was to change when a new supplier in England refused to modify the machines. Some time later, after Mr. Ozouf died, Don became agent for Samro machines.

There were many sides to the business, including plant hire with earth-moving equipment, tower cranes, etc., which began with a Coles crane and a large bulldozer known in the family as Tiger Lille. It was bought for a song from American army surplus auctioned in the Island. It was later used on contract at the airport. A number of other contracts around the Island were undertaken, including laying tarmacadam on public and private roads. L. C. Pallot (Tarmac) Ltd. was formed and run by Sam Pallot. It has since been sold, but still operates from the premises at Rue de Bechet. Yet another of the family's businesses is Windowcare, who manufacture and fit plastic windows.

Entertainment at Rue de Bechet is provided alongside the museum, with rebuilt cinema organ and church organs and the steam railway, which was Don's hobby and part of the business. The railway is complete with steam engines, restored railway carriages, and a railway station using some of the materials from the Snow Hill Station of the Eastern Railway. Now there are the Threshing Days, when the Ransomes steam traction engine is driven out into the field and the threshing machine and baler are lined up and threshing begins. The collectors and restorers of tractors, farmers' lorries, and stationary engines display and operate their latest exhibits. So with organ playing, the museum open, and steam railway rides, there is plenty to see and do. It provides a great day out for all the family! Following the turmoil of the revolution in the farm machinery industry in the 1970s and 1980s, International Harvester Co. have merged with J. I. Case to become Case International, and L. C. Pallot remain the local agents.

Mr. Sam Pallot beside the 25-hp, 50-cwt International lorry he has restored

The organisation and general logistics of running so diverse a business have to be admired. The purchasing of materials, machines, and stock control are aspects that the casual observer would not be aware of, but which went on behind the scenes to support all these activities. Mr. Pallot was fortunate to be blessed with children of whom several went into the business and became as skilled as their father. The business L. C. Pallot & Sons Ltd. still runs today alongside the Steam Museum, selling and servicing agricultural machinery. Don and his family have performed a wonderful service preserving and reconditioning so many pieces of old farm machinery, implements, tools, and tractors, all displayed in their museum. The display includes a portable steam engine, a traction engine, and two steamrollers, one of them a Marshall from the parish of St. Saviour. It is a wonderful display for so many Jersey farming folk and visitors to enjoy.

Today one of Don's sons continues to run the machinery business while Sam Pallot runs the Steam Museum, restoring machinery and vehicles for display. He also organises the steam railway engine and the open days featuring a threshing machine and the Ransomes traction engine, all as an attraction for local folk and holidaymakers. Meanwhile, Lyndon restores old stationary engines, but at present he is working on a sixty-year-old John Deere tractor at his workshop in St. Brelade.

A Gardner no. 2 single-cylinder gas engine, made in 1900, being restored in Lyndon's workshop. The original engine test report is on the next page.

The Merryweather Company bought engines from various engine manufacturers to couple up to their water pumps, afterwards fitting their own nameplate. Note the drip-type lubrication points on the engine, one of glass above the cylinder and the second made of bronze above the connecting rod-bearing. This engine and water pump was installed in the cellar at Steephill, where it pumped water from a well for many years.

Mr. Lyndon Pallot contemplates reconditioning a John Deere gearbox and back axle in his workshop.
Lyndon Pallot is surrounded by machine tools and equipment in his workshop at St. Brelade. A picture and description of the John Deere is featured under 'Tractors'.

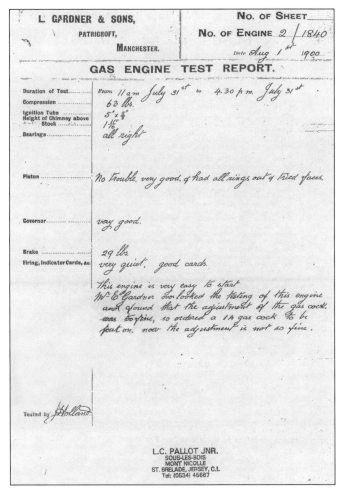

Gardner factory, pre-delivery, engine test report, dated 1900.
While restoring engines, Lyndon has come across all sorts of different items like this pre-delivery test report of a Gardner engine carried out and supervised by Mr. E. Gardner on 31 July 1900 before dispatch.

N° 14,865

A.D. 1915.

Date of Application, 20th Oct., 1915

Complete Specification Left, 18th Apr., 1916—Accepted, 19th Oct., 1916

PROVISIONAL SPECIFICATION.

Improvements in or relating to Fastening Devices for Vehicle Shafts.

I, MOSES ALEXANDER PALLOT, of Mont Pellier Farm, Trinity, Jersey, Saddler, do hereby declare the nature of this invention to be as follows:—

This invention relates to fastening devices for use in maintaining or holding the hinged or pivoted shafts of vehicles in a raised position when not in use.

5 According to the invention I provide means which, on the shafts being raised or elevated, will come into operation automatically to secure them in such position until they are required to be lowered. Said means may comprise a hinged member mounted on the vehicle at or near the point at which the shaft or shafts are hinged or pivoted to the vehicle and adapted when the shaft or 10 shafts are raised to engage therewith so as to prevent the accidental lowering of the same. When requiring to lower or bring the shaft or shafts to the horizontal position the member may be moved out of the way to permit of the shafts resuming their normal position. For the purpose of holding the member against the shaft it will be fitted with a spring adapted to cause the member to 15 engage that portion of the shaft projecting or extending rearwardly beyond the pivot or hinge about which it turns, whilst a suitable handle or projection may be provided to enable the member to be readily moved out of engagement when requiring to again lower the shafts. The spring controlled member may be hinged or pivoted to the body of the vehicle or to the usual shaft supporting 20 means, so as to lie below the shaft, or it may be arranged above or at the side thereof and have a hooked extension capable of engaging an eye or loop fixed at a suitable position on the shaft. If, however, it is preferred that the member shall act simply as an abutment when the shaft is raised, a stop or notch may be provided on the shaft against or into which the member under 25 the action of its spring will take when the shaft is raised.

For shafts mounted to move independently of each other there will usually be one of such fastenings or securing means provided for each shaft, while for shafts which move together or are connected by a footboard or the like, one of such fastenings will usually be found sufficient.

30   Dated this 20th day of October, 1915.

HASELTINE, LAKE & Co.,
28, Southampton Buildings, London, England, and
55, Liberty Street, New York City, U.S.A.,
Agents for the Applicant.

35   ## COMPLETE SPECIFICATION.

Improvements in or relating to Fastening Devices for Vehicle Shafts.

I, MOSES ALEXANDER PALLOT, of Mont Pellier Farm, Trinity, Jersey, Saddler, do hereby declare the nature of this invention and in what manner the same

[*Price 6d.*]

(*facing page*) A patent by a forebear concerning the shafts of horse-drawn vehicles, to enable them to be lifted vertically and locked in position when not in use; and (*below*) the drawing accompanying the patent. Horses' shafts were often an irritation when lying on the ground when a van or carriage, or any four-wheeled vehicle, was not in use. They were always hinged and easily lifted; however, if the vehicle had a footboard it was not always possible to push them over centre, so they would rest back out of the way.

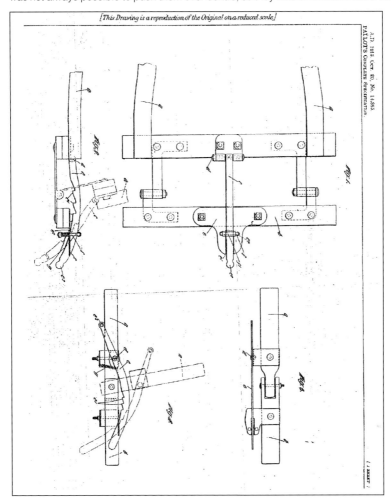

The late Don Pallot, his family, and their collection have helped the author in his endeavour to prepare this history of implements and farm machinery in Jersey.

Philip Messervy (1829–1920)

Mr. Messervy traded between 1860 and 1915, at his forge at Mayfair, Faldouet, St. Martin. He was the earliest blacksmith whose accounts the author was privileged to see. His beautifully hand-written accounts illustrated below reveal a wide range of activities. During the early years he turned out ironwork for ships and boats, mostly in Gorey. As shipping, shipbuilding, and the fisheries reduced and died away at Gorey in the 1880s he was doing rather more agricultural work on pumps, carts, ploughs and farm implements, cartwheels, etc. Among the goods he purchased for sale were anchors, pumps, boxes of wire nails, cartwheels, axles, and potato forks. Other purchases were guano and groceries!

Men's wages were from half a crown (12.5p) a day to 10 shillings (50p) a week. He supplied labour for house repairs, chimney sweeping, and other work. He grew his own early potatoes for

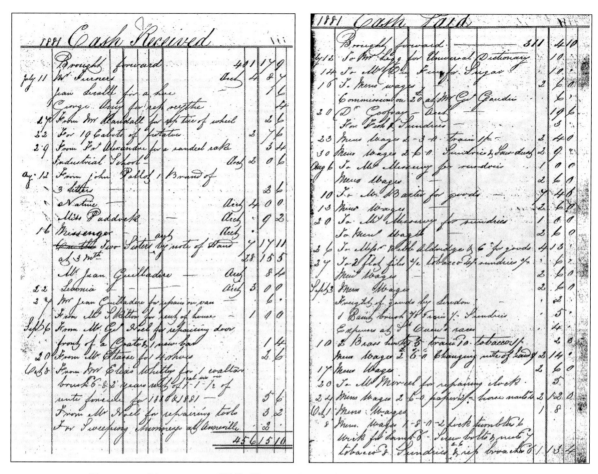

Two pages of the accounts of Philip Messervy in 1881 (courtesy of Miss Mary Billot).

sale, all of which indicated a wider business interest than simply that of a country blacksmith. Above are copies of his account book, illustrating the diverse activities of his business. The first page is from July to October 1881. The second page shows his wage bill and the various goods supplied and paid for over the same period. His accounts in 1902 show that he was selling potato forks through May, June and July to Frenchmen for the potato season, and to take with them back to Brittany after the season; others were sold to the Parish of St. Martin and local folk. These accounts are all in 'old' money, the days of pounds, shillings, and pence. One entry listed the sale of 15 cabots of potatoes at 1s. 9d. (8p) a cabot. One item that appears to be missing from his purchases was coal for his forge.

Charles F. Robin and T. J. Marett & Son

Mr. Tom Marett of T. J. Marett & Son, The Forge, or La Forge, La Grande Route de Rozel, in the parish of St. Martin, kindly provided the author with sufficient details of his business to piece together a short history of a country blacksmith still trading today.

Previously, a Mr. Nicholl owned the property but a Mr. Ferey ran the blacksmithing business. It is thought that the forge had probably been built in the nineteenth century. In 1910 Mr. Charles F. Robin, Junior, bought the business for £400. Work today is supplying horseshoes and using a motor van and a mobile forge to shoe horses at a customer's stables. No longer is the horse taken to the forge for new shoes, as the author had to do with his father's horses.

Mr. Tom Marett and his van, a mobile forge for shoeing horses at the customer's stables. No longer does the horse go to the forge – the forge goes to the horse.

Products in the early years included ploughs, mouldboards, cartwheels and iron tyres for cartwheels, making horse shoes and shoeing horses, making grappins from old potato forks, and sharpening plough shares, etc. Making horseshoes is also a thing of the past; they are now purchased in various sizes and types for different types of horses.

Charles F. Robin, junior, was the great-grandfather on Tom's mother's side of the present proprietor, Mr. Tom Marett, whose father, also named Tom, married Charles Robin's daughter and in due course continued to run the business until he retired. The present Tom Marett, who was born in 1935, joined the business as an apprentice when he left school at the end of the German Occupation.

Mr. Charles Robin had served his apprenticeship at E. Slade, who were also blacksmiths in St Martin. They manufactured the Jersey Scarifier (presumably for potatoes) and zigzag harrows, and were the maker of the Jersey Butter Worker. They were also agents for Blackstone oil engines and cycles. They were also known to many for their bus service to Minden Place, which was Slade's town terminal before the last war. The last time the author travelled on a Slade's navy blue and white bus from town to Maufant was in the summer of 1939, after going to the pictures on a Saturday night.

Charles Robin began in business at Les Hurieux at Rozel in 1907, when we see from his accounts in July that year that he bought:

half a ton of large coal @ 13/- [65p]
half a ton of small coal @ 8/- [40p]

At about the same time he purchased an anvil for 15 shillings (75p) from Messrs. Robert Hunt, at 26 and 27 Conway Street.

Blacksmith's anvil.
A blacksmith's anvil: an iron casting iron probably made by Grandin at their foundry at Commercial Buildings in St. Helier. The dimensions are: height 14 in. (35 cm), length 38 in. (97 cm), width 6.5 in. (16 cm); the length of the horn is 10.5 in. (26.5 cm). The horn has a varying diameter and is necessary for making horses' shoes, among other things. They are never painted and are in constant use. A blacksmith's basic equipment is a forge, his many hand tools, and an anvil, which might almost be described as the symbol of the blacksmiths' craft.

On 7 November at Mr. Elias Billot's sale, Messrs. Charles Perchard, of La Chasse, St. Martin, and no. 4 Halkett Place, were the auctioneers, and Charles purchased a 'meule' (or grindstone) for 10 shillings (50p). This and the following purchases indicate that he was getting the necessary equipment together for his business. Again, on 23 December, he evidently attended a farm sale with the same auctioneers, Messrs. Charles Perchard, and having both home and business in mind he bought 'une herse' (a harrow) for 2 shillings (10p) and a dresser for 18 shillings (90p).

On 2 December 1907 half a ton of small coal was purchased, followed by a similar delivery in May 1908 and again in June, all supplied by the Sunderland, Hartlepool and Newcastle Coal and Coke Depot at no. 6 Don Road. The proprietor was Messrs. J. J. Marett.

Charles was obviously doing well, because also in April 1908 he had a tweed suit made by Messrs. A. L. Mollet, 'High-Class Tailor', at no. 1 Bath Street and no. 1 Peter Street for £8 10s. (£8.50), which was an expensive suit in those days. He was evidently satisfied with his tailor, since he purchased a second suit described on the invoice as a 'Black Diagonal' suit from them for £3 13s. (£3.65) and a discount of 3 shillings.

It is interesting to compare these prices with £2 10s. (£2.50 or 50 shillings) for a suit at the Fifty-Shilling Tailors on the corner of King Street and Halkett Place in the 1930s.

The year 1909 was an exciting one for young Charles Robin, as further examination of the accounts reveals that this young man was planning on marriage. First he purchased the suits in which to woo his lady and then he purchased furniture. An account from Messrs. Horace Fitch, upholsterer, cabinetmaker, and dealer in modern and antique furniture, of 16 Halkett Street lists:

bedstead,
wire mattress,
wool mattress,
fender,
fire brasses
cupboard

all for the princely sum of £5 18s. (£5.90) with two pillows and a bolster gratis! From Messrs. Amy & Fitch, also furnishers, at 41 Don Street came:

dresser to order £3-9-0 [£3.45]
mahogany chest of drawers at £1-12-6d. [£1.62_]
stair rods and clips for 1-6d. [7.5p]

When the great day was at hand on 24 September, he paid for a 'Bride Cake' at £1 16s., evidently delivered to Melton House, St. Martin, along with a delivery of gallons and half-gallons of wines and spirits, including cognac, brandy, port wine, and sherry, all for the sum of 18 shillings! All supplied by Messrs. C. Le Monnier & Co., 36 Bath Street, with vaults in Rouge Rue.

On the following day two wedding carriages were provided by

W. Gregory & Sons, Ltd.,
Royal Livery Stables & Riding Establishment
'By Royal Warrant to the late Queen Victoria' Established 1820.

This was obviously a well-established business with premises all over town (La Motte Street, Ann Street, Wesley Street, David Place), and with branches at Paragon in Halkett Place, St. Clement's Road, and Rouge Bouillon.

The account for £2 was settled on 2 October 1909.

Presumably all went well and he married his bride, having a reception afterwards at Melton House.

The fascination of these different accounts is in the names of his suppliers, almost all of which have disappeared, due largely to the fact that in Jersey, up to a few years ago, businesses were owned by local families who usually ran the business themselves. When the proprietor retired or passed away, if there were no boys to continue running the business, it closed or changed hands, adopting a new trading name. Some, however, continued; one such is Voisin & Company at Commercial House, 24-30 King Street (still in the same family after well over a century). The invoice of 16 October 1909 for a dinner service at £1 1s. is instantly recognisable by the billhead on the invoice having changed very little over the years.

Equally interesting are Mr. Robin's suppliers on the mainland such as

Thomas Reynolds & Son
Iron Merchants, Factors and Wholesale Ironmongers
of 6, 8 & 10 Colston Avenue,
St. Augustine's Bridge, Bristol

who supplied '40 Smith taps 5/16" @ 1/9d each' and 'dies to pattern sent by post'. Presumably smiths' or engineers' taps and dies (for making threads) were unobtainable locally.

Charles Perchard, of La Chasse, the auctioneer, printed his invoice heading in English, but the goods are in French and/or Jersey Norman-French (as for many invoices at the time between local people in the country), such as an invoice at a sale for

3 Roues @ 3/- [15p]
5 Esselet @ 1/- [5p]

Fourteen shillings for three wheels and five axles seems a good bargain, even in those days!

In 1910 Charles was able to buy La Forge, next door to Uplands, a village store on La Grande Route de Rozel, St. Martin, from Mr. Nicholl for £400. There the business has remained in the same family, the name having changed only through marriage.

Charles appears to have been preparing for the move in July 1910, when he purchased some more furniture from

General House Furnishing
16 Halkett Street and No. 47 Lower Bath Street.

including, among other things, a mahogany wash stand for 13 shillings (65p) and a night commode for 14*s*. 6*d*. (72.5p). These prices show how reasonably priced mahogany furniture was in those days, and also just how the value of the pound has fallen over ninety years. The pound today is worth no more than a sixpenny piece of the old money of pre-war and early post-war years! The author still has a 'night commode' at La Porte, left by his forebears, which is a particularly beautifully made piece of furniture; of little use today, but it makes a useful table top in the hallway!

In November, Charles changed his coal supplier when he purchased 2,000 lb of small coal for 16 shillings from R. J. Blampied, at 38 Esplanade, 'Fruit and Potato Exporters and Importers of Guano, Artificial Fertilisers, Hay, Straw, Corn, Forage, and Coal'. The receipt was signed by R. J. Blampied, indicating, as explained above, how so many Jersey businesses were owned and managed on a day-to-day basis by the proprietor. R. J. Blampied was one of the many agricultural merchants along the Esplanade before the Second World War and for a few years after the war. They all packed and shipped tomatoes and potatoes and they all imported the same guano fertilisers, hay, straw, coal, etc. Almost every building along the Esplanade from the JF(T)U, at Olympia to the corner of Conway Street, was an agricultural merchant; there were more in Caledonia Place and along Commercial Buildings, including Norman Ltd.

Farmers would often complain among themselves that these merchants were living off the backs of their industry and hard work. However, change came about when farmers began to pack their own produce and sell it directly through their own groupings to the UK outlets.

Later in the year, it would seem, Charles had some alterations to make, possibly to his forge. He had a pane of glass delivered at 8*d*. (3p),

10 x 53 lbs of cement 2/3d [12p]
8 lbs of paint @ 4/- [20p]
a quantity of coal tar and a pint of turpentine @ 10d [4p]

His wife was busy as well, making sure the home was comfortable, when she went shopping at the Co-operative General Drapery Store, of Waterloo Street, a 'cash terms only' business; She purchased a blanket, various lengths of material including netting and muslin, and a pair of curtains, the most expensive item cost 6*s*. 9*d*. (33.5p), no less than six mats, including one at 2*s*. 4½*d*. (the remainder were 1*s*. 9*d*. and 1*s*. 11*d*.). These items amounted to £1 13*s*. 2*d*. (£1.65), and after a discount of 3 shillings (15p), the total came to £1 10*s*. 2*d*. (£1.51).

Charles continued to attend the sales conducted by Charles Perchard, of La Chasse, buying old iron, or *vieux fer*, at 1*s*. 6*d*. a time, a *griffon à pomme de terre* (a potato scarifier) for 7*s*. 6*d*., and on another occasion a *charrette* or handcart for 5 shillings (which seems to be another bargain), two *charrues* (ploughs) for 10 shillings, a lawnmower for 6*s*. 6*d*., and a press for £5.

The old iron would be for use in the forge while the *griffon*, the *charrette*, and the two *charrues* were probably as a speculation for sale to a customer. It is a pity there is no more detail about the press, but suffice to say that a press in a forge, or any engineering workshop, is an extremely useful piece of equipment. Judging purely on the prices he had been paying for so many items, this press was something substantial, which he found worthwhile, paying up to £5 to acquire.

The move to near Uplands obviously proved successful for the forge. By the spring of 1911 he had increased the frequency of his purchase of 2,000 lb of coal. Among his various activities, he was shoeing horses, as we see from his purchase of requisites for them, such as oil for horses' feet and other items from F. L. Le Chevalier at Five Oaks. The blacksmiths always coated the horse's hooves in oil with a brush after shoeing them, leaving their hooves sparkling clean and shining.

Cartwheel repairs were beginning to feature with the purchase in May 1911 from

Mr. F.J. Nicholle Junr.
Wheelwright, Cart and Van Builder of
Les Vaux in Trinity

of

14 Felloes and 8 Spokes
a pair of van wheels @ £1-5-0 [1.25p]

and in June a pair of van back-wheels at £2 16s. (2.80p) (felloes are the components which form the wooden rim of the wheel, on the outside of which the iron tyre is shrunk on by the black-smith).

At the end of his first full year at Uplands he is looking for business outside the Island by advertising in the *Guernsey Almanac* for 1912 at a cost of 7s. 6d. (37.5p). At the start of the new year in January 1912 he paid 1s. 6d. to

Mr. J.D. Tirel, Cycle Maker and Repairer
of St Martin's Cycle Works

for repairing a carbide lamp.

This was probably for his bicycle; these lamps were very large and very grand-looking chromium affairs, with the usual round glass to the front and two little coloured glasses on each side, which lit up when the lamp was lit. They were mounted on a pair of spring-loaded parallel motion levers to protect them from the bumpy road surfaces of the untarred roads of that period. They were still in use in the late 1920s, when as a small boy the author would push down the top of the lamp on his father's bike with his finger tip and watch it spring up and down.

The St. Martin's Cycle Works also hired bicycles for 2s. 6d. (12.5p) per day.

Later the same month there were preparations for the arrival of a baby with the acquisition of a pram from

Messrs C. Pearce
Dealer in all types of Baby Carriages
29 Hue Street & Old Street.

The deal seemed to be part of an exchange costing £1 10s. (£1.50).

Again, in January he evidently decided it was time to be more businesslike by placing an order for bill heads printed by

Messrs Huelin & Le Feuvre . . . the printers of the 'Nouvelle Chronique De Jersey'
with offices at 11 Royal Square, St Helier.
350 Billheads (3 sizes) 6/6d [32.5p]

An account which ran for a little over a year was for the collection and delivery to La Forge of various implements purchased at various farm sales and deliveries of iron from town, commencing on 27 September 1912 with goods from a sale, and then frequent deliveries of iron from the pier, iron from Albert Hunt at 9, 26, and 27 Conway Street, and on two occasions from the St. Malo boat. Most of these deliveries from town were charged at 4 shillings (20p); after twelve months it amounted to £2 8s. 6d. (£2.48½), which was settled on 14 October 1913.

A noticeable feature in the conduct of business in those years was the credit extended between suppliers and customer: the account for bill heads settled after four or five months! Regular accounts mounting over the year, and settled annually, occur quite frequently and this was evidently an accepted way of doing business. The author recalls that farmers were reputed to settle their accounts once a year at Christmas time, but it would seem to have been general

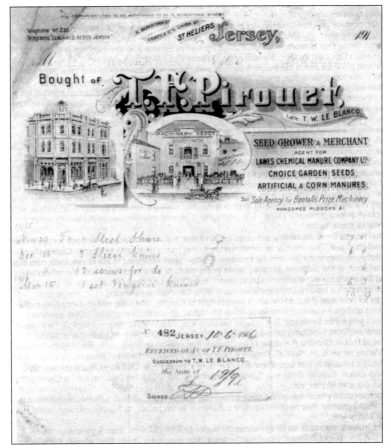

T. F. Pirouet's invoice and receipt for farm machinery parts in 1911. T. F. Pirouet's shop on the left of the bill head above made the corner of Beresford Street and Cattle Street. Later it changed hands to Mr. Le Marquand during the Second World War and the Occupation. Mr. Le Marquand continued to run the business until he retired in the 1970s and it became The Island Lock & Safe Co. Ltd.

practice in those days. Not so today; one pays cash to see the doctor! It is noticeable that during 1914 a change was taking place: monthly statements begin to appear with settlement in the following month.

Coal for the forge was being purchased in ever increasing amounts from different suppliers, probably in an attempt to obtain the best price. Two other commodities which were being supplied frequently were Stockholm tar from Mr. Le Chevalier at Five Oaks and carbide from J. W. Dupré & Co. of Charing Cross. Carbide was used in acetylene lighting, which explains the frequent delivery.

While telephone numbers up to three numerals are included in the bill heads of the businesses in town in 1911 only a few country businesses had a telephone number, and they had only two numerals. In 1913 and particularly in 1914 it was more widespread on the bill heads of the country businesses.

In October 1913 when Charles Robin paid his rates to the parish of St. Martin in the Vingtaine de l'Église he paid 7 shillings (35p) for six quarters. Mr. P. J. Le Huquet, Vingtenier, signed the receipt.

He also did further business with Mr. P. J. Le Huquet of Elmore who invoiced him in March 1913: 'To making Box Cart for Mr. J Renouf of La Gallierie @ £7-0-0'.

The iron plate on which the wooden-spoked cartwheels were assembled and the iron tyre fitted is still in the forge today but rarely if ever used these days.

Other work in the forge included repairing farm implements, making ploughs, making the mouldboards with a press with two shaped cast iron moulds to bend the mouldboard to its precise curve and shape, making and sharpening plough shares, making grappins out of old worn-out forks by bending the tine through 90 degrees and fitting a long straight handle, making flat hoes with blades of 7, 8, and 9 in. (17.7-22.8 cm) wide supplied by Mr. Le Chevalier, of Five Oaks, fitting new handles to hand tools, spades and forks, etc., and, of course, shoeing horses. A stock of nuts and bolts was carried for sale.

Charles, like Philip Messervy, at Faldouet, before him, presumably had a piece of ground, for in January 1914 he bought five sacks of guano from H. Vardon, of Caledonia Place, an importer of fertilisers and exporter of Jersey produce. Charles, like many other Jersey folk, probably liked to grow his own early potatoes. After all there is nothing so satisfying and enjoyable as digging your Jersey Royals in the morning, giving them a wash and having them for your dinner at midday with that other Jersey product, a piece of butter. The very thought makes the mouth water as one writes these words!

What has been so interesting about looking at these accounts of ninety years ago is to see how life has changed. The country communities were very much more self-sufficient. Cars were expensive, so they were few and far between. People were restricted to the horse, cycle, and bus for transport, in the northern parishes, while in the south of the Island there was the railway all along the south coast for commuters to town. Apart from La Forge and the shop at Uplands, which included a bakery, there were so many other businesses operating in St. Martin and nearby. There was P. J. Le Huquet, a wheelwright at Elmore, who later added decorating to his services (and he was also an undertaker); Slades, having a forge, a cycle shop, supplying stationary engines, and a bus service; J. D. Tirel and his St. Martin's cycle and motor works; P. B. Le Huquet at Bandinel Farm, supplying cider by the cask and the pot; F. C. J. Benest 'Ladies' and Gents' Tailor' at Rozel; Charles Perchard of La Chasse, an auctioneer (*encanteur*); who probably farmed La Chasse as well; H. Bendall, 'Draper & Grocer and Wine Merchant' at Orient Place, Rozel (did he land his wine at Rozel from France?); and Philip du Feu of Rozel Bakery, St. Martin's baker, grocer, corn and seed merchant.

All these country businesses supplied a necessary service but, as their sales were restricted to a small community, they doubled up their activities in some cases, such as draper and grocer, baker and grocer.

An interesting invoice is for three pieces of copper at 7s. 6d. (37.5p) from a coppersmith, all including the receipt in French, unusual for an invoice from town. It was from Messrs. F. Hebert (Late P. Guilleaume), of 24 New Street, which the bill head declares is the oldest house in the Island. One wonders whether the claim is true.

Two interesting items in 1914 and 1915: one is a ticket from the States' Weighbridge on behalf of Messrs. Hunt for a three-quarter-ton cartload of iron. The author remembers those notes well, when farmers always weighed their loads of potatoes before selling them to the merchants, then went back to weigh empty. The second item is the increase in the price of coal, presumably influenced by the First World War looming at that time.

In July 1915, Mr. P. Le Huquet, of Elmore invoiced four separate deliveries in April and June for a total of twenty brakeblocks. Bearing in mind the business of La Forge would include fitting hardwood brakeblocks to farmers' vans and carriages, this seems a remarkably high number over three months. Even more surprising is the price 5d. each.

Mr. C. A. Copp also did some work for Charles Robin, supplying two pairs of brakeblocks at 7½d. (6.5p) per pair.

Perhaps the farmers were getting their vans ready for a busy potato season.

Mr. Le Huquet frequently supplied La Forge with a variety of wooden handles for hand tools, spades, potato forks, hay forks, axes, rakes, grappins, and handles for sand-eel rakes, as well as items made of elm for carriages, etc. and of ash for vans.

Things were beginning to change as time went on, as when 1,220 lb of bars of metal were supplied in a range of different sizes, which suggests they were possibly of steel supplied by F. J.

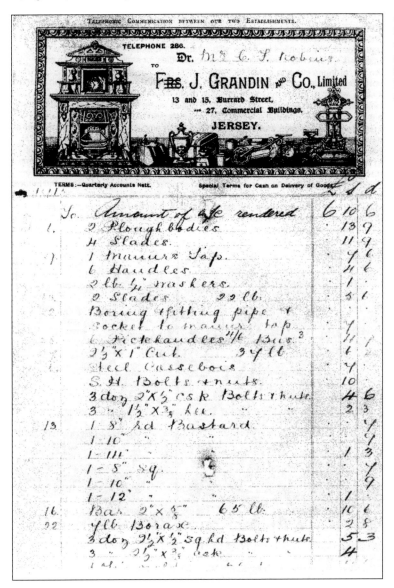

An invoice from Grandin the foundrymen, general engineers and stockists of general hardware at Commercial Buildings, for farm implement parts and sundries.

Grandin & Co., Ltd., who had their own forge and foundry at Commercial Buildings. Up to now deliveries had been of iron, that is wrought iron, the material one tends to associate with black-smiths.

So the business went on thriving and Mr. Charles Robin became a highly respected member of the community in the parish of St. Martin. Unfortunately there is a gap between 1919 and 1935, when suppliers' invoices for that period were presumably lost. There is a noticeable change of suppliers in the late 1930s, as one might expect. Charles was purchasing wooden components from Charles A. Copp, builder and contractor of Wayside, St. Martin, such items as handles for ploughs and hand tools like sickles and spades, and also parts for plough carriages, the felloes for wooden-spoked wheels, panels for Jersey vans, etc. It is interesting to examine Charles A. Copp's invoice bill heads over the years. He starts off as a builder and carpenter, changes to builder and contractor, changes again to builder, carpenter, and painter and decorator, and finally in 1939 to builder, carpenter, and plumber.

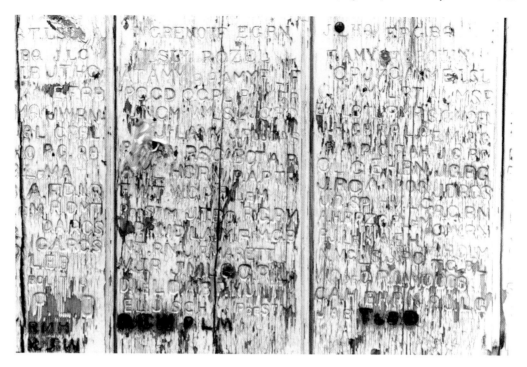

Customers' names burned into the door of the forge with branding irons made for branding cattle; they were also used for marking wooden handles on implements and tools with the customer's name

There was a noticeable change at this time in the bill heads of suppliers' invoices. Gone are the decorative artwork and pictures which adorned the bill heads of earlier years, such as Le Cappelain's below. They were advertisements in themselves. Instead, these new bill heads are plain, with the supplier's name in large black letters and the rest in smaller print, and they are rather dull by comparison.

A Le Cappelain invoice in 1941.

It is interesting that Messrs. Le Cappelain should have four mower knives in stock in December 1941. These would have been complete knives at 4 ft (122 cm) or 5 ft (152 cm) long made up of knife sections for a Bamford reaper/mower.

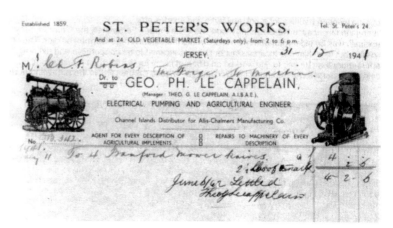

A sign of the times in 1940 was Charles Copp making items for the 'blackout' for Charles Robin. These probably took the form of boards for fitting to windows as darkness fell, to obscure lights in the house from enemy aircraft flying overhead on bombing raids at night. For the benefit of younger readers, the 'blackout' was just that, no lights at night anywhere, any time; no street lighting, etc. The whole of Jersey was blacked out. This went on night after night, and all over the

UK. The blackout was strictly enforced, with heavy fines in the Island. The Honorary Police mounted special patrols in 1939 and 1940 to see that the population complied. One has to remember that pre-war the Island was not lit up after dark as it is today; there were many areas without street lamps, and people including the States and parishes were very careful how money was spent. There were no States police; only St. Helier had a small uniformed police force.

The forge continued to conduct business through the war and Occupation years. In 1942 A. F. Gallichan & Co. at 26 and 27 Commercial Buildings had taken over from the Grandins and supplied components for ploughs, including slades (landsides) and plough bodies and drilling machines. The Iron Stores in the Parade supplied a variety of hardware goods and materials to the forge in 1942. One wonders where they got materials from at that stage of the Occupation, assuming demand would have cleared any pre-war stock. It is interesting to compare this flow of materials through the Occupation with the problems experienced by George Le Cappelain, waiting for rationed iron and steel to make ploughs and cultivators during the First World War in 1917 and 1918, when of course the Island was not occupied.

In 1943, Messrs. Le Huquet of Elmore continued to make and supply the forge with a wide variety of wooden implement handles and bodkins. At the end of 1944 one particular item stands out: it is the frame for a sugar beet press at 3 shillings, a clear indication of the shortage of sugar and the need to make it from the raw materials at home. In 1945 Mr. Le Huquet had given up trading as an undertaker, as indicated by the crossing through the word on his bill heads. Perhaps that is not surprising in view of frequent invoices to La Forge with long lists of wooden components being turned out by his workshop for the customers. A. F. Gallichan & Co. continued to supply bars of iron and bundles of horseshoes. Mr. Gordon A. Le Breton at Eden (who many years later became the Constable of St. Saviour, and later Jurat) was also making and supplying wooden handles for forks, hay forks, and spades.

During the Occupation the Germans made use of La Forge. Fortunately, the German Army blacksmith was an older man of more mature years than the average German soldier. They had no choice but to let him use their facilities, but he was inclined to be co-operative and did not interfere more than he had to. He worked on different items for the German forces, including shoeing their horses. At the end of the Occupation he gave Charles Robin the remaining horseshoes, but to quote Mr. Marett, 'they were rather big and heavy, made for road work and were not hugely popular with the farmers'.

Mr. Tom Marett beside the forge in his blacksmith's shop; empty horseshoe boxes on the forge are ready to be used to light the fire

So the business survived the Occupation, and by July 1945 they were re-establishing their connections with pre-war suppliers in England. One statement in particular stands out and brings a memory back to the author. It comes from Messrs. Godwin Warren and Co. Ltd. of Bristol, with whom Charles Robin had been doing business for many years. This statement is typed and dated: 'July 1945 . . . To goods . . . £2.12. 9.'; but underneath in ink is added '1940 12/-'. A supplier with a long memory! The account was promptly settled on 23 August 1945.

Pre-war, the author's father, who farmed at Beau Désert, St. Saviour, ran a milk round from the farm. One of his customers was Mr. Grummet, the headmaster at Victoria College, living at College House. At the end of the war he was living in Dublin. When the author's mother was going through the farm accounts in 1945, which was her province, she noticed an outstanding amount for Mr. Grummet for several shillings for milk supplied just before the Occupation. The account was sent to him and he paid by return of post!

Godwin, Warren & Co. Ltd. were steel and iron stockholders and through the last six months of 1945 Charles Robin was restocking with goods from the company, including nuts and bolts, twist drills, taps and dies, horseshoes, and welding materials. Godwin's also supplied reciprocating water pumps, driven by either electric motor or petrol engine. Many of them were used on Jersey farms for pumping water from wells.

A noticeable item missing from the accounts of the wartime years is coal deliveries to the forge. These start again in July 1945. It is quite clear that he is both busy and stocking up with a ton of open-cast coal priced at £4 10s. a ton.

It is interesting to note the changes in the price of coal, which increased enormously during the First World War: 13 shillings per half-ton (1,100 lb) in 1907, £2 10s. per 2,000 lb in 1915, £4 10s. per ton at the end of the war (1918), and £4 10s. per ton of open-cast coal in 1945.

In 1945 Tom Marett, the present proprietor, left school and began his apprenticeship to become a blacksmith in the family business. Tom's son, also named Tom, is in the business travelling with a portable forge, shoeing horses on customers' premises. What is extraordinary, however, is the need to go away to the UK to technical college during the apprenticeship to obtain a qualification in order to shoe horses. So Tom, senior, an apprenticed blacksmith with a lifetime's experience, would be unable to shoe horses in the UK today! However, the business continues to serve the customers and, although the work has changed, no longer building ploughs and implements but carrying out repairs to tools and implements and shoeing horses, it keeps La Forge, one of our few remaining blacksmiths, busy.

C. G. Le Breuilly

Mr. Clem Le Breuilly ran a blacksmith business at La Forge, Rue de la Guillaumerie, Victoria Village, in Trinity. He started in business in the 1930s after serving as an apprentice with William Henry Gough, opposite Trinity Church, where the pub stands today. In due course he started his own business at Rue de la Guillaumerie, opposite the turning into Rue des Boulées. A new dwelling stands on the site today, named La Forge. Earlier in the 1920s Clem was an active sportsman, frequently taking part in the Bouley Bay hill climbs. At La Forge he carried out repairs on tools and implements, shoeing horses and selling Oliver ploughs and components from the USA. The author recalls taking his uncle's horse along La Rue du Pont, past La Guillaumerie, to be shod at Clem Le Breuilly's smithy in 1939. As well as selling Oliver ploughs, Clem fitted Oliver plough bodies and mouldboards to his own plough frames, producing both digger ploughs and breezing ploughs. He supplied other blacksmiths with Oliver bodies and mouldboards. They were a favourite of his and with many farmers; they had the reputation for polishing up to a beautiful shine so the soil slid over them easily, and as a consequence they would wear well, having a long life.

When the first Ferguson-Brown tractor, with its three-point hydraulic lift, came to Jersey Clem began to make implements for it. Other blacksmiths also saw the opportunity, but Clem went one step further. He designed and built the first mounted, quarter-turn, one-way plough. There was a story about the difficulty with his one-way plough working satisfactorily when ploughing across sloping land, or 'contrepy', as it is known in Jersey. The plough would tend to turn a wide or narrow furrow depending on the direction of ploughing across the slope. Clem in fact was not alone with this problem. It did not only apply to one-way ploughs; it affected all mounted ploughs in the early days, but it was foreseen on the conventional plough by fitting an adjustment facility to the crossbar, which could alter the line of draught. Eventually the adjustment could be made on the move. The problem was made worse on one-way ploughs because they were heavier and did not have a satisfactory adjustment for it. Another problem some manufacturers had with early designs of one-way ploughs was making the plough swing over and latch in place each time it was reversed or turned. In due course all these problems were overcome on later designs. The author recalls having difficulties with the width of the front furrow on two-furrow, reversible, one-way ploughs on the mountainsides of Wales as a young service engineer with Ransomes in the 1950s, and later on hillsides in East Germany.

Mr. Le Breuilly also made a simple potato planter, using plastic drainpipes, down which the operator dropped the potato, spacing in the row being set by a 'clicking' mechanism on a landwheel. He also made large numbers of Jersey hoes. The author purchased some from him for his customers in the 1970s. Clem must have been one of the last to make them. Mr. Harold Perchard, who lives now at Clos des Sables, once worked for Mr. Le Breuilly. In due course Mr. Le Breuilly moved his forge in Victoria Village to La Rocque, where he continued to run his business, producing his planters and hand tools, particularly Jersey pattern hoes.

Clem Le Breuilly's advertisement for his five-row potato planter. Note the telephone number!

Lanz potato diggers lined up in the yard in St. Clement ready for delivery.

The year 1956 seemed to mark a change in the supply of labour. Up to that time, Breton farm workers, short of work in Brittany, were pleased to come over to Jersey for the summer season to dig potatoes and help with the tomato crop. However, the economy was evidently improving in western France, with full employment, so local farmers had to think again. One answer was mechanisation, hence the importation of a consignment of Lanz potato diggers. What is surprising is that they are trailed diggers, rather than mounted. Mounted potato diggers driven off the PTO had been available from UK farm machinery manufacturers for the previous ten years, and many were already in use in the Island. The author's father had a mounted spinner-type digger in 1947, supplied by the CGA, who were then on the Esplanade.

Jack Marett

Mr. Jack Marett started at The Forge at Five Oaks, in St. Saviour, in the 1920s. The forge was on the corner of Rue à La Dame and St. Martin's Main Road, surrounded by a brick wall, where the Five Oaks pub is today. At that time it was next to Huelin's brickworks; the area is occupied today by Norman Ltd. Mr. Marett was an agent for Ransomes. His work was making and shoeing horses, of course, and making mounted ploughs, single-furrow, deep-digging ploughs, twin-furrow breezing ploughs, mouldboards, and mounted spring-tine cultivators with starwheel rotors. He also sharpened plough shares. During school holidays the author often took his father's horses there to be shod; while waiting, he spent many a happy hour watching the blacksmiths working at the anvil or fitting a new iron tyre to a cartwheel, and watching the water boil as the wheel was plunged into the cooling tank to shrink the tyre in place. On other occasions a red-hot iron plate would be placed between moulds in a press, which was screwed down to make a plough mouldboard. When the author's father bought a Ferguson Brown tractor in the late 1930s, Jack made the mounted implements, a single-furrow digger plough, a twin-furrow breezing plough, and a C-spring-tine mounted cultivator with a starwheel crumbler on the back of it. The unique thing common to these three implements was that none of them had a landwheel; they were carried on the three-point linkage both in and out of work. Depth of work was set with a depth-control lever in a quadrant on the tractor beside the tractor seat controlling the lift linkage.

Jack Marett frequently travelled on the Southern Railway ship the *SS Brittany* to France to purchase tools and implements. He eventually retired to take over the old Five Oaks pub, which stood on the corner where today the ramp descends to an underground car park adjacent to the shops opposite Jones's Garage.

Thérin and others

Mr. Thérin was another well-known blacksmith, with a forge in Trinity. He was known for his ploughs, among other things, and converted trailed ploughs into mounted ploughs. In the 1960s he imported Bomford two-furrow reversible ploughs, supplying one to Mr. Charles Billot, in St. Martin.

Mr. Le Lay was a blacksmith who worked before the war for Mr. Thérin, but later he set up in business at East Grave, St. John, where he converted some pre-war trailed or horse-drawn ploughs into mounted ploughs for use with the Ferguson tractor. Yet another country blacksmith in St. John was Mr. Picot, at Green Farm, and two more in the west were Mr. Le Cornu, at Rue de Vinchelez, St. Ouen, and Mr. Syvret. They all did much the same sort of work, repairing implements, shoeing horses, etc. There were many more all over the Island, but most have disappeared. Many blacksmiths were called upon to make road bands for tractors.

Mr. Charles Perchard, of Trinity recalls seeing his first tractor in St. Martin while he was still at school. He estimates that this would have been in 1920. The tractor was a Fordson belonging to Smith & Coles, who farmed at Wrentham Hall between the wars. The Fordson had steel wheels with angled cleats on the wheels instead of spade lugs. The object of this was to obtain a good grip in the field when ploughing, but also to allow the tractor to be driven on the road without damaging the road surface. The idea was not good enough for the Constables who were responsible for the maintenance of the roads in their parish. It soon became the law that road bands had to be fitted over the cleats before driving on the road, to prevent the cleats and lugs digging up the road surface. When spade lugs came into use only a few years later it was even more important. Fitting the bands was a laborious, time-consuming task and a way to take skin off the knuckles of the unwary. The rear wheels had to be jacked up, first on one side and then on the other, to get the bands on each wheel. The imported road bands were better at keeping their shape, because the blacksmiths could not make them hard enough, and the locally made bands eventually become flat between the lugs or cleats, making the ride bumpy and fitting them more difficult. Some imported bands were made with a flange around the inside of the outer edge of the band, which added to the strength to hold the shape.

Ozouf, Augrès Garage

Mr. Ozouf at Les Augrès Garage on Trinity Main Rroad started as a blacksmith in 1945 in an existing blacksmith's premises. Mr. Ozouf eventually extended the building to make a garage and filling station that became known as Augrès Garage. His daughter Olga, while studying French in Paris, visited the Salon Agricultural Exhibition there which, as any one who has visited the show will know, is a vast international show with displays of farm machinery among many other items including wine and cattle. She saw a wide variety of farm machinery, some of which she felt sure would be of interest in Jersey, and told her father.

The result of this was that he imported first the Pulverjet fertiliser spreader followed by Viaud reversible ploughs, then Ritmic planters, Remy elevator potato diggers, and lastly Samro potato harvesters. These Samro machines were first imported from Germany, where the machines were fitted with wheels with an adjustable track width. They performed perfectly. However, when the importer in England got wind of this he insisted that he was to supply the machines, as Jersey was part of his franchise. The Swiss factory which supplied the UK would not supply the machines with the adjustable track. Mr. Ozouf tried to overcome this problem by making up the adjustable track in his workshop. This was not successful and the UK distributor was not at all helpful.

As a result, the dozen or so machines supplied by the Swiss gave endless trouble in that first season. Unfortunately, during the following winter Mr. Ozouf died, and his widow and daughter continued to run the business but gave up the Samro machines, which were taken over by Mr. Don Pallot.

At about this time, the importers of Remy elevator potato diggers in England had a surplus of these diggers with a quantity of spares. Mrs. Ozouf purchased a number of them for sale in Jersey. Mrs. Ozouf went on supplying machines and spare parts for several years, even after the business closed at Augrès.

T. F. Pirouet

T. F. Pirouet, at 5 Beresford Street and 1 Cattle Street, formerly run by T. W. Le Blancq, were among the merchants who supplied farm machinery. Their activities included supplying seeds for farmers, and they were agents for Bentall, of Maldon, Essex, who manufactured farm shed (barn) machinery, Ransomes ploughs and spraying machines, and the MG2 tractor. Other items they sold were Choice Garden Seeds and Lawes Chemical Manure Company's Artificial and Corn Manures.

During the 1940s the business was taken over by the late Mr. Brian Le Marquand, who continued to run it in much the same way. He handled farm machinery manufactured by Nicholsons of Newark, including fertiliser distributors, and while not supplying Ransomes agricultural machines, he did sell their lawnmowers.

La Motte Street Garage

La Motte Street Garage, the main Ford dealers, sold Fordson and Ford tractors, Ransomes MG tractors, and implements. Fordson tractors were first brought into the Island by Messrs. Bougourd Bros. of Guernsey; this changed during the 1920s, when Mr. Noel, a brother of Mr. Noel of Noel & Porter in King Street, took over the Ford business. He had started a motorcycle business in the former stables of the Imperial Hotel in La Motte Street after the First World War. He went on to sell Ford cars, the famous Model T, etc., and also the Fordson Model F tractor. Unfortunately, the business failed in 1935, when a customer who had paid for a tractor did not get delivery and complained to Ford Motor Company.

Mr. Bill Sutton, in his capacity as the Fordson sales representative and dealership supervisor for the Ford Motor Company in the southern region of England and Ireland, was asked by Ford Motor Company to investigate. He came to Jersey at a difficult time in the Depression, when cars were not selling and nobody wanted the Ford dealership. He took a liking to the Island and went back to England to seek the finance to start a Ford dealership in Jersey. He successfully persuaded Hendys, the Ford dealers in Southampton, to back him. So he took over the business in the stables in La Motte Street and moved his family to Jersey in 1936. This was timely, just as production of the Fordson Model N tractor was getting into full swing in Dagenham. La Motte Street Garage were appointed the Ford dealers for Jersey and all the Channel Islands for Fordson tractors. However, business continued to be difficult, so when cars did not sell, Bill Sutton started a taxi business, known as Luxicabs. The cabs were Ford V8 cars painted black and white. The drivers wore a smart uniform and a peaked cap and always opened the door of the cab for their customers with a smart salute.

In due course business began to pick up; Fordson tractors were selling. Ford main dealers were often appointed by Ransomes to be their agents, so Ransomes implements and the Ransomes MG2 tractor were stocked. When the American company began manufacturing the Ford-Ferguson 9N tractor in 1939, a number of them were delivered to La Motte Street Garage in Jersey. The first demonstration of the 9N tractor was to Mr. Emile Pallot, of Petit Ménage Farm, in Fountain Lane, St. Saviour; the Ransomes MG2 was also demonstrated.

In 1940 complications arose with the mortgage on the property, and to solve the problem the Imperial Hotel next door was purchased. During the Occupation the States commandeered all the Fordson tractors on rubber tyres; not all were engaged in agriculture. There were about eighteen in total and all were sent to France under the supervision of Bill Sutton to be converted to burn charcoal gas. Mr. Sutton served on the Essential Commodities Commission, frequently going to France to purchase farm machinery including threshing machines. After the war there were patent problems between Ford and Ferguson, halting the sale of the 9N tractor. But by this time Harry Ferguson was producing his tractors at Banner Lane, in Coventry, and selling them in Jersey through St. Helier Garages at First Tower, and they were selling well. Towards the end of the 1950s the Ford Dexta came along; it was a very similar tractor to the Ferguson and was a success, with a range of Ransomes implements designed for it.

The Jersey Farmers' (Trading) Union Ltd.

The JF(T)U Ltd. first traded and for many years remained at Olympia on the Esplanade. The business originally started life in February 1927 as the trading arm of the Jersey Farmers' Union, which was founded just after the First World War. Eventually the business developed into a private trading company with many farmers holding shares, and was managed for many years by the late Mr. Frank Perrée who had followed his father into the business. At the end of the lease for Olympia, the business was sold to the Jersey Farmers' Co-operative in 1969 and the organisation moved into the premises at Commercial Buildings.

They were agents for David Brown Tractors and implements from 1939, Alfa Laval milking machines, Howard Rotavators, Hayter machines, E. V. Twose and Tong's equipment, and for a period, Walthambury potato-packing machinery, and other farm and garden machinery companies

However, business has changed resulting from the rash of takeovers among manufacturers in recent years, David Brown suffering the same fate in the 1970s following a marketing agreement with American White Tractors. They in turn were eventually taken over by Tenneco, a group which owned J. I. Case. so JF(T)U no longer handle tractors. Today at the premises at Commercial Buildings they have a large department concerned with water, Grundfos submersible water pumps for boreholes, water pipes, and Wright Rain irrigation equipment, and a store with hand tools, sundries, and clothing. At their premises at Les Ruettes in St. John are showrooms and workshops; they continue as agents for Alfa Laval dairy equipment and a range of garden machinery.

James E. Colback and St. Mary's Garage

James E. Colback ran a garage in town and were the Jersey agents for International Harvester, selling the range of tractors, implements, and harvesting machinery, including trailed harvesters and pick-up balers such as the well-known B45. They also ran a contracting business with their tractors and harvesting equipment.

St. Mary's Garage, run by the Renouf family, were agents for the widely popular Coleby two-wheel tractor and other two-wheel tractors for planting, scarifying, and banking potatoes.

St. Helier Garages Ltd. (suppliers of Ferguson tractors and equipment)

The company which first imported Ferguson tractors in 1936 started life in St. Aubin with horse-drawn vehicles, trading as St. Aubin's Coach & Car Co. Ltd., run from Bulwark House. The move to Bath Street in St. Helier and the change of name took place in 1920; the owner was Mr. Harry Mell. Mr. Briginshaw was appointed managing director in 1924, when the company began to sell Clyno cars. In 1925 they installed a petrol pump and began selling Standard cars and Imperial motorcycles. By 1929/30 they offered a wide range of vehicles: Singer, Humber, Hillman, Riley, Guy, and Chevrolet lorries, buses, and coaches. The company continued to expand its properties, extending in Bath Street and opening in Don Road and First Tower Garage, when Duvey's Garage, a property owned by the late Lord Trent, was acquired. A branch was opened in Guernsey.

When the Ferguson Brown tractors were first imported into the Island, it was necessary to demonstrate the Ferguson system to the farming community because of the tractor's unique method of draught and traction control that enabled so small a tractor to pull a deep digger plough with ease. The Ferguson tractor had an 18-20-hp Coventry Climax engine compared with 29 hp on the Fordson model N, a popular tractor in the Island at the time, and the Ferguson was physically smaller.

Details of the tractor will be found in Chapter 9. The slope of a côtil was selected as the ideal way to demonstrate the tractor pulling a deep-digger plough, and St. Helier Garages set about doing just that at a number of sites in different parts of the Island. The demonstrations were successful; the author's father and his brothers along with others, ordered Ferguson tractors, which were delivered in 1937. Sales continued through 1938. The company also offered a range of Ferguson implements for use with the unique three-point attachment and lift system.

After the war Mr. Briginshaw returned to the Island to become joint managing director with Mr. Harry Bree, and with Mrs. Mary Anderton as chairman. Mrs. Anderton was by then quite elderly. The arrival on the market of the entirely new and highly successful TE20 Ferguson tractor on rubber tyres, then built at Banner Lane, Coventry, saw tractor sales continue in ever-increasing numbers from the First Tower Garage. Again, the author's father and his brothers were among the many who ordered the new tractors. Farming in those days was a very different game; early potatoes mostly enjoyed good seasons and outdoor tomatoes were grown in many parts of the Island, but were subject to the occasional glut.

The company offered a wide range of Ferguson implements and attachments, and implements made by other manufacturers designed for use with Ferguson's unique lift system, including a rear-mounted loader. As time went on models changed, with the TEA and the TEF having different fuel-burning engines, petrol, petrol/paraffin (TVO), and diesel oil. Horsepowers varied between 18 and 16 for the diesel. The author can recall attending a course at the Ferguson School at Stoneleigh during his student days, which included a visit to the factory at Banner Lane, in Coventry. On arrival we entered a large foyer where the famous 'black' tractor was displayed. It was, of course, the first tractor which was built for experiment and development. In the factory there was a ripple of excitement when a number of four-cylinder diesel engines were spotted lining a wall in the assembly shop beside the production line. (Ferguson did not have a tractor with a diesel engine at that time in 1951.) Students' questions were answered with a numbed silence, but on returning to Stoneleigh we were told yes, they were going to build a small number of tractors fitted with a diesel engine and put them on test at Stoneleigh and with a number of selected farmers. We were sworn to secrecy never to utter a word! Testing proved successful, and in due course a diesel model went into production.

One of the problems with the lightweight Ferguson tractor had been the introduction of the pick-up baler. The Ferguson was too light and not quite powerful enough to drive it. Along came the grey-and-gold-painted FE35 tractors, just that bit heavier and sturdier and with a more powerful engine sufficient to handle a baler like the International B45. At this time Harry Ferguson was negotiating with Massey Harris to merge the two companies that were in so many respects poles apart. However, the red and grey Massey Ferguson 35X tractor appeared following the merger.

Among the implements sold were the Ferguson solid tine, spring-loaded tine, and finally the spring-tine cultivators, the Ferguson 16-in. (45 cm), quarter-turn, one-way plough. The early Howard Rotavator posed a problem: the TEF tractor had to be split at the centre to fit a lower gear, slightly lengthening the tractor, and the Rotavator had to be bolted to the tractor. Eventually the difficulty was overcome with design changes in both tractors and Rotavators. Other machines handled by St. Helier Garages included Allman sprayers, followed by the Caruelle sprayer from France. They were more expensive but were able to cope with a wider range of insecticides, including injectors and spraying beans, which had been a problem to avoid killing the bees necessary for germination. The Caruelle attracted the attention of agricultural contractors in the UK, and a number were sold there. Huard, another French manufacturer, supplied reversible ploughs. Other suppliers were Greys, of Feterangus, in Scotland, well-known manufacturers of farm machinery, from whom front loaders, rollers, and buckrakes were ordered. Two Massey Ferguson combined harvesters were sold.

Well-known employees were David Quérée, Brian Rondel, Phil Perrée, and Edgar J. Deffain.

In 1972 Mr. Briginshaw was to receive a severe shock one morning when he received a phone call telling him to 'get rid of those tractors'. The company had been sold and the new owners were not interested in the Massey Ferguson business, resulting in the disposal of a successful business. The Ferguson agency passed out of the hands of St. Helier Garages to be acquired by Mr. R. G. Romeril, of Le Couvent, St. Lawrence. Thus St. Helier Garages' long association with Ferguson and the farming industry came to an end.

The Ferguson tractor was highly successful in Jersey. It was the right size for the Island, and the three-point hydraulic lift, with a range of implements to suit, added to the attraction. The early popularity is reflected in the low serial numbers, many of them with only two numerals, such as no. 97. Probably due to our relatively small farms, many farmers had continued to use horses and they had no problem with ordering new mounted implements when they bought a tractor, whereas those farmers who had used a Fordson, an International, or a John Deere, either hauled horse implements or they had tractor-trailed implements that would have to be replaced or modified. There was a similar problem in England, where the deterrent was not only the small size of the Ferguson tractor, but the additional cost of buying a whole range of mounted implements.

The Ford Motor Company had established a tractor training school and testing ground at Boreham, in Essex, many years before, and Harry Ferguson set up a similar school at Stoneleigh Abbey, in Warwickshire. The author had the unique experience of attending both schools for long weekend courses: at Boreham for the Dexta tractor and its range of implements, the author having spent many months working on the development of those new implements.

The range of implements and machines that have been designed and manufactured in local blacksmiths' and engineering workshops is quite remarkable There were people like Clem Le Breuilly making the first mounted, quarter-turn, one-way plough. Other ploughs and similar implements were those of Mr. Thérin; Don Pallot's quarter-turn, one-way ploughs and last-furrow attachment, and his elevator potato digger; Jack Marett's mounted ploughs and cultivators; and Le Cappelain's self-lift ploughs and cultivators during the First World War. Considering the humble nature of these highly skilled craftsmen, they were often greatly respected for their skill by the farmers who benefited, but strangely the wider community considered them to be simply blacksmiths. Unfortunately, the market place in Jersey is minute and, being surrounded by water, the growth and expansion of these businesses was impossible.

The changing world of farm machinery

Looking outside the Island at the wide world, so many of the most famous international companies manufacturing a wide range of agricultural machinery started in the same humble way as our Jersey blacksmiths and engineers, such as J. I. Case. Jerome Increase Case was a farmer's son from Williamstown, New York state. He started in business with his Groundhog threshing machine, which was simply a wooden peg drum mounted in a stout wooden box. In 1830 he took it across country to the Midwest. At first he hired it out with an operator on contract to farmers; then he made many more of them for sale, developing them over the years and eventually making the complete threshing machine; then he set about making steam engines to drive them.

Another even earlier example in England was Robert Ransome, who was apprenticed to an iron-monger in Norwich and later set up in business as a foundryman, producing plough shares. As so often happens, he discovered quite by accident that when molten iron fell on a piece of iron the surface in contact with the cold iron was particularly hard. He realised the value of applying it to plough shares: it would extend the life of the cast-iron ploughshare. He took out a patent in 1785. His shares were so successful that he moved to Ipswich in 1789 where. after arranging the finance, he set up his world-famous Plough Works beside the River Orwell. After further experiment and development he produced the first chilled cast iron share in 1803. Ransomes went on to manufacture a whole range of cultivating implements, threshing machines, and steam traction engines. In 1841 Ransome exhibited the first steam powered threshing set. The rest of the story is well known.

J. I. Case are still very much alive, having recently joined forces with the ailing International Harvester Company. Sadly, the Ransomes name is no more in the agricultural world; their products are now manufactured in continental Europe and the USA. The name continues only in grass machinery for sports fields, etc. The company suffered during the vicious spate of buying and selling of successful internationally famous companies by foreign predators as the manufacturing base shrank in recent years.

Ford Tractors are produced under the banner formed by the previously close association of Ford and New Holland, both American-based companies but with a big presence in the UK, now trading as Ford New Holland.

The farm machine industry has become a lottery for survival, having to shrink as a result of the ending of some farm subsidies and allowances for new machinery. The changes in commodity prices and the pressures on prices at the farm gate from the supermarkets, are forcing many farmers to move out of the industry. As a result we have fewer, but larger, farms. The production engineers have been so successful in manufacturing the whole range of farm machinery so quickly and economically that fewer companies are able to meet the demand for machinery of world agriculture. The process is repeated in the heavy-lorry and car industries, with the disappearance in the UK alone, of Austin, Morris, the Rootes group, Singer, Triumph, and Standard cars.

Agricultural contractors

Mr. Buesnel

The business at Carrefour au Clerq, next to the old East Exchange, in St. Saviour, was one of the first agricultural contractors to use tractors. Mr. Buesnel started immediately after he was demobilised from the Royal Flying Corps in 1919. He had a Fordson model F tractor and International Junior operating various implements, ploughing in the winter with the old Jersey horse plough, mowing hay in the summer, and harvesting with a binder. He later moved into more modern equipment, including a liquid manure tank for emptying the cisterns on dairy farms, the pump driven by the tractor PTO.

P. J. Blandin and Sons

The family business of contractors of agricultural machinery at Le Hocq, St. Clement, was well known in the Island for many years. As can be seen from their advertisement below they operated a fleet of tractors with ploughs and other cultivating implements, tractor-mounted mowers, hedge cutters, haymaking machinery and Jones balers, front loaders and manure spreaders, to mention only some. The later generations are still in the business, but mostly with industrial equipment.

P. J. Blandin and Sons, agricultural contractors, advertise their services to farmers.

Glossary

adze cutting tool for dressing timber

ard primitive cultivator first pulled by Neolithic man and later by oxen

auger tool for boring holes in wood, soil, etc. and also used as a conveyor in a pipe or channel

bachîn (Jersey French) a large diameter cooking utensil, usually made of brass

batchu (Jersey French) a bodkin; an English expression used in Jersey or in England a whipple-tree

bodkin *see batchu*

branchage roadside hedge cutting, as required by law

breezing shallow, autumn ploughing

buckrake tractor-mounted implement for carrying silage

cabot measurement by volume: cabot = sixtonniers (6) = 40 pints

cas-chrom cultivating tool similar to spade with a bend at the bottom of the handle and a foot tread to apply weight to push into the soil and lever up the soil

caster wheel a wheel mounted on a vertical swivel to enable it to follow the direction of travel

CAV the name of a manufacturer of diesel fuel injection equipment

cavings waste material produced when threshing: husk, short straw, etc.

centres centre to centre dimension e.g. as between the rungs of a ladder

chaff cutter a machine for cutting hay or straw into short lengths

cleat a bracket with two horns around which a cord can be wound to restrain it or angled lugs/cleats on the steel wheels of an iron-wheeled tractor as on the Fordson F

compound engine a steam engine with two cylinders for high- and low-pressure steam

cotil a steep slope that is cultivated to catch the sun and will be warm earlier than flat land

cotter pin a pin to lock a component to a shaft

coulter; disc-coulter a vertical knife or disc (on edge) to make a vertical cut in the soil

crownwheel and pinion a pair of gear wheels; the crownwheel has the bigger diameter

crumbler a tool for crumbling soil, a knife roller

dog clutch a mechanical castellated clutch

ducksfoot a wide cultivating point

felloe a section of the rim of a wooden wheel

foreshare the share at the front of an ard that penetrates the soil

frog that part of a plough body to which all the components, mouldboard, share, and landside, are fitted

grappin a cultivating hand tool with four or five long tines arranged side by side at right angles to the handle

groundwrest that part of an ard that rests on the ground when the ard is in work

harrow a cultivating frame with tines on one side for dragging over the soil

hay tedder a machine for tedding hay; it has a number of forks for kicking the hay upward to dry it

hay wilter a machine to squeeze cut grass to dry it

headland the land at each end of a field upon which an implement, machine, or tractor will turn or stop for a tea break

heel the back of the landside (slade) of a plough that rests on the ground, it helps to control the depth of work

knife-roller/crumbler *see* crumbler

la grande tchéthue (Jersey French) the Jersey big plough

landside a plate that is fitted to the land side of a plough body to prevent the plough body moving sideways into the unploughed land and helps to set the depth of work, also known as a slade

landwheel the wheel that supports the weight of an implement

live electrical equipment when switched on would be live; a power take-off (pto) would be live while the pto clutch is engaged, connecting it to a running engine

mattock a cultivating hand tool with a blade at right angles to the handle used to break up the soil

milking bail a mobile milking parlour

mouldboard the component on a plough behind the share for turning the soil

OHV overhead valves on an engine

OTA Oak Tree Appliances

palstave Neolithic bronze axe with wings at the top which are wrapped around the stub at right angles to the handle

peen beaten, as with a hammer

peg-drum threshing drum with pegs rather than rasp bars

Petter engine manufacturer

pinion a gearwheel; the smaller of two gearwheels, e.g. crownwheel and pinion

potato banker an implement to bank the soil around potatoes

pto/PTO power take-off

quadrant a quarter of the circumference of a circle; a quarter of a sphere

quern two stones, one like a ball and the second much larger with a central bowl; the ball is used to pound and grind grain in the bowl to make flour

ram/baler a plunger for ramming hay or straw in the bale chamber of a baling machine

reciprocating mower a mower with a reciprocating blade

road band a steel band placed over the spade lugs, cleats, or spuds on the wheel of an iron-wheeled tractor or machine to prevent damage to the road surface

scarifier cultivating implement with spring or solid tines

silage cattle fodder made by compressing grass in a silage pit or silage tower

skimmer an implement similar to a small plough body for skimming off the top soil when ploughing and depositing it in the furrow bottom

spade lugs also known as spuds or cleats, on the rim of the rear wheels of a tractor to obtain traction or a grip; also used on the rim of the landwheel of a machine such as a potato digger

splines a number of relatively narrow equally spaced longitudinal grooves machined with a milling machine on a short shaft which will match when inserted into the internal splines in a short hole on the end of a driven shaft

spuds *see* spade lugs

spur gear the teeth of a gearwheel set at right angles to the rim

stilt the handle of an ard that supports the share on some ards

straw walker long channel section components at the top of and towards the back of a threshing machine for shaking and walking the straw to the discharge point. Any remaining grains in the straw fall into the channels and are carried forward by the motion to fall on the sieves

stroke the stroke of a piston or ram, e.g. upstroke or downstroke of the piston in an engine

tâch'ron (Jersey French) also known as a fork, a team of three people to dig and pick Jersey Royals (potatoes)

tail the handle of an ard and some early ploughs

tang that part of the implement that is fitted into the handle

tear load factor the load imposed on a buckrake when it is tearing out a load of silage from a silage pit. The load factor is critical to avoid imposing too big a load on the buckrake which might damage it, i.e. bending the tines or frame or damaging the tractor's hydraulic lift system

threshing (thrashing; it is spelt both ways and a manufacturer will choose one or the other) to extract the grains out of cereals

tracklayer a tractor which lays a track like a flexible band on the ground it will pass over, then picks up the tracks as it moves on

trembler coil an early idea to generate a spark at the spark plug on an internal combustion engine, located in the flywheel of the Fordson F tractor

trusser a machine to compress and tie hay or straw into trusses or low-density bales

turnwrest a one-way single-furrow horse plough, the body of which rotates longitudinally complete with mouldboard and share etc.

tvo tractor vaporizing oil

whippletree also known as a bodkin or *batchu*: harness, a bar usually made of wood with a U bolt at each end and a U bolt at the centre with a free swinging hook, for use with a horse in traces to keep the chains separated behind the horse

wilter a machine to squeeze freshly cut grass/hay

windrow when the hay is dry during haymaking it is raked into a row, known as a windrow, preparatory to baling (or collecting in haycocks in the days before pick-up balers)

worm and segment the worm takes the form of a spiral which engages in the gear teeth of a segment of a gearwheel

Index